The Handbook of Data Communications and Computer Networks

Dimitris N. Chorafas

PETROCELLI BOOKS
Princeton, New Jersey

Library of Congress Cataloging in Publication Data

Chorafas, Dimitris N.
   The handbook of data communications and computer networks.

   Includes index.
   1. Computer networks. 2. Data transmission systems. I. Title.
TK5105.5.C487 1984   001.64'404   84-20762
ISBN 0-89433-244-9

Contents

Introduction   xiii

PART ONE   **MICROPROCESSOR-BASED ENGINES**   xvii

Chapter 1   **Distributed Information Systems**   1

One Microcomputer per Desk 1
Three Levels of Sophistication 5
Other Dimensions of DIS 6   Division of Labor 7
Alternatives: Vertical and Horizontal 9   Conclusion 12

Chapter 2   **R&D and Semiconductor Technology**   15

From Transistors to Biochips 16
The Pace of Microelectronics 19
An Inventory of New Images 21   Essence of Change 23
Market Characteristics 24

Chapter 3   **Cost-Benefit with the New Technologies**   29

Getting On-line 29
Decentralization and Centralization 32

Facing the Constraints 33   Criteria for Choice 34
Cost Issues with Future Systems 37
Supporting Services and Management Decisions 40

Chapter 4   From Data Processing to Data Communications   43

User Levels in Data Communications 44
System Perspectives 46
The Three Main Classes of Communications 50
Electronic Message Systems 52   A Message Service: Ontyme 54

PART TWO   TELECOMMUNICATIONS   57

Chapter 5   What is Telecommunications?   59

The Investment 61   Communications Costs 63
Estimating Communications Requirements 64
Calculating Unit Charges 68   Expected Benefits 70
New Perspectives 71

Chapter 6   Space, Frequency, and Time   73

Space Division 74   Frequency and Time Division 75
Code Conversion 78   Time Slots and Alohanet 79
Time Assignment Speech Interpolation 81
Intelligent TDM 83   The Problem of Vocabulary 85

Chapter 7   Switching Technology and the PBX   87

Switching Functions 88
Quality Service and the Erlang Algorithm 90
Analog and Digital Private Branch Exchanges 93
Cost Control and Service Features with the PBX 95

Chapter 8   Transmission Media: From Coaxial to Satellites   99

Coaxial Cable Installations 100
Experiences with Cable Television 102
Optical Fibers Technology 105
Communications by Satellite 107
Coaxial vs. Satellite Transmission 109

Chapter 9   Terminals   115

The Use of Terminals 116   Building Blocks 119
Transmission Speed and Interfacing 122

The Line Controller 123
Computers, Microcomputers, Microprocessors, and Terminals 126

Chapter 10 **Modems** 131

The Use of Modems 132   Noise and Line Losses 135
Technical Issues with Modem Selection 136
Agile Modems 140   The User Site 141
Standard Interfaces: RS 232, RS 422, and RS 449 142

Chapter 11 **Multiplexers, Concentrators and Front-ends** 151

The Process of Multiplexing 152
Betting on Concentrators 154
Assisting the Central Resources 159
Breaking Down the Front-end Tasks 161
The Data Communications Machine 165

PART THREE **PROTOCOLS** 171

Chapter 12 **What is a Protocol?** 173

Protocol Reliability 174   Access Methods 176
Procedural Requirements 178
Synchronous and Asynchronous Transmission 178
Synchronous Protocols 180
Terminals for Synchronous and Asynchronous Protocols 183

Chapter 13 **Circuit Switching and the Polling/Selecting Option** 187

Circuit Switching Principles 188
Control Procedures: Fixed, Switched, and Multipoint 189
The Coming Possibilities 194

Chapter 14 **Bit-Oriented Protocols** 197

The Data Link 198
The Fields of XDLC 202   Frame Sequence and
Acknowledgment 207
Using a Bit-Oriented Protocol in a Loop 208   Objectives of XDLC 211

Chapter 15 **The Nesting of Protocols** 215

Standards for the Physical Circuit 216
Second-Level Protocols 217

Framing and Link Management 218
The Higher Levels 219   Applications Protocols 222

Chapter 16   Networking Functions   225

Routing 226   Virtual Circuits and Datagrams 230
Choosing Virtual Circuits or Datagram 232
Connection and Transmission 233
Node-to-Node Protocols 234
The IMP-to-IMP Protocol 235
The IMP-to-Host Protocol 236   Host-to-Host Protocols 236

Chapter 17   X.25   237

What is X.25? 238
The Communications Session 241
Comparing Protocols 242   Flow Control 245
Goals in Flow Control 247
Congestion Control 247   Internetworking 248

Chapter 18   Session and Presentation Control   251

The Purpose of Session Control 253
ANSI and Session Control 255   Presentation Control 256
A Process Level Protocol 258

Chapter 19   Standards for Presentation Level Protocol   261

The Observance of Protocols 261
Presentation Control 263
The CEPT Standard 266   The PLP Standard 267
Handling Graphics 273   International Coordination 276

PART FOUR   NETWORKS   281

Chapter 20   Three Generations of Networks   283

The Early Periods 284   Point-to-Point 284
The First Generation 285   The Second Generation 287
Merging Technologies 288   Network Interfaces 292
The Third Generation 294

Chapter 21   Competitive Offerings and International Standards   299

The ISO/OSI Model 301
A System Network Architecture? 305

SNA Compatibility and User-Oriented Supports 307
The Encryption Standard 308   Using Value-Added Networks 309

Chapter 22   Toward Local Area Solutions   313

Assuring Connectivity 314
Benefits from a Packet Switching Network 316
The Local Area Network Concept 318
A Relative Standardization 320
Cost/Effectiveness with LAN Solutions 321

Chapter 23   Backbone Operations   325

Topological Description 326   Topological Solutions 327
Sender and Receiver 329   Sharing Tasks 331
Datapac—An Example of Network Service 332   Gateways 334

Chapter 24   Basic Definitions for Architectural Design   337

Systems and Network Architecture 337
The Nodes of a Network 339   Basic Definitions 341
Projecting an Architecture 344   Conclusion 345

Chapter 25   Functions and Objectives in Network Architecture   347

Layered Solutions 347
Duties of the Network Architect 350
Protocols and Interfacing 351   The Grand Design 352
Impact at the Workplace 354

Chapter 26   The Tradeoffs   357

Network Requirements 358   The Seven Basic Steps 361
Layered Communications Principles 365
Implementing a Layered Solution 368

Chapter 27   Circuit, Message and Packet Switching   371

Circuit Switching 373   Message Switching 378
Packet Switching 381
Comparison of the Three Basic Methods 383

PART FIVE   MESSAGES AND TRANSACTIONS   385

Chapter 28   Transaction-Based Systems   387

The Transaction Network Service 387
The Choice of Facilities 389

Types of Communications Links 391
Change in Structure 393   System Requirements 395

Chapter 29   **Message Theory**   397

Message Technology 397
Principles of Message Systems 398   Conventions 401
Performance Criteria 402   The User's Requirements 403
Examples with Message Systems 404

Chapter 30   **From Electronic Mail to Funds Transfer**   407

A Telemail Application 408
Operating Through Workstations 413
Perspectives in Electronic Funds Transfer 414
EFT in the Supermarket 416   Foreign Payments Procedure 417

Chapter 31   **Videotex in the 1980s**   423

Personal Computers and Videotex 423
Developing Videotex Systems 425
The Mechanics of a Videotex Facility 426
Connections, Transmission, Disconnection 429
Lessons from the Market Trial 435

Chapter 32   **Retail Banking Through Videotex**   437

Subscriber Agreement at the First Bank System 438
Placing Emphasis on Marketing 440
The Database and the Network 442
Videotex Payments by the Bank of America 445

PART SIX   **SOFTWARE PREROGATIVES**   447

Chapter 33   **Communications Software**   449

Developing the Software 451   Software Functions 452
Downline Loading, Upline Dumping, and Loopback 456
Database Support 457   System Design Requirements 458
The Implementation Schedule 460

Chapter 34   **A Network Operating System**   463

Designing a Basic Operating System 464
The Software "Constant" 466
Operating Systems Background 468

Executive Functions 471   System Management 472
Data Maintenance 472   Terminal Handling 472
The Server System 474   Distributed Operating Systems 477

Chapter 35   **Error Detection and Correction**   479

Errors and the System View 480   Error Reduction 480
An Integrated Approach to EDC 482
The Cyclic Redundancy Check 483   Bit Error Rate 483
Error Rate and the Dependability of Carriers 485
Control of Errors on Voice-Grade Lines 486
Testing the Network 488

Chapter 36   **Journaling**   489

The Journal is the Means 491
Procedural Prerequisites 492
Distributed Recovery and Restart 493
Failure Isolation 496   Security, Privacy, and Auditability 498

PART SEVEN   **NETWORK MAINTENANCE**   501

Chapter 37   **Life Cycle Maintainability**   503

Requirements for Life Cycle Performance 506
Availability and Reliability 508
Software Reliability 511   Portability 515

Chapter 38   **Systems Maintenance**   521

Time of Systems Interrupt 521
Preventive Maintenance 525   Repairability 527
Diagnostic Centers 528   Do-It-Yourself Maintenance 530

Chapter 39   **The Network Control Center**   533

Environmental Factors 535
A Maintenance Architecture 537
Implementing the Maintenance Architecture 540

Chapter 40   **Network Diagnostics and Monitoring**   543

Applications with Remote Diagnostics 545
A Case Study with the Danish Savings Banks 550

Introduction

This handbook has been written as a graduate and professional text to help computer scientists and practitioners in the expanding field of data communications and computer networks. Prime importance has been given to interleaving theory with examples, thus allowing the reader to progress smoothly from concept to concept and one new term at a time.

We are living in an age when human knowledge doubles every 15 years. Every 10 years technology makes tremendous jumps, and the life cycle of 50 percent of our expertise is only 5 years. We must work and produce in this fast-changing environment, but our job is not to operate large machines or to build elegant systems. It is to solve business problems. Providing the most efficient software or hardware is only part of the problem. The *real* issue is how to make information work for the people who need it.

The starting point is understanding how information capabilities are received by and delivered to the end users. To do this requires a profound knowledge of the business—how it operates, and what the important issues are.

The implementation process of computers and communications includes:

Gaining management's recognition and acceptance.

Obtaining a commitment to the tangible and intangible costs of change.

Involving the end user in the design of change (he won't change unless he wants to).

Acquiring technologies that match needs and that people will accept.

Designing man-machine interfaces and limiting the impact on organizational structures and relationships.

Planning the gradual evolution of information technology within the organization.

Assuring that the benefit from computers and communications is tangible, factual and documented.

Keeping costs low so that benefits always exceed costs.

Implementing the change effectively (with the appropriate training and sales effort).

Training the user to the new system and demonstrating costs/benefits in a simple, efficient, understandable manner.

This handbook is divided into seven parts. Part One is devoted to microprocessor-based engines. It introduces the concept of distributed information systems; reviews the most advanced R&D efforts in semiconductor technology; shows how to gain cost/benefit; and leads the way to data processing and data communications.

Part Two is devoted to telecommunications. It explains the requirements; treats technologies such as space, frequency and time division multiplexing; examines switching technology and computer-based private branch exchanges (PBX); and includes such topics as transmission media (from coaxial cable to satellites), terminals, modems, multiplexers, concentrators, and frontends.

The theme of Part Three is protocols. What is a protocol; circuit switching and the polling/selecting option; bit-oriented protocols; the nesting of protocols; networking functions; X.25; session and presentation control; and the new standards for PLP.

Part Four concentrates on networks. Three generations of networks are presented; competitive offerings and international standards are explained; a discussion on backbone operations is followed by basic definitions for architectural design; functions and objectives in network architecture—including tradeoffs—are outlined; emphasis is placed on circuit, message, and packet switching.

Messages and transactions are the subjects to which Part Five addresses itself, including transaction-based systems, message theory, electronic mail, electronic funds transfer, videotex and its impact in the 1980s, and an American application of retail banking through Videotex.

Part Six underlines the software prerogatives: communications software, network operating systems, error detection and correction, and journaling.

Finally, Part Seven is devoted to network maintenance. The issues are life cycle maintainability, systems maintenance, the functions of a network control center, and network diagnostics and monitoring.

This choice of subjects has been made in the understanding that the rapid increase in the demand for data communications and computer networks has elicited a need for more efficient structures than those presently available.

Though we still learn on databases, we know beyond doubt that data communications, databasing, and data processing are converging. Before long, there will be no distinction between them at all. The common ground is distributed information systems. Its impact will transform our professional and personal interests.

Let me close by expressing my thanks to everyone who contributed to this book, from my colleagues for their advice, to the organizations I visited in my research for their insight; and to Eva-Maria Binder for the drawings and typing of the manuscript.

Valmer and Vitznau
Dimitris N. Chorafas

PART ONE

Microprocessor-Based Engines

1

Distributed Information Systems

Technology has advanced to the point where computer power is economically available at all levels of company operations. Distributed information systems are tools which enhance the productivity of organizations with widespread operating facilities. Productivity gains can only be expected, however, if system tools are used easily, by authorized individuals, for a variety of purposes, and can be adapted readily as requirements change.

Distributed information systems, DIS, increasingly draw attention, yet have a meaning that is not totally understood. DIS is an evolution from centralized processing, which in turn evolved from "free-standing" modes. Although it combines certain strengths of its two predecessors, DIS is unique in its own right. It represents a break from the past.

The implementation of a distributed information system rests both on Logical and on Physical premises. The logical functions center on the procedural design for channeling the flow of information, and controlling the physical faculty throughout the projected systems configuration. The object of the physical functions is the engineering of the hardware and hard software devices to provide a specific level of capability.

Figure 1.1 outlines the chronological order of development from the information service request to the logical and the physical design phases. The information service request can be motivated by the need for cost reduction in data processing, clerical operations or other sectors, and/or by requests for improving the current information handling service and bringing it nearer to the user.

We shall take factual and documented examples to back up these references.

One Microcomputer per Desk

Typically, in the 1950s and 1960s, information handling was centralized, batch-oriented and costly, and encountered an inordinate number of errors and delays.

1

Figure 1.1

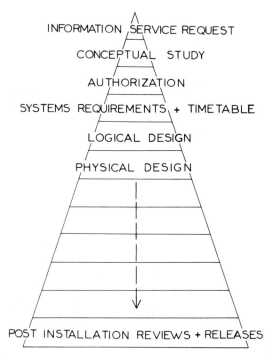

By the late 1960s there was plenty of evidence that this state of affairs was not satisfactory. Management needed to do something about this situation, and knew it. It was assisted in opening a new frontier by the system analysts' own realization that new ways were badly needed to master complex information systems.

In the late 1960s information system designers started to realize that software projects could not (and should not) always be behind schedule, taking more memory than planned, costing several times more than the original estimate, and performing less than projected. But it took another ten years to bring into perspective the fact that such results were the direct effect of underestimating complexity: there is no one-dimensional way from systems analysis to programming, but a four-dimensional approach past the architectural level involving noncomputerized procedural design, data base (DB) organization, software design, and hardware engineering. Figure 1.2 gives a snapshot of this organization. We shall return to it later at greater length.

The second vital element in opening the new frontier has been brought about by the cutting edge of technology which made it possible to bring computer power to the workplace at a lower cost than the previous mammoth solutions. Incorrectly called "minicomputers," this generation of information equipment made feasible both the division and the multiplication of computer power. Introduced in the mid-1960s, the minicomputer (based on semiconductors) exploded in the 1970s into three families each with its own market and price range: the maximini (or

Figure 1.2

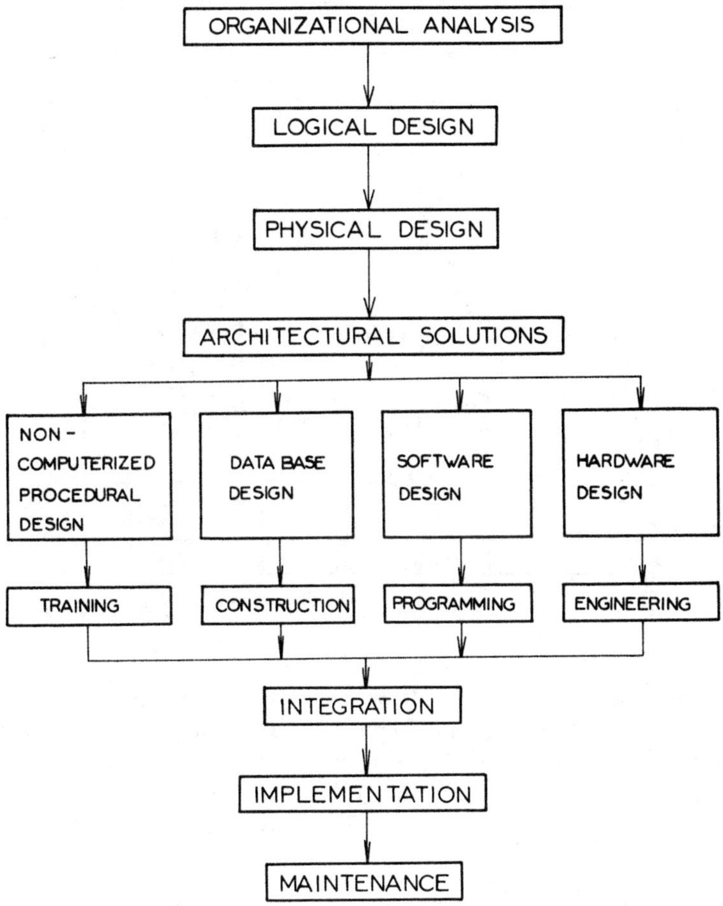

```
┌─────────────────────────────────────┐
│      ORGANIZATIONAL  ANALYSIS        │
└─────────────────────────────────────┘
                  │
                  ▼
        ┌─────────────────────┐
        │   LOGICAL  DESIGN    │
        └─────────────────────┘
                  │
                  ▼
        ┌─────────────────────┐
        │  PHYSICAL  DESIGN    │
        └─────────────────────┘
                  │
                  ▼
    ┌───────────────────────────────┐
    │  ARCHITECTURAL  SOLUTIONS      │
    └───────────────────────────────┘
```

NON‑COMPUTERIZED PROCEDURAL DESIGN	DATA BASE DESIGN	SOFTWARE DESIGN	HARDWARE DESIGN
TRAINING	CONSTRUCTION	PROGRAMMING	ENGINEERING

```
              ┌──────────────────┐
              │   INTEGRATION    │
              └──────────────────┘
                       │
                       ▼
              ┌──────────────────┐
              │ IMPLEMENTATION   │
              └──────────────────┘
                       │
                       ▼
              ┌──────────────────┐
              │   MAINTENANCE    │
              └──────────────────┘
```

midi), the mini proper, the micromini. Figure 1.3 shows the perspectives for the 1980s, and the specific orientation of each of these markets.

Technologically, the evolution of the maxicomputer resembled the "big motor" approach with the main drive shaft which we had in factories at the beginning of the Industrial Revolution. The evolution of the mini can be considered as a data handling counterpart to that of small motors (fractional power): "one motor per tool," "one mini per office."

For the 1980s, the master of the marketplace is the personal computer (PC). Microprocessor-based, with capabilities which exceed those of 1960 mainframes (and, in some cases, of big computers of the 1970s), the PC has gone through an evolution characterized so far by two generations.

1. The first generation of PCs came onto the market between 1976 and 1979, but began to receive major attention only since 1980.

Figure 1.3

Introduction of minicomputers based on semiconductors

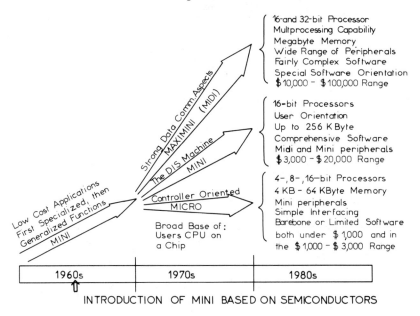

INTRODUCTION OF MINI BASED ON SEMICONDUCTORS

Typically, these are 8 bit-per-word (BPW) engines; have a central memory (CM, high speed memory, semiconductor memory) of 16 kilobytes (KB); use for external storage a cassette, eventually changing to floppy disc; have native support for a 40-column video, or 80 columns through a special printed circuit board (PCB); and have no capability for networking. (The latter can also be added through a PCB.)

2. The second generation of PCs entered the market after 1981 and attracted immediate market interest.

The central processing unit (CPU) of this generation is characterized by two types of commercially available microprocessors, though a few machines feature special LSI (large scale integration) semiconductor units or other than the two leading microprocessors:

the Intel 8086, with 16 BPW and a 16-bit bus (though some PCs have the Intel 8088 with 16 BPW and an 8-bit bus), and

the Motorola 68000, with 32 BPW and a 16-bit bus.

Though comparisons in terms of CPU power are quite abstract unless one knows and considers the machine's internal design, there is as an order of magnitude—a 30% rule—for comparison, with other things being equal. Benchmarks which I have done tend to indicate that, for currently available microprocessors, a 16/16 architecture is 30 percent faster than a 16/8 one, and a 32/16 is 30 percent to 35 percent faster than a 16/16.

As usual, other things are not equal. For example, 80186—the new Intel micro-processor—is said to be twice as powerful as the 8086; and the 80286 four times as powerful as the 8086 engine. One may even question the purpose of all that power on a chip to serve the workstation until if we consider the principle of one PC for one WS at each desk.

The PC should be dedicated to the manager, the professional, the secretary, and the clerk. A PC may have one or more microprocessors—but more than one person should not share the same PC. The objective of this investment is individual productivity—both mental and clerical.

Furthermore, PCs should communicate with one another: within the office through local area networks (LAN), and over long distances through data communications gateways. Standalone PCs are of little value; they just emulate machines which are now "dead." A communicating PC is the true distributed information system for the mid-to-late 1980s.

Three Levels of Sophistication

Figure 1.2 underscored the issue of noncomputerized procedures. Typically, such procedures either escaped the attention of the analyst because their user was reluctant to identify them, or did not justify their handling by computer for cost/benefit reasons. DIS takes a totally new approach. We may now speak of the effective distribution of functions to be done locally. This definitely has an impact on computer design, input–output processors, front-end communications processors, intelligent terminals, etc., as a means of performing given functions. But the underlying issue is much broader than the functions referred to.

The salient problem in DIS design is the decision to use one of three levels of sophistication in projecting the new system.

The first level is *distributed processing* which is the implementation of one set of logical functions within multiple physical devices. Basically, it is the standalone minicomputer. The distribution of processing is realized through local or remote computers, with or without their own input–output devices and data base.

The second level of sophistication, which necessarily demands much more in terms of systems studies, is that of the *distributed data base*. It is one logical set of data stored at multiple physical locations interconnected and integrated among themselves. It is here that the avant-garde companies and financial institutions did their homework. A great deal of intellectual effort centered on this field. Its results decided which organizations pushed ahead. The distribution of the data base poses many systems challenges, among them the definition of the "primary" files needed to tune the DB in the case of mutations and discrepancies.

The next, higher level of sophistication is the *distributed operating system* involving the distribution of DB processing and network control. This is the true distributed intelligence system. It embraces such features as downline loading unattended operations, total network control, and other key features which find their fulfillment in the 1980s. In the evolving symmetric or balanced networks, no single host is in total control of the system and all computers within the network can control their own processes. We shall return to this issue and treat it in detail. Let us summarize these definitions. Distributed processing involves systems where large amounts of information are stored on media. But the data is *not* organized as a data base. This is the aim of distributed data bases. In turn, DDP† and DDB among themselves do not necessarily make a data communications system. This is the goal of distributed operating systems whose aim is to assure communications control while avoiding highly redundant storage.

At each level of sophistication, the designer must be aware that a basic reason for distributed intelligence is the impossibility of mastering extreme complexity. Large systems projects suffer problems different than those of small systems.

Other Dimensions of DIS

Three additional dimensions of distributed information systems are operations, management, and applications development. A basic factor here is the logical structure of the applications segments or functions to be performed. Are the tasks or functions mutually dependent, or are they independent from one another? Inventory management, personnel systems, manufacturing control, order entry, accounts receivable and payable may be either totally independent or interdependent to a greater or lesser degree. With maxicomputers most of these systems have been operated (with duplications, discrepancies, and incompatibilities) independently from one another because of the dual influence of the accounting machines era and the remoteness of the central installation.

But times have changed. The minicomputer brought the equipment capability near the user and with it the problems and responsibilities. Users became responsible for entering their own data into the system correctly.

Clearly, however, we must teach the end user how to work with the tools we offer. One example in this regard is that of one thousand United Technologies executives who took three-day courses on personal computers. Upon graduation, each was issued a PC with video, printer and other accessories to use in any suitable manner.

In the background of this policy is a major switch in management attitude toward the use of computers as an individual, intelligent workstation. So far, while computers are commonplace at lower corporate levels, they are not routinely used in the executive suite. This attitude must change.

More useful to corporation executives will be the next generation of multifunctional, communicating workstations. They will include not only computing power but also

---

† "Distributed data processing" as distinguished from the classic DP, "data processing."

word processing,

file access,

telephone facilities, and

dictating machines that respond to spoken commands.

The ws will be linked through local area networks and to other stations, minis and mainframes so that managers can share data and exchange messages. They will provide a wide range of services including electronic mail, financial control, strategic analysis, and graphics preparation.

This book does not advocate blind progress towards *personal computing*. Quite to the contrary, the company, its executives, and its system analysts must watch:

1. Cost of accomplishing a desired processing or logical function
2. Time needed to develop and implement the process
3. Maintenance requirements
4. Controls and standards relating to the process
5. Utility or relative priority of a given function
6. Expected results
7. Risks associated with a decentralized, distributed approach

There is no central computer department to blame anymore and to complain about to top management.

However, DIS is not certain to be an outright success just because it is modern. The procedural and the logical studies hold the key to success or to failure, and with them the architectural project which we shall be discussing.

Division of Labor

The division of labor and the specialization of functions have become possible with distributed processing. The integration of these functions into a working ensemble comes about with the study and implementation of distributed data bases. Does distribution of processing mean no centralized standards with everyone getting a computer and doing as he wants? Definitely not. This would be chaos. But what is the "right" level of distributed functions? This is, indeed, very debatable.

Centralization and decentralization vary over time by broad function, by specific task, by topology and local problem. The same is true when you look at the means for implementing a distributed information system. Some companies just distribute the hardware, leaving all organizational studies, system analysis, and programming centralized. Others also decentralize some of the software development functions. Those who distribute everything, including the control, are rare.

No matter which policy is chosen, there is a need for coordination. This involves:

1. Planning the use of all resources—human capital and equipment—under one authority.

Figure 1.4

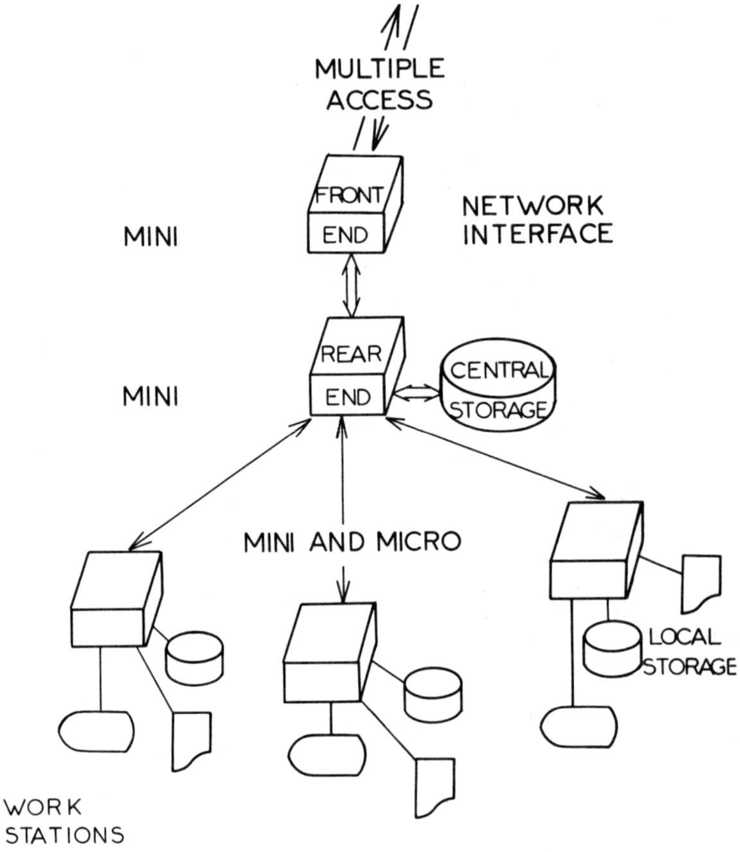

MULTIPLE ACCESS

MINI   FRONT END   NETWORK INTERFACE

MINI   REAR END   CENTRAL STORAGE

MINI AND MICRO

LOCAL STORAGE

WORK STATIONS

2. Communicating with users on current requirements and on projected requirements for the next one to three years.
3. Integrating the job of software analysts and programmers with the current requirements and within the longer range plan.
4. Projecting the system architecture for the development of network approaches (including host and terminal topology and usage).
5. Providing for "user exits" to help develop a creative effort at the periphery.
6. Projecting the use of packages to bring future requirements for software usage within a nearly 50–50 basis between packages and homemade programs.
7. Maintaining and updating the timetable for all the above-mentioned functions.
8. Initiating and administering design reviews.

Provided that these functions are carried out ably, centralization or decentralization becomes an option to be decided by management.

Figure 1.5

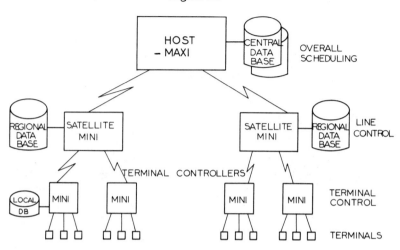

What must be done in DIS is to match the management organization, functions, and operating principle of the industry or financial institution contemplating a change from a centralized to a decentralized approach. However, for this to be done properly we must formulate a total DIS solution.

Let us take as an example the guiding principles followed by the Bank of America and Citibank. They may be stated in three main points:

1. Put the computer power into the hands of the decision maker.
2. Build the concept of the individual task, but keep in operation a central DB accessible to all.
3. Project a data communication network for system access and project it in a cost-effective manner.

Work stations are installed at the branch-office level. Each work station is dedicated to a particular task or function. Microcomputers in this local area network are peer systems linked in a hierarchical structure to central resources. But hierarchy does not necessarily mean a vertical organization.

Alternatives: Vertical and Horizontal

A distributed information system may be organized along centralized control* (asymmetric, vertical, hierarchical), decentralized control (symmetric, bus, ring, horizontal), or hybrid lines. The choice depends on the system architecture to be adopted.

Figure 1.5 illustrates an asymmetric centralized control approach with a host

*A centralized control solution which should not be confused with a "centralized system."

Figure 1.6

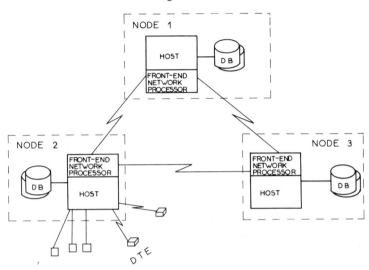

processor, satellite processors (usually mini), terminal controllers, and near-by and remote terminals. This equipment is connected vertically and the whole system is controlled by the host processor. The *host* is an information processor which provides supporting services to users and/or other processors. The *satellite* is an information processor which communicates with and depends on a host for services and guidance.

One should not confuse a vertical or hierarchical control system with a hierarchical information system, which may be totally decentralized in terms of architecture and control.

Two or more processors operating in an "equal partner" relationship constitute a symmetric or horizontal system. For instance, three minicomputer centers may be maintained in different cities provided with links which allow them to communicate freely; see Figure 1.6. Jobs may be transfered between centers; data load may be leveled. The failure of one center will *not* affect the whole system. Each center may control one or more front ends, FE, and each front end one or more terminals. For their part, the front end and terminal controllers support data entry operations by providing the appropriate screen format for data input; assist in detecting errors and report them back to the terminal user for corrective action; send correct transactions to the host (whether horizontal or vertical); and help the host's data load by removing and handling locally a considerable amount of processing and data storage functions.

Thus, the distributed information system reflects logical relationships among functional jobs and physical relationships among components. Actual implementations may use a variety of physical communications network structures.

The data communications, DC, functions include polling/selecting in long haul,

Figure 1.7.

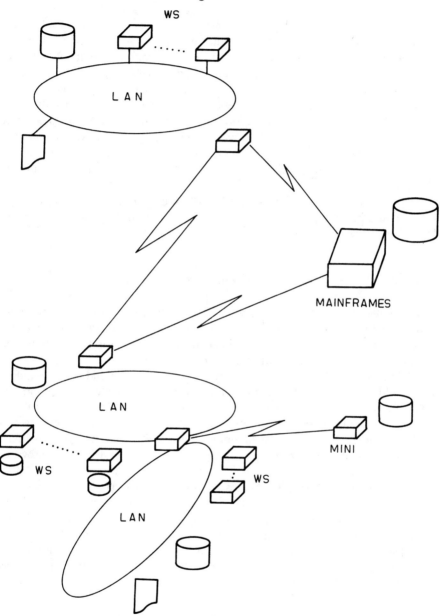

carrier sensing multiple access or token mechanism, in LAN, the choice of lines, the choice of architecture, code translation, data verification and data blocking, band rates, and line disciplines.

In general, the data communications work can be effectively done by gateways on a LAN; by the PC through proper routines; by distributed minicomputers, or by maxicomputers with colossal memory-eating operating systems.

Suppose, as Figure 1.7 does, that we have a number of PC's connected through a local area network. This LAN communicates with central mainframes which are now acting as large switches and global database engines. Through its gateway, the LAN also communicates with a number of other established resources, such as minis programmed in the 1970s for specific areas of application. The LAN features its own database—while each workstation may have an individual *microfile*. The system therefore supports not only individual computing but also individual data-basing—and does so in a cost/effective manner. (The cost of a workstation currently stands at or below $5,000. For an executive this represents a month's salary, yet it can increase his productivity 10 percent to 20 percent, recovering investments in less than a year.)

Cost features bring forward the wisdom of using distributed resources in computers and communications. Efficiency further underlines this solution. In the last analysis, the critical question for any system is, "Does it pay for itself?".

Conclusion

A distributed information system is *not* a decentralized system, as commonly spoken about. It is a hierarchical, structured, organized system with discipline and rules to be enforced at all times. Violation of these rules results in the negation of its advantages—and an eventual disintegration of the system.

In a hierarchical system, the rules have to do with security and protection, data accessibility, the use of shared resources, timeliness, accuracy, and economics. Standards are also necessarily directed to the issues of transferability of programs between computer resources, common data definitions, common operating procedures, and line of command or unity. Rules and standards applied within a DIS environment will help move processing close to the end users, improve response, decrease transit delays, and dwarf costs.

Not only can the PC workstations and local databases perform functions cost effectively, but the benefits to be derived range from reliability and maintainability, to modularity, expandability throughput, response time, workplace terminal independence, low implementation cost, and simplicity in applications software.

Table 1.1 identifies the factors entering a DIS design. Some constitute the basic background of the new information systems. User acceptance is acquired from the momentum of accomplishment.

10. Maintenance	9. Operation	8. Installation	6–7. Test	4–5. Construction	3. Physical design	2. Logical design	1. System planning	
								1. DIS concept: processing, data base, operating system
								2. New systems methodology
								3. Microelectronics
								4. Personal computing Workstations links: LAN, Long haul
								5. Communications
								6. Protocols
								7. Networking: routing and recovery
								8. Systems architecture
								9. Data base management
								10. Security, privacy, encryption recovery
								11. Interactive approach and user exits
								12. Operating system support
								13. Maintenance
								14. Cost effectiveness

Table 1.1

2
R&D and Semiconductor Technology

In 1982, Bell Telephone Laboratories spent $275 million on basic research, more than the rest of the U.S. industries. Although basic research accounts for only slightly more than 10 percent of Bell Labs' $2 billion annual budget, it has produced a prodigious flow of technology that has given the laboratories its formidable reputation.

Bell Labs now has 10,000 patents in effect and is receiving new ones at the rate of one a day. Under a 1956 antitrust consent decree, AT&T was required to license those patents. It has 400 licensing agreements with U.S. companies and nearly 200 more overseas. Without Bell Labs, there would be no Silicon Valley.

The drive to acquire larger markets also has economic reasons behind it. There is a basic law with semiconductors resulting from the large fixed capital investments needed for design and manufacturing: All things equal, every time production doubles, the price can be reduced by 20 percent—and price is the bottom line in electronics competition.

The other side of the coin is steady advancement. Microelectronics chips that contain nearly a half-million circuit elements and which are hundreds of times faster than currently available devices are being developed for a wide range of uses. The first Very High-Speed Integrated Circuits (VHSIC) are made using photolithography and have device geometries (the smallest dimension on the chip) as small as 1.25 micrometers. Chips in the mid-1980s will be made with electron beam lithography and will boast device geometries at the submicron level.

The new technology permits electronic circuits as complex as 100 Los Angeles street maps to be printed on a thumb tack. VHSIC will give electronics systems a tenfold increase in data processing capability. These "superchips" will be more reliable and need less power than the integrated circuits now in use.

Early applications include processors for multimode radar, communication systems, sonar, electro-optical systems, and advanced multimode fire-and-forget missiles. But the range of possible applications is much broader. As always, implementation in the commercial domain exceeds that in the military market.

At Bell Labs, systems engineers are working hard to convert the entire phone system into a digital communications network, substituting the off-on computer code of digital signals for continuous-wave voice signals all the way to each handset. When that process is completed, computerized information technologies such as videotex will be easily plugged into the system.

This merger of computer and communications takes advantage of microelectronics and computers, computer software, and photonics (using light-like electricity in switching and computing devices). The building of the next generation of semiconductor chips is a crucial technology.

Quite importantly, software now accounts for nearly half the research effort of Bell Labs, as management believes that it has a commanding expertise in software design. UNIX, the operating system two Bell computer scientists began developing in the late 1960s, is now a favorite in a race to become the standard operating software for the 16- and 32-bit microcomputer market. Bell Labs also considers itself a leader in developing *friendly software* that makes it easier to use a computer. To support this work, psychologists and human factors experts have a mission to develop a friendlier interface between man and machine.

From Transistors to Biochips

In 1947, Bardeen, Brattain and Shockley at Bell Labs invented the transistor, a solid-state device with the ability both to amplify an electric current and to act as a simple switch. It was the major invention of this century.

The early transistors were made of germanium, a material of the same chemical group as silicon. But germanium is fairly rare, and germanium transistors had a limited temperature range. Silicon had most of the advantages of germanium and few drawbacks.

The first silicon transistor was made by Texas Instruments in 1954. Silicon is cheap, plentiful, easy to handle, and has an oxide which is useful in the fabrication of semiconductor devices and can also be used as a dielectric.

A good example of step-by-step improvements is silicon-on-sapphire (pioneered by Hewlett-Packard), involving the laying of fine silicon tracks on a slice of sapphire, providing a better combination of speed and power than conventional silicon chips. Semiconductor designers also strive to pack the components on the silicon chips closer together because the electronic circuits can then operate more quickly since the electronic signals have less distance to travel. With memory circuits, the aim is to cram more storage space in a smaller area. This solves some of the problems, but in the longer run the development curve tappers off.

Because silicon has its limitations, there is interest to develop and use other materials, such as gallium arsenide (GaAs) which can run twice as fast. Presently, gallium arsenide is probably the most important of the newer semiconductor materials. Research into its properties and potential is being undertaken at a series of commercial laboratories throughout the world. Bell Labs has, for example, built an integrated circuit from gallium arsenide that incorporates 16 tiny lasers along its edge. That chip will be used in converting electrical signals to light. The high-power lasers used for communications through fiber optics utilize complex compounds such as GaAs to achieve exactly the right wavelength. Gallium arsenide circuitry offers the possibility of high-speed computation in a system which would not need elaborate cooling methods because of the lower power requirements.

Concurrently, *field effect transistors* (FET) are emerging as strong contenders for microwave switch applications in communications satellites. Gallium arsenide FETs are likely to replace PIN diodes in satellites due to higher speeds and lower power consumption. Using arrays of FETs, researchers built an 8x8 switch matrix for time division multiple-access (TDM) applications at 4 GHz. The device (built by Hughes) achieved a 1-nanosecond transition time at 10 milliwatts drive control power.

This is in line with a general trend in making the basic electronics circuitry faster, smaller, and cheaper. These aims are always at the top of a semiconductor designer's list. Since the early 1960s, it has been the pattern that every two or three years the complexity of a silicon chip doubles but the price continues to fall.

The introduction of the first microprocessor—a computer on a chip—in the early 1970s marked a new phase in both electronics and computing. It lowered the cost of computing to a level where it could be employed in almost any application imaginable, and set the grounds for the appearance of equipment as diverse as electronic games, new aircraft navigation systems, aids for the disabled, heart pacemakers and a totally new generation of industrial controls.

While the developmental trend is expected to continue, we are also at the beginning of a different era. The *why* is self-evident through the steady process of evolution. The *how* calls for a reference to another basic invention seemingly unrelated to electronics, yet which constitutes part of the same major trend.

The first historic development in learning how information systems are organized in living matter took place in the early 1950s. In England, two scientists—James Watson and Francis Crick—discovered the double helix, thus exposing the gene to human scrutiny for the first time in history.

Some 20 years later, in 1973, the second development took place. Biologists Stanley Cohen of Stanford University and Herbert Boyer of the University of California took two unrelated organisms *that would not mate in nature*, isolated a piece of DNA from each, and then combined the two pieces of genetic material. The result was a new form of life that never before existed. *Recombinant DNA* is a kind of biological engine that can be used to glue together the genetic fabric of unrelated organisms. Intensive research throughout the world is now thrusting mankind into the era of *biotechnology* and promises new markets greater than ever (Figure 2.1)—but also new risks as the effects of the new evolution cannot be foreseen.

As scientists, we are learning how to manipulate, recombine, and reorganize living tissue into forms and shapes which never existed in nature. Biological knowledge is currently doubling every five years, and in genetics the quantity of informa-

Figure 2.1.

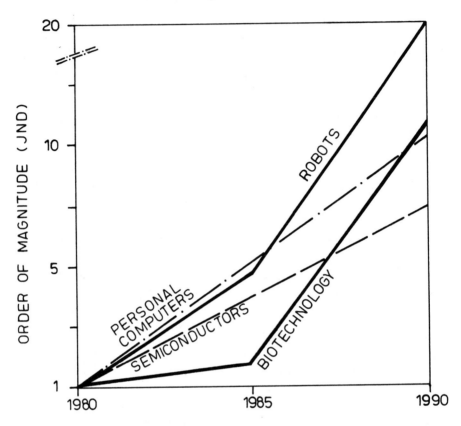

tion is doubling every two years. In this regard, research is being done to replace the microchip with the *biochip* and the microcomputer with the *biocomputer.*

Within a delicate protein latticework of a biocomputer will be organic molecules (the biochips) that act and react under an electric current, winding or unwinding, and passing hydrogen atoms from one end to the other. As they shift positions and shapes, the biochips (molecules) pass along information in the manner of integrated circuits. Since they are so tiny and close together, they can perform a calculation in about a millionth the time of today's best VLSI. These molecular diodes, transistors, wires—generally protein architectures—will most likley be manufactured by simple E.coli bacteria through genetic engineering.

A future aim of biotechnology is to build a computer that can design and assemble itself by using the same mechanism common to all living creatures: The coding of genetic information in the self-replicating DNA double helix and the transaction of this chemical code into the structure of protein. This is the *key vector,* or vehicle, through which the computer industry and the life sciences may be joining together in a new field: *molecular electronics.* Eventually, man will turn living material into *biocomputers* and use them to further engineer living materials. Biocomputers may be engineered into living systems, just as microcomputers are incorporated into mechanical systems today. They will monitor activity, adjust performance, speed up and slow down metabolic processes, transform living matter into products, and perform many other functions. Such computers may even reproduce themselves, cancelling the remaining distinctions between living and nonliving processes.

The Pace of Microelectronics

To appreciate the facilities we have now available to work with in terms of products and processes, let's recall that just 30 years ago some of these were unavailable. It's only in the mid-1950s that semiconductors substituted vacuum tubes as the main logical element in electronic circuits.

In the early 1960s, manufacturing technology made a big step forward: It became possible to realize 20 (elementary) logical functions in one circuit. In the late 1960s, TTL (transistor/transistor/logic) came into being. However, the decade of the 60s is generally characterized by small scale integration (SSI).

In the early 1970s, integrated circuits were first regrouped on chip electronic components to form a complex logical function, and each chip was caged in a box. To make this feasible, multilayer manufacturing processes (for instance, printed circuits in six layers) were needed to realize some 800 elementary logical functions on one PCB.

In the mid-1970s, CML (current mode logic) substituted TTL, which had reached its limits. In the late 1970s, CML technology permitted up to 8,000 logical functions on a PCB. In 1983, the 256 kilobit chip became the first significant component of the early 1980s, which also saw complex logical functions on a chip with Intel's 80286 microprocessor having 130,000 transistors.

Designing a new integrated circuit board from scratch is a major undertaking. The development cycle typically takes about a year, and the cost is very high. Therefore, circits are only economically viable when very large quantities of the special circuit would be required. Hence the trend toward commercially available microprocessors, such as the Intel and Motorola offerings. At the same time, by making considerable use of computer-aided design systems, chipmakers can now tailor circuits from a library of predefined functions. Development time can thus be halved, while costs are reduced and quality significantly bettered.

By using technology to project new products, we obtain many advantages in terms of system performance and reliability. For instance, integrated circuits save money, by placing more of the functions needed for a new electronic system on a single chip, production costs can be reduced. Integrated circuits are also more reliable. Reducing components cuts down on the number of possible system failures.

Microcoding is another area of electronics which is now much more effective through IC. It can help accomplish three things:

1. Enforces standards.

   A microcode is very expensive to change and so impedes changes in microcode, while changes are simpler and faster with software.

2. Provides parallelism.

   In microcode we can do many things at the same time. In software we can do essentially one.

3. Eliminates duplication, particularly in support for virtual machine assistance and the extended control program.

But the real mark of the early 1980s is the wide use of microprocessors at an affordable price. Microcomputers include a microprocessor, some form of RAM (random access memory) and ROM (read only memory), input/output control facilities, and communications interfaces. They can be classified by:

Word length expressed in BPW, typically: 4, 8, 12, 16, and 32 bits;

Chip count: single, dual, multiple; and

Application: logic replacement, calculator, general purpose microcomputer.

Various types of microprocessor chips are available and include calculator-type units, fixed instruction set units, bit slice machines, and microprogrammable engines. The range of applications covers logic network replacement, program controllers and calculators, and small system configurations with varying architectures.

The 8 BPW design is being phased out of the PC market and into handheld devices and calculators, replacing the 4 BPW designs. By 1985, 8 BPW PCs will have run their course. The 16 BPW and 32 BPW designs have entered PCs. The latter is the engine of CAD-oriented PCs and of many minis.

Internal design, BPW, speed, and programming considerations must be made in selecting a microprocessor. Other critical variables include system costs, availability and second-source constraints, flexibility for expansion of the basic system, user groups, documentation, power supplies, and noise immunity. Eventually, broad new markets will absorb more microprocessors than currently established products—even if currently some of these products look like fad. As personal computers evolve into functioning, intelligent workstations, their contribution to mental and clerical productivity will be beyond question. For instance, a new microcomputer system may someday bring paralyzed limbs to life again, allowing some paraplegics to walk and stroke victims to use their arms once more. This device has been tried with preliminary success on animals. The computer package, installed above the paralyzed limb, acts as an outpost of the brain. It is linked to a set of implanted electrodes that trigger muscle movement on command of the computer. It not only provides nerve signals to formerly inactive muscles but also listens to feedback from the muscles, keeping constant track of motion so that complex movements can be made smoothly.

Making subtler, coordinated movements with artificial stimulation has turned out to be a far more difficult problem. Walking, for example, involves many muscles contracting and relaxing in rapid sequence, using feedback from the muscles and the brain to keep a steady motion while swinging the body's weight forward from foot to foot. Using a microcomputer to govern nerve and muscle action, it is now feasible to move smoothly and to coordinate the eight muscles necessary for walking forward in the leg of a cat. This experiment took place on a lab table with the cat anesthetized and held in place upright while the computer moved its leg.

An obstacle to computer-actuated approaches has been the sophisticated, rapid control necessary to coordinate the movement of many muscles. After studying the motion of cats' legs, the inventor, made a computer program that will give movement signals to the paralyzed leg based on information from two sources:

The motion of one leg is translated into signals triggering motion of the other leg.

As it moves, the paralyzed leg provides feedback about its own position and muscle tension to continue smooth motion.

This computer-assisted but still mechanical approach to the engineering of the human body may give way to new modes of thought and new solutions brought about by bioengineering.

An Inventory of New Images

The early 1950s and the early 1980s have this in common—they present new horizons in terms of professional perspectives, systems development, and machine components. One of the most significant breakthroughs is in semiconductor technology: the computers and communications industry—from supplier activity to user costs—will account for 13 percent of the nation's GNP by 1990. Further:

Some 20 percent of the total U.S. labor force will be required to have some knowledge of data processing.

About 65 percent of that labor force will be dependent to some measure on the use of data processing.

There will be approximately 175,000 large-scale general-purpose computer sites at various parts in the U.S., not including the close to 10,000,000 dedicated systems for such applications areas as process control, inventory management, and data entry including local area networks and dedicated PCs.

The new market horizons which are now opening will require a good six years before they are in full swing. In another decade or so they will reach maturity, but until nearly the end of the twentieth century, we shall see a time of transition.

To appreciate the impact on our lives of these new technologies, we should return to the fundamentals. First we have to focus on the right image.

A person's mental inventory of images largely determines his ability to understand events. The General Motors Corporation, for instance, would be quite inconceivable in ancient Greece because the people of that age did not possess the requisite set of images for industrial and commercial operations of that type and size. Columbus would never have set sail westward had he not had an image of the round world and a high value system for spices. The Industrial Revolution in England cannot be simply explained by the availability of coal and iron, it was much more determined by a change in basic images.

Without the requisite images of simple concepts, more complex ones cannot be understood. Basic images are so important that the ideas or concepts necessary for progress will always precede the actual development.

The importance of having the necessary images before a new development can come into common use can hardly be underestimated. Market research tells us not so much whether or not a product or service will be accepted; it points out what necessary images of perceived value or functional importance are already publicly accepted. If important images are missing, then it will be necessary to create them before the service will be commonly accepted.

The pioneers in new services often find slow acceptance. This is precisely because they are in a new-image-building business. The second and third entries into the marketplace benefit from the expensive image-building activities of the first. Nevertheless, the first has an important asset, if he knows how to use it. He has the opportunity to formulate the new service image and thus dictate the basis for new additional service options that can be added to the service at a later time.

This is what is happening today with rising markets and falling prices.

Since 1975, vast improvements in price/performance ratios have become commonplace. The trend is continuing—

Since 1950 the cost-per-bit of information in high-speed storage has decreased 2000-fold.

Since 1950, the price of 100,000 calculations has dropped from $1.56 to 0.3 cents.*

In the past few years the cost of computer memory declined at the rate of 40 percent per year. In the mid-60s memory devices cost 3 to 5 cents per bit. They now cost 1/2,000 of a cent per bit.

Costs for discs dropped by 40 percent in 2 years.

Costs for computer-logic decline by 25 percent per year.

*Significantly, that cost stood at 5 cents in 1970.

New innovations have a high probability of being called obsolete before instal-lation. Obsolete, though, does not mean useless. Rather, better, more cost/effective alternatives are steadily made available. Such alternatives radically alter informa-tion systems concepts and their implementation.

Essence of Change

In the information systems profession, change is the essence of our work as we strive for continuing productivity improvement as much in equipment as in people. The manager who cannot cope with and plan for change, *and* produce continuing change, will not be effective. This role is something new and different from the traditional roles of management. Change brings to professionals both risk and op-portunity, but definitely the greatest opportunity (and test) is in the marketplace.

If the automobile industry had progressed on the same curve as computers in the last 25 years, we would have been able to buy a medium-sized car for under 10 dollars, and this price would have dropped to less than 3 dollars within 5 years. On average, computer power prices have dropped by a factor of 50 during the last two decades, as concerns system prices.

The decline is much more dramatic for some components. For example, memory (RAM) prices declined by about 30 percent to 40 percent annually between 1971–82, to a level approaching .001 cent, and with a million components or bits per IC.

Three variables characterize the bit of information in 30 years of development (1953-1983).

cost (the reduction has been 2,000 : 1);

volume (here the ratio is 1,000 : 1);

speed (with a ratio of 150,000 : 1).

Cost reductions in computer technology were the result of:

1. A better fundamental understanding of the materials used
2. The development of computerized design techniques
3. Sophisticated manufacturing tools
4. New techniques used to package increasingly dense circuits
5. Volume production
6. The push of competition.

Today, a microcomputer with 64 KB* can be brought for less than $500. It is projected that by 1985 advances in microelectronics will bring the cost of the 64 KB chip to about 10 dollars.

Disc drive capacity has jumped from 5 M bytes in the early 1960s to over 3

*10^3 bytes; a byte is 8 bits.

gigabytes today. This is nearly three orders of magnitude. The price per MB (megabyte) has decreased nearly a hundredfold during this same period.

The basic rule aptly states that *when something changes by a factor of 10, fundamental new effects will be presented, and management decisions will change.* Such changes will be reflected in every walk of industrial and business life in terms of costs, speed, and facilities.

Throughout this decade, and in the 1990's, every time we take a step we shall find that—within the short span of 2 to 4 years—*a product which is overtaken by developments* must *leave the "normal" curve and sell at a dramatically lower cost—or nobody will buy it anymore.*

By the late 1980s, we should expect 10,000 times greater performance from Josephson (tunnel junction) technology. A MB storage chip may cost approximately $30 by 1985–1987. The entire systems profession will be affected by this. A 100- to 500-fold improvement in performance over current levels if practical by 1985, will be sufficient to change our style of programming. A further 500-fold increase in speeds and capacities will dramatically alter the way we program future computers. There will no longer be much concern about efficient code or wasteful use of main memory. Working on-line, programmers and analysts will be able to try all possible solutions to a problem since it takes a few nanoseconds per try. Trial and error, interactive analysis and programming analysis will dramatically change the way we create software.

Cost considerations will be radically altered in the near future. Today it costs 5 times the price of a minicomputer to do the analysis and programming for just one shift per day. It costs easily 20 times the price of a PC to program a general ledger application. With 500-fold speeds, one hour of computer time may take a million-and-a-half man-hours to program.

For the programmer, the problems of constructing and verifying software should be met at the chip level. On-line analysis, on-line programming, and even specialized AP computers (which are rarities today) may become commonplace tomorrow.

In considering computer-aided analysis and programming we should not forget that although the computer industry has been successful at expanding equipment capabilities while reducing costs and package size, there's still quite a way left to go before the ultramicrocomputer or picocomputer becomes a reality. Picocomputers will find their way into a wide range of audio-visual materials and workbooks, in-structor-led and laboratory sessions, and on-line or standalone terminals to serve professionals and for the training of a vast population of users.

Market Characteristics

The most striking characteristic of the microelectronics industry has been a persis-tent and *rapid decline in the cost of a given electronic function.*

It is now possible to put the computing power* of a computer that cost $1

---

*Excluding auxiliary equipment and the power supply of peripherals.

Figure 2.2. Medium Cost of a PDP-8 with 4 KB

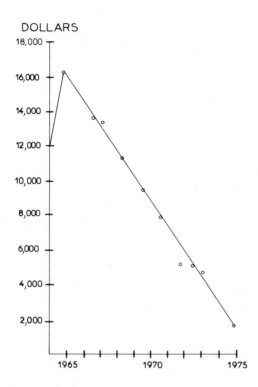

million in the early 1950s on a chip that now costs $20. That same chip cost $100 a few years ago and probably will cost less than $10 in 1985.

Minicomputers originally evolved as small processors that were almost like components. They were almost always a part of a larger, more complex system. Now, users have become so sophisticated, and the PC so powerful and flexible, that the same machine can be used as a component of totally different systems, or as complete standalone equipment.

This story is not exclusive to the 1980s, and neither is the PC the sole engine to experience the dramatic effects of dropping prices. For instance, PDP 8, which more than any other machine helped put DEC on the way to becoming a multibillion dollar corporation, also had a dramatic cost-reduction story (see Figure 2.2).

Another reason for the rapid decline in cost is due to the "learning curve": the more experience an industry has, the more efficient it becomes. Thus, the PDP 11, introduced in 1970, cost its manufacturer in hardware and software investment an estimated 1 billion dollars, with the lion's share on the software side. Being a highly successful computer, it has given its manufacturer many billions of dollars in return.

Such investments are justified because of the size of the market. As already underlined, well-run industries reduce their costs (in constant dollars) *by 20 percent or more* each time their cumulative output doubles. For the semiconductor industry, we find that integrated circuit costs have declined by 28 percent with each doubling of the industry's experience. Some of the costs, though, tend to remain steady or even increase—particularly those having a human labor component. Maintenance is an example, yet self-maintenance, assisted by on-line diagnostics, is a good way to cut costs.

Another major impact of inexpensive circuitry is on the location of computer power. It is becoming more and more feasible to *distribute computer power* to the points where information originates or is needed instead of transmitting all data to and from a central computer installation. It is no wonder that there is a shift in the nature of the computer population (Figure 2.3).

Not all firms entering the field of PCs can be successful. In 1983, as many as 40 companies introduced portables that range in size from a bulky 30-pounder to lap-size models that weigh about 4 pounds. Sales are growing incredibly fast: from $4.7 billion in 1982 to an estimated $7.7 billion in 1983 and a projected $21.6 billion by 1987.

As the industry grows, the entry level changes. No longer can someone launch a company from a garage with pocket money. Carving out a piece of the market is expensive. Advertising used to consist of just a few homemade ads in electronic hobby magazines. In 1983, some companies will spend tens of millions of dollars on publicity. Compaq, which makes a portable IBM work-alike computer, spent $30 million getting started.

Table 2.1 identifies the early entries into the PC field who have been able to maintain relative market leadership. However, about 30 companies who exhibited at the 1982 National Computer Conference in Houston did not show up for 1983.

Because of their technological lead, American and Japanese semiconductor firms have left most of their European counterparts far behind. European chip suppliers now control less than 35 percent of their own market.

In machine tools, Japan has been taking business from Europe by using microelectronics to build extra-value features into equipment. To survive companies must incorporate high technology into communications equipment faster than their competitors.

Combining market potential with the competitive advantages offered by integrated circuits, communications firms are also competing with the development of intelligent lines and feature phones. The latter use electronics to perform such sophisticated functions as call-forwarding, two-digit dialing, and conference calling. At least 15 such telephone systems are being produced. Chip- or biochip-based information systems distributed at the level of personal computing serve as a focal point around which users can bring the latest technology into the organization.

New technology is important not because of scientific excitement—no matter how great this may be—but as a function of economic considerations as they impact the end user. When the end user buys a product, he doesn't want one at the end of its life or one which is new and may have "bugs." He aims to get a service

Figure 2.3.
Small Business System
Personal Computers

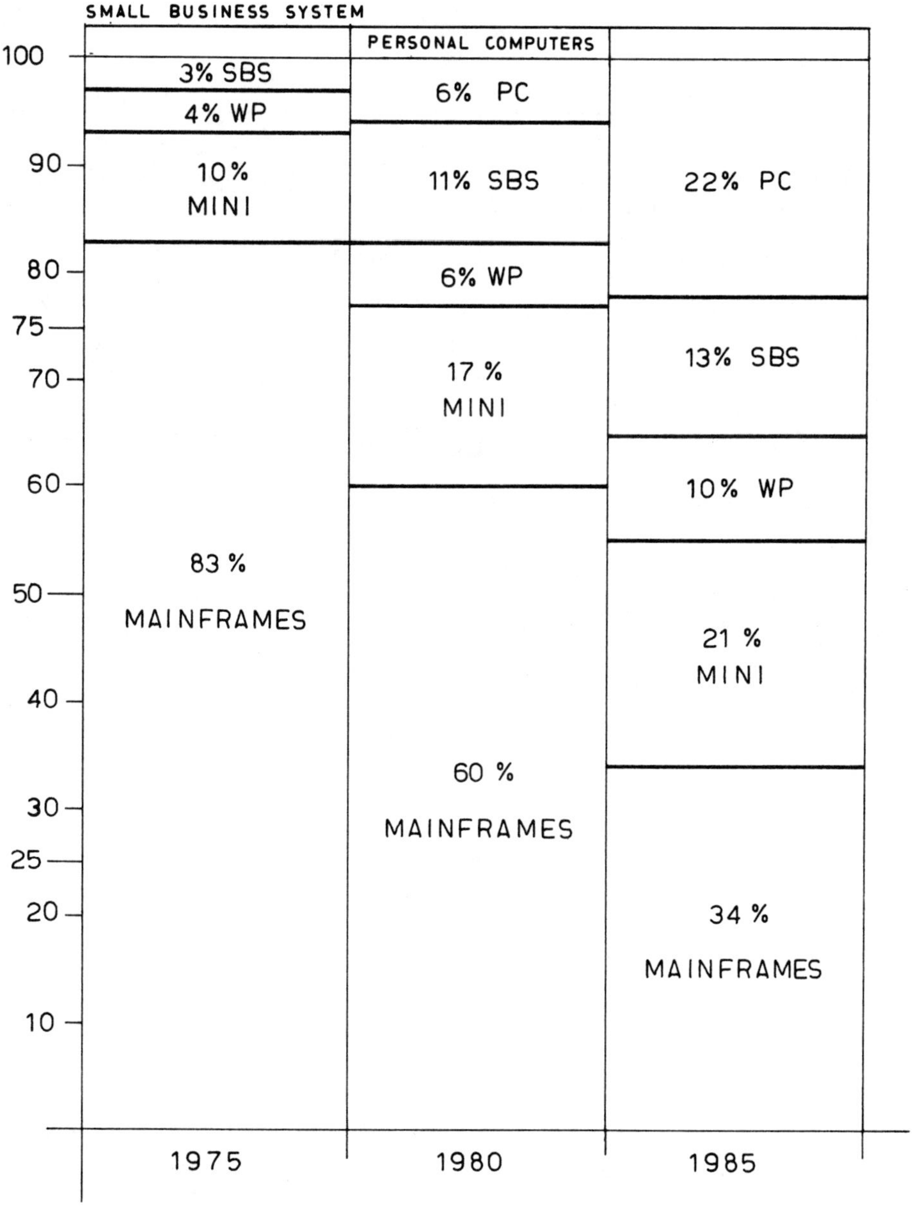

SMALL BUSINESS SYSTEM

3% SBS	6% PC	
4% WP		22% PC
10% MINI	11% SBS	
	6% WP	13% SBS
	17 % MINI	10% WP
83 % MAINFRAMES		21 % MINI
	60 % MAINFRAMES	34 % MAINFRAMES
1975	1980	1985

Table 2.1.

The Early Entries in the PC Field.

| Company | Billing in Millions of Dollars | | | |
	Entry Date	1978	1979	1980
Apple Computer	February 1977	10	75	166
Commodore	September 1977	22	55	110
Tandy Radio Shack	October 1977	57	150	400

from the product which is able to grow and develop and to have a "company relation" with the supplier:

Is the supplier commited to him and to his market?

Does the supplier understand his problem?

Will the supplier support the product?

3

Cost-Benefit with the New Technologies

We have been discussing distributed information systems as an overall term for a variety of processing structures whose common goal is the placement of local computer power at the disposal of every unit of business. The purposes have been described as enhancing each unit's operations, controlling a timely flow of intelligence among these units, and reducing data-handling costs.

Every phase of data processing has a cost in time and in money; both must be accounted for along with the conceptual integrity of the system determining its ease of use. In terms of time, money, and intervening errors, the cost is higher the further out the sources and the destination of the data; see Figure 3.1

This is why the traditional batch-processing channel did not work well. In a batch-processing environment data is grouped in order to be transmitted in the same data-handling operation. The disadvantages are obvious: delays, costs, and errors. At the point of origin, clerical hours are spent in the transcribing, batching, and expediting of the support media (usually paper) to the central location. Then time will be spent on data-entry equipment; computer runs will be needed to weed out errors; more clerical time will be required to check the computer outputs; and a sequential treatment is necessary to update files: the operating system launches the program on the basis of job control cards.

This operation is obsolete, slow, and clumsy. We have available today the methodology and the systems necessary for moving information from a *source* location to the *processing* sites and on to the *destination*. Modern technology provides a set of functions necessary for the manipulation of the *input* information to produce the desired *output* (results) and this can be done on-line.

Getting On-Line

One of the biggest breakthroughs in data processing has been the development of the on-line access terminal. For the first time management has data that is up to the

Figure 3.1
Computer use on an integrated basis should start at point of origin (as early as possible) and end at point of destination (as late as feasible). Only then can computer use give profitable results.

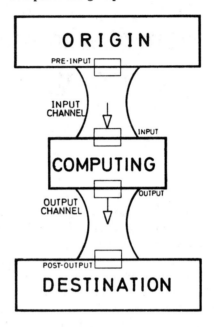

minute. Today, the on-line method is the basic design of a whole new generation of inexpensive computers. Forward-looking industries and financial institutions are using them for better management control and more efficient operation throughout decisions issues, scheduling processes, and settlement procedures; see Figure 3.2.

A description of the elements which define a distributed information system distinguishes four basic aspects:

Distributed processing at transaction level

Distributed communications (not only transmission)

Distributed data bases

Distributed procedures (restructured to fit the organizational requirements and to profit from the new technological realities)

The days when state-of-the-art limitations forced users to place all their computer resources at a distant central site are past. There is today no reason for adjusting business operations to meet the restrictions imposed by such centralization.

Distribution of computer power is made feasible by technology in a way that best fits the user's needs by locating processing and storage capabilities *close* to the

Figure 3.2

Information handling in an organization can be divided into three large families of problems

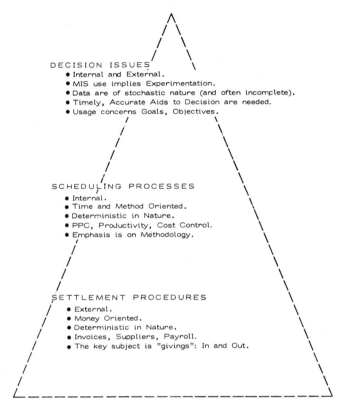

DECISION ISSUES
- Internal and External.
- MIS use implies Experimentation.
- Data are of stochastic nature (and often incomplete).
- Timely, Accurate Aids to Decision are needed.
- Usage concerns Goals, Objectives.

SCHEDULING PROCESSES
- Internal.
- Time and Method Oriented.
- Deterministic in Nature.
- PPC, Productivity, Cost Control.
- Emphasis is on Methodology.

SETTLEMENT PROCEDURES
- External.
- Money Oriented.
- Deterministic in Nature.
- Invoices, Suppliers, Payroll.
- The key subject is "givings": In and Out.

workplace: the individual office at headquarters, the factory floor, the sales or inventory management outlet, or the branch office. Whether on-line terminals or minicomputers are installed at remote locations, it becomes feasible to:

1. Shorten the data input route
2. Avoid repetitive clerical operations
3. Provide for error detection and protection as the data is captured and transcribed
4. Improve the response time
5. Eliminate the delay inherent in round trips
6. Assure an interactive type of man-machine communication
7. Reduce the costs of data handling
8. Simplify programming tasks and handle more transaction in the process
9. Automate the fringes of the operations in the periphery—which so far have defied computers

The organizational study and the definition of the logical functions are the pillars on which a good solution will rest.

One reason for distributed networks not becoming widespread overnight is that the currently installed base of computer systems is primarily centralized and batch oriented. That investment in equipment and software cannot be lightly tossed aside and will continue in place until depreciated.

Another basic reason why DIS has not become widespread overnight is the lack of images in the minds of both analysts and users with which to explore the new frontiers. A terminal for each user is an efficient solution which quite often makes economic sense. But where will the drive come from to put into action departures from the past which often negate what people have been taught to believe whether formally or through personal experience?

Decentralization and Centralization

The evolution of new concepts is necessarily based on two pillars: the issue of human effectiveness versus system efficiency (i.e., hardware performance per dollar versus people producitivity), and corporate issues and current pactices such as the use of centralized information systems—now a vital part of the headquarters' management—functioning in today's decentralized organizational management. Information requirements are best answered through a transition, rather than by a total negation of current facts.

Because control over information means greater political power, the corporation and its organizational subentities are increasingly dependent on data processing systems. This makes availability and reliability of the information resources, a critical issue. This used to be the case in some industries (e.g., airlines), but by now it is widespread—the whole financial sector being a specific case.

On the other hand, it is just as true that data processing's growing percentage of total budgets is causing corporations to seek means to optimize their computer expenses while caring for and feeding this vital resource. While the larger organizations look for economics and for alternatives, technological improvements and developments such as microprocessors, minicomputers, and input–output devices mean that smaller company organizational units can now afford their own equipment. The classic accounting machine gives way to the minicomputer at least, to the sophisticated terminal systems with full processing capabilities.

But management also has other concerns to look after: security of information system resources when centralized sites are possible targets of dissident groups is a factor in some decisions to distribute the corporation's nerve center and data bases. The decentralization of information systems is no eccentricity on the behalf of organizations. It is a hard fact of life. Security, privacy, even survival may depend on it.

Facing the Constraints

We can say easily that of all the constraints and factors involved, hardware represents one of the least important, whereas software and management issues are very significant, perhaps even paramount.

The evolution toward DIS passed through the phase of centralized real-time operations. This left its mark on present-day systems. Of the systems labeled as distributed, many prove to be centralized data bases that have been divided among several sites.

A survey revealed the following statistics among the companies interviewed. Users of truly distributed systems accounted for only 60 percent of the population surveyed. But, only 20 percent of the computer users had split their databases among several remote locations.

Only one of the users interviewed rejected distributed processing outright after thoroughly evaluating the alternatives. Other users, however, were undecided about the approach either because they suspected that distributed databases would clash with their existing procedures or because their data processing plans were still in the formative stage.

However, it is a common weakness of surveys that they fail to identify the transition concepts in management thinking as new systems and components arise. Delay in application is directly related to this transition.

The first big move was made not in the 1970s but in the 1950s with the transition from punched card (unit record) equipment to computers. Such equipment was so deeply imbedded in thinking—both among specialists and at the management level—that it dominated computer usage until practically today. We can only hope that this sort of failure will not repeat itself with DIS—treating minicomputers as large-scale equipment.

The next major transition took place with the move from reasonably small to big machines, naturally for reasons of cost effectiveness.

Finally we now realize how inefficient we are with big systems. We tried for too long and too hard to run the big machines like small ones. We found out the hard way that even scale has its diseconomics: you have to keep the system running, find experienced operators, and hire more people. All this costs so much more money. And software costs outrun the user's budget. This is the problem with project management; it is made for the small, sharp team of experts. Man-made software is also too slow and not big enough for large-scale computer systems. As a result, the systems profession is retooling for new horizons where the impact of the computer will be felt to its fullest extent.

Computers must make their own software—or at least assist the expert in constructing it on-line. Hardware interfaces, controllers, peripherals, and communications devices must be studied in detail. They should have sufficient intelligence to enable timely hook-ups and plug-to-plug compatibility. A plug-to-plug compatibility goal for both hardware and software will enable capitalizing on the coming technical breakthroughs in mass memories, data communications, and a range of peripherals. Plug-to-plug compatible software can and should be attained. Most importantly, we must make the machine (terminal, front-end, local minicomputer) work unattended. If in a network, we must assure that the power is kept on so that a host computer can call it automatically.

The human elements are the most vital but also the most expensive components of the information system. We should be thrifty in the use of clerical help in general and of the computer operators in particular—but not when it comes to putting systems talent to work.

Financial Criteria for Choice

One of the subjects which the current literature leaves unexplained is the criteria for choosing microcomputers and related equipment when confronted with a specific choice. This lack of guidelines leads to difficulties which are compounded by the fact that personal computers are predominantly installed near operating entities— while operating entities dislike becoming involved in matters of technology, including programming, operations, standards, and communications.

Below is a list of criteria for evaluating alternative approaches and guidelines compiled from visits with leading American and European industrial and financial institutions.

If the minicomputer is projected for use in multiple installations (e.g., branch offices, factories, sales offices), then choose only one type of equipment.

If the machine is to be used only for *one* installation (e.g., foreign operations, commercial paper, the management of a large client), then choose the equipment with the characteristics which indicate the best way of tackling the job.

The software accompanying the machine should always be considered, but its availability is much more crucial where the machine will be used for only one installation.

There should be no more than one basic application on the microcomputer at any time, unless the applications are very similar. A multiprogramming/multiprocessing environment should be avoided.

The creation (and, hence, proliferation) of peripheral data processing centers, in the classic way we know them, is an expensive mistake. There should be *no* minicenters, no professional operators.

The microcomputer software should be purchased. If written, then this should be done at the center, but a wise policy is to allow for "user exits" and to let it be known that contributions are welcomed. Periodically, these should be examined and pruned.

Site selection should be evaluated in the light of service both to the branch and to the organization. The proper topology can make it feasible that less than 20 percent of the operations in the periphery interest the center, and less than 2 percent touch other regions. (the 80/20 rule).

The justification of a microcomputer and local area network installations should definitely respond to basic economics.

Table 3.1 presents a cost comparison between a batch job and a German industrial firm. Two procedures are considered and each costed on a maxicomputer and a minicomputer. The difference is striking. For the same applications, the ratio between maxicomputer and minicomputer yearly costs is 2.97:1. Fringe benefits, for example, easier access, are at the minicomputer's side.

Now look at a real-time environment; Table 3.2 gives the data. It compares a minicomputer installation's ability to handle seven terminals in a bank's branch office to a starlike network's ability. Here the cost ratio between maxicomputer and minicomputer is greater: 3.12:1. In addition to financial benefits, the minicomputer provides better client service, reliability/availability, and software development and maintenance.

Now let's compare the minicomputer solution with an implementation of PCs and LAN. Figure 3.3 gives the financial data expressed in thousands of dollars. Six alternatives are considered within the framework of four solutions.

Table 3.1

Cost Comparison of a Batch Job from a German Industrial Firm

	Cost (1,000 Deutsche marks, KDM)	
	Procedure I	*Procedure II*
Maxicomputer		
Hardware	160	45
Operational expenses	130	36
Supplies	150	56
Data entry	220	36
	660	173
	833 KDM/YEAR	
Minicomputer		
Hardware	140	40
Operational expenses	30	10
Supplies	20	10
Different expenses and reserve	(20	10)
	210	70
	280 KDM/YEAR	

Table 3.2

Cost Comparison of a Maxicomputer and a Minicomputer in a Real-time Environment

Service	Maxicomputer Starlike Network	Minicomputer
1. Central processor	Rental $$\frac{\$100,000/m}{250\ T} = \$400/m,T$$	Purchase $$\frac{\$110,000}{5\ years} = \begin{array}{l}\$2,000/ \\ year\ for\ 7 \\ terminals\end{array}$$
2. Terminals	Purchase $$\frac{\$10,000/year}{5Y} = \$2,000/Y,T$$	
3. Lines	$$\frac{\$600,000/year}{250\ T} = \$2,400/Y,T$$	At 1/5 this cost x 7 (for 7 terminals) = $3,360/year
4. Operations expenses	Take 100% of central processor expenses: $4,800/Y,T	Must be nil but, say, 1/4 of 1 man-year, at $24,000/man-year = $6,000/year
Summary	$14,000/Y.T for 7 terminals = $98,000/year	$31,360/year
5. Client service		+
6. Reliability/availability		+
7. Software development and maintenance		+

Key: m = month
    Y = year
    T = terminal

Solution 1 shows the substitution of conventional equipment (typewriters, calculators, nonintelligent terminals) of a medium-sized bank by similar but modern units.

Solution 2 took the approach of changing from a centralized realtime option to locally installed minis able to support less than 5 to 6 seconds in response time.

Two options fit within this approach: The one would give one minicomputer-based, nonintelligent terminal to each of the department's 35 employees. The other would do so for only the managers and the secretaries, while giving one terminal per two professional employees for a total of 23.

Solutions 3 and 4 adopt the PC and LAN approach. The former would put a personal computer under every desk, and the latter would give machines to only 23 people (like one of the No. 2 choices). Furthermore, with Solution 3 there are two alternatives. The more expensive one incorporates a 10 MB hard disc (HD) per PC over and above the 40 MB File Server of the LAN. The other alternative does away with the HD.

Also, as the figure demonstrates, three different vendor sources of practically equal potential have been examined. The one (supplier B) is definitely very expensive and out of range, and as a result has been dropped. Suppliers C and E are quite comparable price-wise.

Comparing PC/LAN to minicomputer solutions, we see that the cost per intelligent workstation vs. the nonintelligent one stands at about $6,200 vs. $16,700 for each of the 23 WS, and $6,600 vs. $17,000 for each of the 35 WS. The per unit difference is attributable to system configuration. This still leaves an average ratio of 2.65 in favor of the PC.

On the average, the comparison we have made suggests that the minicomputer solution with its "stupid" terminals is many times more expensive than PC/LAN which brings programmable workstations to every bench. Since the maxi to mini cost ratio for supported terminals hovers around 3.1, and the difference of the mainframe to PC/LAN is roughly 8:1, we see that personal computing is a much better and more affordable service.

Cost Issues with Future Systems

Organizations with DIS experience are quick to emphasize that such systems must be powerful and flexible enough to meet users' current needs and that they should have sufficient expansion capacity to provide for future needs.

If we wish to take advantage of the possibilities which present-day technology makes feasible, namely, the distribution of computer power in a way that best fits the user's needs, we must be on the look out for the bottomless pits which absorb money—programs and data bases. These are the two areas where the highest costs lie. The interests of future buyers and sellers will center here. The pertinent factors in these areas must be carefully studied and analyzed. Available resources must be optimized and shared to the fullest possible extent. The degree to which a careful, well-implemented study can change yesterday's economic or operational criteria is often surprising.

The selection of a programming language is important to users both during and after system development, since the time and costs involved in programming can exceed those involved in hardware implementation. Users are well advised to look for fully implemented interactive language capabilities, industry standard high-level language if available, the ability to use different languages if need be, and programmability down to the single terminal level.

Then, to economize on the data base side, users should appreciate that it is not sufficient enough to locate the processing and storage capabilities close to the workplace—the office at headquarters, the factory floor, the sales and inventory outlet, or the branch office—but they must also

1. Rethink the data bases
2. Shorten the data input route
3. Provide for error detection and correction
4. Improve the response time
5. Eliminate the delay inherent in round trips
6. Ensure interactive man-machine communication
7. Handle more transactions in the process
8. Automate the fringes of the operations in the periphery—which so far defied the computers
9. Simplify the programming tasks
10. Study maintainability in advance and allow the basic system to evolve toward larger configurations
11. Ensure that future developments will safeguard the software made today

In regard to this last aspect, as management becomes keener to automate clerical jobs and to shorten the path to decision, the cost is often paid in an accelerated obsolescence of the software. By putting the user directly into the picture, on-line solutions may help increase both the portability and the longevity of the computer programs.

Over the last twenty-five years of computer use we often lost sight of the fact that hardware and even software are not the really dominant issues in establishing and running computerized solutions. The real problems are organizational and psychological ones.

For on-line approaches to be successful, the overriding need is to study, quantify, and convince. Planning tasks are a prerequisite. The seven major steps in this planning process are:

1. Determine current work load of the data center
2. Determine future work load requirements
3. Define work load capacity and performance of current configuration (hardware and software)
4. Define projected (required) capacity and performance of minicomputer configuration (hardware and software)
5. Determine user response times and other production requirements
6. Determine overall minicomputer site performance criteria
7. Determine planned costs and performance of the minicomputer site

Data load at any computer site grows. Tomorrow, which way will "transactions per second" be better handled?

We can now integrate into a comprehensive list the lessons to be learned and the advantages to be derived from on-line processing made feasible through cheaper technology and the advent of distributed information systems.

Comparative lower costs of components will alter historical design rules, since

Figure 3.3

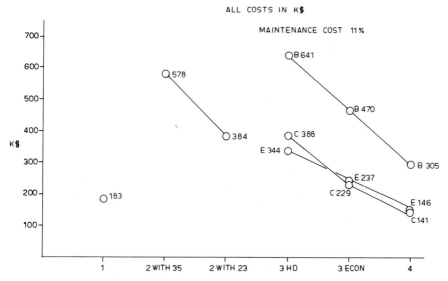

the price cuts will be industrywide and widespread. The "new" systems will substitute through electronics the functions now performed by more expensive methods, including those performed through people.

Prior to the end of this decade, all installed computer systems will use some kind of communications facility, devices or lines. New systems being installed will be communications oriented. The overwhelming trend will be that of soft copy (CRT, video) use, with many computer installations moving away from hard copy; on-line capabilities will accelerate this trend.

The research and development budget for hardware development, software construction, data communications research, and applications evolution will increase sharply. For hardware and software only, $2 billion annually is a conservative figure for the United States. Figure 3.4 gives a glimpse of R + D expenditures as man-made systems move further away from the Stone Age.

Volume is a good measure of where the R + D money goes. In the early 1950s, a 650 would have occupied 400 ft³ if 1 megabyte were available. By 1962 (with 7070 and 360/30) this volume was reduced to 100 ft³. By 1972 (with the 370/135 and 145) it went down to 8 ft³. By 1975 it further decreased to 0.5 ft³. The ratio is 0.5/400 = 1/800 in 20 years! It is anticipated that with 256 kB chips as the workhorse it will take only 0.006 ft³ for 1 megabyte and the ratio will be 1/65,000 in only 30 years!

Equally impressive is the drop in disc storage: from 5 megabytes in the late 1950s to the curent capacity of 5 gB. This is three orders of magnitude again, in only 30 years.

Before the end of the decade, among computer manufacturers the hardware will look alike and will be inexpensive. What they will be selling is systems software, programmed applications, and expertise. Computer manufacturers now spend

Figure 3.4

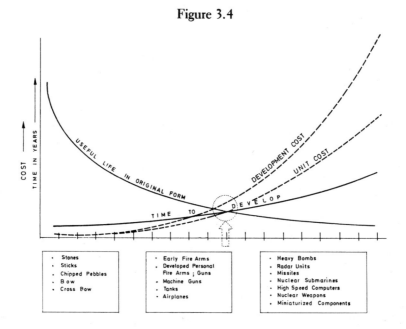

much more on software than on hardware development. Thus it is logical that they will derive more income from their know-how. This means that the computer user should expect to pay dearly for software and services. It is better to be aware of this now, rather than later.

New applications developments may have been the bottleneck in the last decade, and as Professor Schmidt* said: "The bottleneck is always at the top of the bottle." In fact, the growth of the market will be limited more severely by the lack of knowledge. This is just as true of the capacity to process data on-line.

Supporting Services and Management Decisions

Let's now take another look at network requirements.

Each host (processor) attached to a network has a CPU and a local addressable memory. What it needs is a transport facility to send and receive data to-and-from the other processors.

This is precisely the goal of the different network architectures. The network (transport facility) level is implemented through physical and logical media. The physical can be optical fibers, coaxial cable, radio links, and satellite broadcasts. The logical media are algorithms. A search for possible paths calls for a communications model.

*Formerly chief executive officer of Brown Bovery, Germany, and Board Member of Nestle.

A communications model can have sequential logic, decoding logic, and store and forward characteristics. It can be split into two parts—control and transfer. Control concerns requests (per input), origins (per input), presences (per output), priorities (per output), and data paths per I/O line. Modeling starts with the data path, as its aim is communication.

It is possible to build a number of systems with such elementary switching and transport elements, each with handshaking and simultaneous transfer facilities. The network opeating system must be able to cover communications management. Preferably, it will be composed of short programs with many elaborate actions. But in reality, the needed DB/DC software will include operating system functions, database management requirements, message handling and message concentration.

The software functions involve transport time allocation, communication among the transport mechanism and the hosts, the databases, and the terminal devices. The message handling functions include message management, routing, traffic accounting and protection.

File and message format should be given due attention. All messages, regardless of size, source or destination should answer formatting requirements. All approaches underline the need for increased address range to provide a logical address space large enough to encompass programs *and* files.

Users at most locations can access resources attached to the network through connected workstations, bulk telecommunications facilities, and interactive terminals. In the past, authorization for on-line handling was a subject for thorough investigation, and the initial justification for connection of a computer system to the network was made on the basis of experimentation, particular application needs, contingencies, and a factual, documented study showing cost and benefit. When a new connection is made, the availability of (still unused) network communication facilities tends to lead rapidly to its utilization.

In many cases, new systems connections to the network materialize through communication links already installed for use by other kinds of support. Equipment is acquired with a view to its possible integration in the network, but machines brought prior to the now-established architectural perspectives present problems of interfacing.

Computers in close physical proximity are internally linked by high-speed telecommunications lines or channel-to-channel adaptors. These links tend to be employed largely for batch job entry and management reporting purposes. Management oriented output is rapidly being converted to interactive approaches.

Over the last ten years, slower-speed long-line telecommunications links interconnected the computer centers, but these links were used primarily for file and message transfer. As databases became distributed, the lines were converted to high speed to meet bulk transfer requirements.

Optimization of network connectivity is usually addressed at the local level, whereas alternate path routing is sometimes used to balance long distance traffic between the computer centers. This overall view allows a more effective utilization of the available resources—both sharing their capacity and providing back-up capabilities in case of emergency.

The administration of the network has a resemblance to its logical structure. Routing control, traffic management, and database organization are distributed across the participating systems, but system management and software development are centralized. Just the same, coordination of network maintenance is accomplished through a central location. Each installation chooses location identification for its own connected computer systems (minis, mainframes) and data terminating equipment (work stations). These are communicated to the network control center and stored on machine-readable network connectivity maps which are distributed but with centralized management.

Where more than one routing possibility exists between one connected location and another, the choice is made by the routing algorithms according to established criteria. Such choices can result in looping network paths. Hence, the routing decisions must also be coordinated and supervised.

Network utilization now encompasses practically all areas of internal computer use to the point where the network has become an integrated and indispensable part of normal information system operations. Accounting records are kept for all files shipped "to" and "from," and such journals are used to prepare periodic network utilization reports which typically show steady increases in file traffic.

The availability of reliable data communications and database access has spawned an array of application support packages. There is a growing selection of application programs for automatic memo and mail composition; electronic mail delivery and logging; and document distribution and teleconferencing. Virtual machine concepts have been employed to receive and execute requests from remote users for automatic file retrieval and transfer.

This description exemplifies the macroscopic view of a network which supports computers, databases and terminal equipment. There could not be a functioning on-line network without establishing the finer programmatic interfaces required to implement total information systems engine.

4

From Data Processing to
Data Communications

Having covered some of the broader perspectives in telecommunications, the time has come to clarify the boundary between data communications and data processing.

Data communications concerns the transmission and distribution functions, in which the data are unaltered, the network control (and on-line maintenance), and the link establishment, routing, virtual circuit and Datagram, flow control, store-and-forward, and error detection and correction.

Data processing concerns the use of computers for processing information, in which the semantic content, or meaning, of input data is transferred, the storage and retrieval take place for purposes other than those of store-and-forward and error detection and control, and the output data constitute a programmed response to the input data.

The unit of output in data processing used to include such diverse variables as the following:

Tons of paper printed per day

Number of jobs multiprocessed

Number of on-line terminals allowed in data processing access

Megabytes (usually in the hundreds) available on-line (random access)

Throughput

Turnaround

Uptime

Availability

The unit of output in telecommunications may be just as diverse:

Channel facility

Transmission characteristics

Number of terminals managed by the system

Response time

Size of memory at the terminal and access methods

Allowed protocols

Switching characteristics

Line dependability

System reliability (including concentrators, front end, and terminals)

Bandwidth

Distance

Assurance that data going out of the link are the same as the data entering the link

Regarding the overall systems in data communications, we talk of physical resources and logical resources, and we refer in data processing, correspondingly, to hardware and software.

User Levels in Data Communications

It is wise to separate the computing function from the communicating function so that each may be optimized. Data communications systems must accommodate a wide variety of lines, devices, and geographically dispersed facilities for handling in an expandable network. The structure of the system must meet diverse and constantly evolving needs.

ITT's network distinguishes five levels of service:

Facsimile to facsimile

Terminal to facsimile

Terminal to terminal

Terminal to computer

Computer to computer

Rockwell Collins, too, proposes five general levels, but with a different classification:

Host to host (particularly oriented to bulk data transfer)

Terminal to host (switching message and data)

Terminal to terminal (specifically for message-switching)

Terminal to data base (for inquiry–response; this is terminal to host at "disc level")

Data collection (if host has time out)

The functions to be performed at these levels are composed of the following elements: real-time update, remote batch data transmission, remote concentration, and test systems (loopbacks, downline loading, upline dumping). This approach emphasizes connectability, expandability, improved utilization, and reliability.

IBM proposes three basic levels for the electronic office:

Terminal to terminal, for the distribution of priority messages and batches of routine correspondence

Terminal to computer, including the terminal-to-terminal functions and adding on-line processing and on-line merging of file and text

Computer to computer, implementing a protected message-switching system, storing, screening, and transmitting information to and from remote locations.

These are increased levels of sophistication which, like every data communications network, require software modules, protocols, hardware, and support services for overall design and construction of distributed computer networks.

Different levels of sophistication offer options in organizing a network to meet specific communication requirements. We must start with the study of our requirements, both qualitative and quantitative. The more complex they are, the higher the level needed. The services such solutions can offer are valuable: timely documents and messages, improved pace of information flow, reduced paper-handling, increased efficiency in written communication, remote revision capability, and faster response time. Some typical applications are letters, memos, specifications, contracts, confirmation, personnel data, spares and inventories, schedules, and progress reports.

A higher level of sophistication can go further, for instance, by merging electronic mail and point-of-sales equipment (POS) and by creating and maintaining support files, which will be transferred to low-cost media as computer output to microfilm, or microform (COM), today, and eventually to optical disks.

To appreciate the reach of such applications, note that there were about 350,000 word processors in the United States in 1980, less than 10 percent on-line. The number grew at the rate of 35 to 40 percent per year; by 1985, 90 percent will be on-line. The United States Postal Service alone spent $180 million in 1982 for research and development on computerized mass mail service. And mail in the form of communications of all sorts is one of the great frontiers of tomorrow, from electronic mail to Videotex.

System Perspectives

Data processing and data communications need thorough studies. Not only do they interact with and complement each other, but also they influence the solutions to be given to the other side by presenting both requirements and limitations. Data processing and data communications come together in a variety of on-line applications, which may be divided into two groups:

1	2
Direct delivery (to host)	Correspondence
Data collection	Reports
Inquiry response	Message broadcast
On-line update	

The services may be installed at the same time or sequentially, if the project takes them into account in the first place, thus avoiding mistakes of the past.

To understand some of the requirements we are faced with today, we ought to look at the way data processing has developed. Let us consider the branch office of a typical bank as an example; see Figure 4.1.

In the first phase, in the early 1950s, service to the client (an audit, for example) was done by means of a classic electromechanical device installed on the branch-office premises. The balance was registered black-on-white on a personal card and could be consulted and updated at any time. Then in the late 1950s came the central computers and associated machinery. The electromechanical audit at the branch office disappeared, and the data were carried to the data processing center. Delays developed, and with them, errors. This phase left something to be wanted. The third phase promised to correct all that. By the middle and late 1960s the starlike real-time network appeared. The central computer remained king, but the branch office got its equipment back in the form of a terminal.

On paper, it looked wonderful, as if we could eat the pie and have it, too. But snags were cropping up. The terminal, usually unintelligent, would not perform if the line was "down." Sometimes it cuts off fifteen terminals. Worse yet, the central computer's down time made for networkwide blackouts. That was the third phase. Now, in Phase 4, we are in a new era of dependability; see Figure 4.2. Immediate availability of needed information at the branch office is one aspect, but there are others. We must redefine the topology and all devices, support, facilities, native commands, applications, growth potential, restart and recovery, error rates, and maintainability.

The logical support should handle the DTE characteristics, which involves mainframes, front ends, rear ends—in general, minicomputers operating as nodes and hosts.

Figure 4.1
Data processing from the 1950s to now

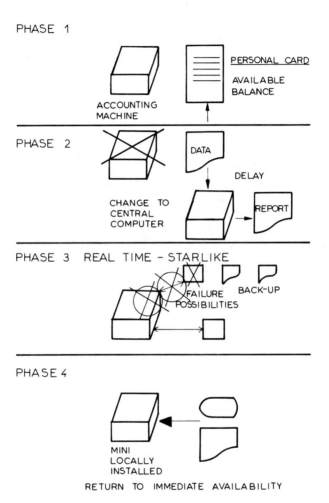

PHASE 1

PERSONAL CARD
AVAILABLE
BALANCE

ACCOUNTING
MACHINE

PHASE 2

DATA

DELAY

CHANGE TO
CENTRAL
COMPUTER

REPORT

PHASE 3   REAL TIME – STARLIKE

FAILURE   BACK-UP
POSSIBILITIES

PHASE 4

MINI
LOCALLY
INSTALLED

RETURN TO IMMEDIATE AVAILABILITY

Figure 4.2
History of systems

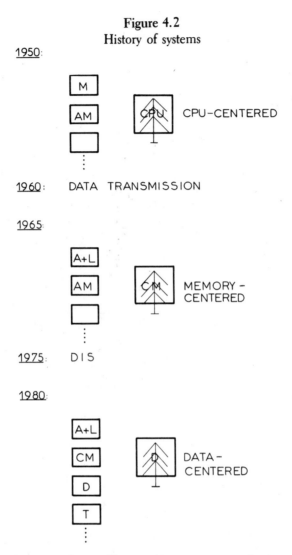

1950:

M
AM
□
⋮

1960:   DATA TRANSMISSION

CPU–CENTERED

1965:

A+L
AM
□
⋮

1975:   DIS

MEMORY –
CENTERED

1980:

A+L
CM
D
T
⋮

DATA –
CENTERED

Another matter to study is traffic as it relates to communications and networking (Table 4.1). The object here is dimensioning, and this necessarily involves both topology and the design of lines, modems, DTEs, and nodes and switches. Decisions on design parameters are vital, as Table 4.2 shows.

The user's needs must be studied. This usually involves data bases, file access, user access, tracing of mailbox, sender, and author, protection and security, and the ever important applied-programming library.

All this is in terms of facilities. There is another prerequisite: know-how: an understanding of the great steps we have taken over the last twenty-five years and of the horizons that have been opened by the new tools themselves.

Table 4.1
Traffic Description

Application Type	Message Requirements							
	Average Length in Characters		Arrival Rate			Priority	Editing Requirements
	Input	Output	Monthly	Daily	Peak Hour		

Table 4.2
Design Parameters

1. Format
2. Acknowledgment Procedure
3. Growth Rate per Year (by application)
4. Data Link
5. Routing
6. Flow Control
7. Communications Procedures
   Switching and transmission
   Store and forward
   Data-base access
   Message multiplication factor (number of output messages per input message)
8. Bit Error Rate
9. Security/Encryption
10. Journaling of All Messages
    Retention Time
       On-line
       Off-line
11. Objectives
    Hosts
    Terminals
       Message switch capability
    Broadcasting
12. Response Time Requirements (by application)

From the central processing unit of the 1950s, we have moved to the memory-centered computer system of the mid-1960s, and we are going on to the data-centered system of the 1980s. The faculties we have at our disposition have changed and, with them, the outlook.

The Three Main Classes of Communications

Currently there are three main classes of communications systems used in business. The telephone is by far the most frequently used means of communicating. The postal service is the second class, consisting of private couriers and intercompany mail-delivery networks that carry messages physically instead of electronically. Finally there is the electrical message system, such as facsimile, Telex, and telegrams, electronic mail and videotex.

About 90 billion pieces of mail move per year in the United States. About 9 billion are writer-to-reader correspondence, of which 4 billion are business mail; interoffice correspondence in the form of letters and memos is estimated at 12 to 15 billion. In addition, there are 220 to 250 billion telephone calls per year and 50 million Telex messages.

Interesting is the question of the lengths of messages. One study shows that 58 percent of management's messages are one page or less, 28 percent are two or four pages, and 14 percent are five pages or more. Electronic message systems (EMS) carry much shorter texts; some 73 percent are less than 100 characters each. Of all messages sent, 45 percent are addressed to one person, 35 percent to more than one, 18 percent to groups, and 2 percent to a combination of groups and individuals. Electronic and videotex mail finds their strength in these statistics.

PCs and videotex are no competitors to one another; they are complementary. In 1979, Prestel (the British Viewdata system) went public, with considerable excitement about videotex. In 1980, the need for communicating databases brought forward Bildschirmtext (the German videotex version). In 1981, the Apple microcomputer caught the attention of many prospective buyers who thought quite highly of its processing power. In 1982, the IBM Personal Computer received attention much notoriety with its enlarged memory capacity and the 16-bit microprocessor. In 1983, the Apple and original IBM PC announcements were overshadowed by products offering bigger, better, faster, and less expensive capabilities—including a 2 MB hard disc of central memory and 32-bit microprocessors.

During the same timeframe, videotex moved from mainframes to minis, and then to PC/LAN. This completely changes the type of offering by reducing costs, increasing the population base, and expanding the application horizon. On these grounds is based the projected videotex usage in the 1980s. An estimate by the National Science Foundation reveals that by the end of the century, 40 percent of American households will be using two-way videotex services. This will lead to changes in economic and social organization as great as those created by mass ownership of televisions and motor cars. Home videotex will allow users to tap enormous computer databanks and to communicate their own information, needs and options directly to manufacturers, providers of services, and politicians. These videotex machines may be the most important products of the new *information technology* which is now being developed by combining communications and computers.

Other predictions point out that both videotex and teletext will be operating profitably in U.S. cities by 1990. The pace is gaining momentum. In 1982, eight companies were testing teletext systems—while a year earlier only a few technical experiments were under way—and 14 videotex systems were being tested, mostly by banks, or were already operating on a permanent basis.

Such experiments are bringing closer the day when people will use television screens in their homes to shop, bank, read about traffic conditions, get the latest stock market figures, or access other information. Videotex will draw many entrepreneurs with diverse information to attract consumers. The key driving force behind the spread of videotex in the home will be the extent to which advertisers are prepared to use it. Services offered by advertisers will eventually sharply reduce the cost of videotex to subscribers.

Once videotex becomes firmly established it will have profound external effects in seemingly unconnected social areas as industrial relations, architecture, and manufacturing design. The home will become a place of work, most of which will be done at the videotex terminal. Distinctions between residential and business area in cities may be blurred, and there will be a drop in the demand for office space. The shift away from conventional workplaces will change industrial relations and corporate structures. Homebased shopping will profoundly alter not only retailing patterns but also manufacturing processes and design.

The impact of these facts can hardly be underestimated. A study found that 40 percent of a manager's time is spent on mail, telephone, and business travel and 12 to 35 percent on writing and reading. Another study identified the percentage of working time some professionals spent handling paper. Statistics show that 550 kilograms of paper are printed each year for every man, woman, and child in the United States, of these a good share being computer output. Other statistics show that a given technical article is read by an average of six readers. The computer was originally thought to be a means of reducing the paper jungle; it has increased it. It is now hoped that data communications will turn the trick.

Electronic Message Systems

Electronic message systems can carry two types of message, hard copy and soft copy, but still the telephone and postal service dwarf other message systems in size. The United States Postal Service revenues break down in this manner: $5.5 billion from first-class mail and $5 billion from other mail (magazines, advertising, and packages, etc.). It must all be delivered by hand.

If these statistics are looked at from another angle, data communications revenues have already surpassed those that the postal service receives as a business-to-business message carrier of first-class mail (44 percent of $5.5 billion).

Further, we observe that electronic messages usually want a higher priority than do others and that they may be delivered in many different ways.

Data communications networks are used for financial transactions, order entry, and associated teleprocessing applications. Formerly quite separate from administrative message systems, data communications networks are now developing at a rapid pace.

Among many possibilities for the future is voice store-and-forward capability for use on the telephone and, maybe, the television network. The sender directs a verbal message to the recipient's "in-box," and the recipient calls the in-box from any telephone and gets the message waiting for him. Hotels might provide a means of coupling the telephone and the television set, to offer terminal capabilities to the guests for receiving and sending messages.

The merging of written and oral messages on the principles of packet switching does offer the following advantages: decoupling of sender and receiver, so that there is no need of both to be present, electronic speeds and geographic independence, and better composition, storage, retrieval, and reading. Such solutions can operate within different environments: exclusive station-to-station calls, primary addressing with copies to other stations, broadcasts, with messages sent from one station to a distribution list, and teleconferencing (group participation).

At present, experience pinpoints several problems: explaining to users what to do in time out, helping users having difficulties, training the end user on all modifications as they appear, and expanding the topology without increasing the costs. Equipment that now is in development will be able to meet such needs. What is missing are the procedural and end-user studies to help in projecting, evaluating, implementing, and maintaining the systems to come.

Here are some examples. Wideband communications would allow a copier to produce a remote image at the same speed at which it produces a copy locally. This would make facsimile an adjunct of copying. The unit would be reserved for local copying during the day, and it would receive only when it was being used locally. At night a single copier would receive a few thousand pages. Data compression units can receive at best about eight hundred pages in eight hours. A facsimile transmission that now takes six minutes will, by means of wideband, take only about eight seconds.

While long haul communications will maintain their vital importance in electronic message systems, significant interest will be channeled to the implementation of local area networks (LAN). Among the issues to attract the greatest amount of interest are:

1. The design and operation of local area computer networks.
2. The correct positioning of a LAN within the context of merging data processing/word processing, realtime operations, office automation, management graphics, and decision support systems.
3. The component parts of a LAN: distributed databases, communications faculties, personal computers.
4. The results obtained by "avant garde" organizations which implemented LAN in their daily operations.

As previously underlined, PCs and LAN help make distributed information work for the people who need it. Computers and communications are part and parcel of the tight interrelationships that exist among productivity, job performance, and the need for understanding the services to be derived from computer support. By bringing under perspective low-cost techniques associated with local systems and personal computers, management's attention is focused on the positive nature of the microprocessor revolution.

A Message Service: Ontyme

For an example of current developments we shall consider Ontyme, a carrier service projected as an alternative to other message-switching systems. It is designed to appeal to geographically dispersed organizations that wish to converse rapidly and economically in forms readable by either a machine or a person, including interoffice correspondence and other data to be collected or disseminated. It would also incorporate separate technologies: store and forward, on-line computers, packet data communications, and terminal independence and error control transmission. The following is a list of its functions:

Verifies authorized use at log-in.

Allows user inquiry of message status.

Provides optional on-line message preparation and editing.

Adds time and date to all messages.

Assigns a unique master message number.

Holds or dials out for delivery at the user's option.

Assigns an output sequence number at time of delivery.

Delivers to group-coded destinations.

Responds with error messages to users.

Provides on-line file storage for frequently used messages or data.

Holds all messages three days for on-line retrieval.

Saves archive messages on tape for 90 days.

Provides data on traffic for management control.

Store and forward has given experience in stamping of time and date on all messages and in master control numbering, output sequence, and on-line retrieval of recently sent messages. Further extensive traffic data are captured and made available to users so that they may have the information necessary to control their own costs. From on-line systems have come the following features:

Verification of authorized access

User's inquiry about message status

A straightforward appearance to users, complemented by error messages to assist in application

An optional on-line message-preparation facility that allows messages to be economically prepared and edited at the user's terminal

Optional on-line file storage that allows users to store the text of anything that might be useful to them

An example of the last is a message that may be sent often but with minor modifications each time; it may be stored on-line and then easily retrieved whenever needed.

Packet technology as applied to message-switching brings to the user a heightened reliability. Errors in transmission are detected within the network, and the affected data are retransmitted until they are received accurately. Alternate routing enhances reliability by providing more than one path between nearly all points in the network.

A packet system is designed around a few simple operations common to all users: entering, sending, and reading messages. By customizing the documentation and training the users, the system can take on a variety of forms. In other words, user organizations can shape even a public service to their own needs.

Another freedom has been introduced in the form of terminal independence. Virtually all terminals in the range of 110 to 1,200 bits per second are supported by Ontyme, and any type of terminal can send and receive messages from any other type. Low-volume stations can be served by inexpensive low-speed terminals, while high-volume locations can use video displays for preparation and higher-speed printers for receiving. Moreover, the terminals do not have to be dedicated to the network but may be employed for any other application a user wishes.

Ontyme can be used either for dialing in or dialing out or both; that is, some locations may install dial-in terminal equipment and use the system as a sort of mail box, while others, equipped with the proper terminals, may be called by the system for message pickup and delivery. The choice is up to the user. The sender of a message does not need to know this or any other characteristic of the recipient's terminal.

PART TWO

Telecommunications

5

What Is Telecommunications?

Telecommunications encompasses all transfer of information, both internal and external to an organization, by electromagnetic means. This includes voice telephone, data transmission, telegram and facsimile, and picture transmission.

The term *network* is often used in a broad sense to designate not only the circuits (and lines) for voice and data transmission but also terminal equipment, such as telephones, teletypewriters, switching equipment (PBXs, computers, etc.), and operating personnel.

Telecommunications and data processing both continue to penetrate the mainstream of the business and scientific environments. We see the combination of both in office products and services. And where previously the responsibilities for telecommunications, data processing, and office facilities were divided, we now see large, integrated departments that encompass all three. It is clear that very soon the telecommunications function will be everywhere one of management's most powerful tools.

The emergence of telecommunications as a key management discipline has several causes: (1) the growing demonstration of benefits to management functions, such as marketing, production, and finance; (2) the explosion of telecommunications technology, enriched by inventions in electronics and in production technology; (3) the increasing role of telecommunications at the corporate level, where it is easier to move information electronically than by the traveling of people and paper; (4) the advent of alternative suppliers in both equipment and services; (5) the increasing sophistication required for optimal choice; and (6) the alternatives in ways of spending the telecommunications dollars (Figure 5.1).

Today *telecommunications is one of business's biggest and fastest-rising expenses.* In the United States the cost is between $15 billion and $20 billion annually, or about 1 percent of the nation's gross national product. Some companies spend as much as 12 percent of their annual operating expenses on telecommunications.

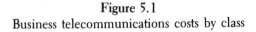

Figure 5.1
Business telecommunications costs by class

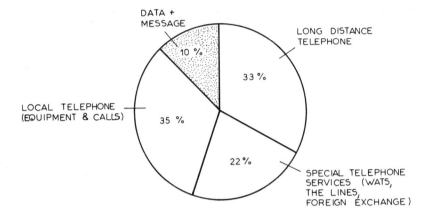

The national average is somewhat below 4 percent (Table 5.1). In the past these costs rose somewhat in line with sales; nowadays they rise much faster (Table 5.2). There are three reasons for this. First, new uses, such as data and facsimile, have only recently emerged in a service that otherwise remained basically unchanged for thirty or forty years. Second, corporate management is beginning to regard telecommunications less as a necessary evil and more as a vital management tool. Third, the effects of inflation are especially bad in some areas of telecommunications, particularly those that are noncompetitive, such as local services. This means that increasing professionalism is required to cope with costs.

Table 5.1
Telecommunications Cost Ratio by Industry

Industry	Communications Costs		Of Total
	Range (%)	Average (%)	
Manufacturing	0.3–1.0	0.5	Turnover
Retailing	0.2–0.7	0.4	Turnover
Insurance	1–3	2	Premium income
Banking, Finance	0.6–4.2	1.5	Operating expenses
Airlines	3–7	4	Operating expenses
Securities	8–12	10	Operating Expenses

Table 5.2
Telecommunications Markets/Carrier Only

	Billions of Dollars			Annual Growth Rate (%)
	1978	*1980*	*1984*	
Voice	45.00	54.00	80.00	10.9
Message	0.95	1.10	1.30	5.6
Data	3.80	5.60	8.50	20.0
	49.75	60.70	89.80	

The Investment

There are 200 million telephones in the United States and American Telephone and Telegraph, AT&T, serves 82 percent of them. Telephone equipment costs represent only 20 percent of the total telephone bills; 80 percent is for use. This is the area that has the greatest potential for cost control.

Capital investments are made in telephones, data sets (modems), private branch exchanges, switching centers, short lines (loops), long lines, the installation system, and the mainenance network. The station (telephone) in terms of telephone company investments cost is 2 percent. The rest is the network, the switching centers, and the overall services. All this capital investment and operating expense is financed by the household market and by business and industry.

In early 1983 it was projected that in that year alone in the United States the telephones would carry more than 400 billion calls. Let us see what the share of a single function would be: cheque clearance, performed by the banking sector. The cheques processed by the banking system in 1983 were projected to be more than 60 billion. The ratio of calls to cleared cheques is 7.5 to 1. Approximately 75 percent of the cheques required bank clearance. Each clearance message is about 1,000 bits long; this means that 30 *trillion bits* are transmitted over lines for cheque clearance alone. If a telephone is used in every American home for direct access to computer memory at the local bank and for subsequent processing of payment orders and money transfers, then 50 percent of the current volume of cheques may be eliminated. This is one of the new frontiers for computers and data communications.

Statistics from the Department of Commerce show that telephone and teletypewriter traffic alone will constitute a $100-billion industry by 1986. By that year—or sooner, according to AT&T—it will cost less to transmit a facsimile letter than to send a conventional letter through the mail. By 1980 or '81 from 80 to 85 percent of all computers in the world had at least one remote terminal on-line. In the same period more than 30 percent of the hardware budget went to communications-related products and by 1986, more than 50 percent.

A variety of services can be provided by data communications, from sub-voice-grade lines (Telex being an example) to specific data communications-oriented networks (Figure 5.2). Packet switching is a special subject, which will be treated later in detail.

Is industry ready for this changeover? Statistics—and a good number of executives—say it is not. A couple of years ago a study made among seven medium-sized United States firms showed the following:

	Cumulatively spend	*While employing*
For computer gear	$56 million	1,089 persons
For communications	$20 million	15 persons

In terms of know-how in systems applications and cost effectiveness, in 1983 we stood in the field of data communications exactly where we were in 1953 with computers. Yet in terms of money it is projected that the budget for equipment in the mid-1980s might be as follows: 40 to 45 percent for data communications, 30 percent for data processing, and 25 to 30 percent for terminals.

By 1980 data communications would amount to a 30 percent share of expenditures for electronics data processing (Figure 5.3). As time passes, communications costs will represent 40 percent or more of the total budget. Already with Arpanet, a network developed by the Department of Defense, the cost of data communica-

Figure 5.2

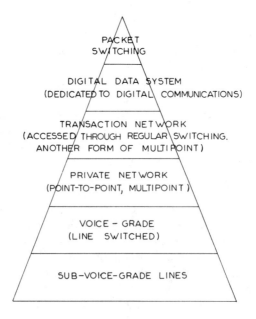

tions is greater than the cost of data processing, and this is the best teleprocessing example we have today. With private lines the costs can even be higher. One telephone company (SIP, in Italy) stated that on the average the telephone lines cost $2,250 per year per terminal, for more than 200 terminals, as over against $1,500 per year for the terminal itself—and the terminal cost decreases sharply.

International Business Machines (IBM) predicts, however, that with satellites, optical fibers, and microelectronics the communications costs may drop dramatically, by the late 1980s, to a fortieth or a fiftieth of those prevailing today.

Communications Costs

Most companies look upon communications expenditures as a bothersome but necessary cost of doing business. Despite the magnitude of the costs, decision-making in this area is often fragmented among local offices or purchasing managers who have little or no technical experience in communications.

The essentials of the current situation are these: First, manageable telecommunications costs are rising because of inadequate controls. Secondly, the technology is proceeding at an extremely rapid pace, opening up innovative ways of deploying communications to competitive advantage. Thirdly, advanced products and services are being introduced, offering every firm an opportunity to upgrade its service and reduce its "fixed" costs.

Contrast, for example, the typical decision-making process concerning communications hardware with that of acquiring a medium-scale computer. In the case of the computer the lessons of the 1960s taught everyone that a great deal of analysis, planning, and weighing of alternatives is needed before any decisions are made, yet a 500-line private branch exchange system (PBX) is equivalent in leased cost and service charges to a fully equipped medium-scale computer. Further, the new PBX system will incur a firm a contractual liability of three to five years, making this decision a $1-million commitment.

Telephone communications expenses involve both direct and indirect costs.

Figure 5.3

Estimated telecommunications costs versus electronic data processing costs

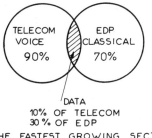

TELECOM VOICE 90%   EDP CLASSICAL 70%

DATA
10% OF TELECOM
30% OF EDP
THE FASTEST GROWING SECTOR

IF DIMENSIONED AT DATA COMMUNICATIONS LEVEL

The *direct-cost* elements are the easier to pinpoint and analyze; examples are the telephone company's charges for service and equipment, salaries associated with switchboard attendants, and the value of the floor space used by the telephone plant. The *indirect costs* are involved in establishing general criteria of cost-benefits that suit the organization as a whole and its operating departments.

It is equally important to determine the degree or quality of telecommunications service to be purchased. This requires a comprehensive analysis of the entire telephone network, the communications loads imposed by different functional organizations within the corporation, and the effectiveness of the present service.

Some employees have so-called telephone-intensive job requirements. Purchasing agents, reservations clerks, and sales persons, for example, often require a higher degree of service than many middle-management and junior executives. These people deliver messages to a client, to a supplier, to the company's own factories or sales offices, often by voice.

Voice, however, is not an efficient medium. A message delivered by voice must be transcribed; then it must be transported as hard copy, transcribed again onto a computer support medium, and then checked, validated, and processed. Transcriptions mean opportunities for errors and errors always cost.

It is not necessary to talk of computer networks to dramatize the issues of choice and the costs that lie behind them. We can stick, for that purpose, to the simpler example of a PBX, which is able to answer the voice requirements. The number of trunks needed to serve a specific PBX system is determined by an Erlang analysis and a queueing study. Erlang's formula may be used to postulate the probability that a randomly arriving call will encounter a busy condition. Because the caller must hang up if the line is busy, the call is lost in the network. A queueing analysis determines the number of attendants needed to ensure a high probability that all calls will be answered within a predetermined time. Response-time requirements are not the same for every class of PBX user nor for the normal or peak-hour use by the same subscriber. In determining the type of PBX needed it is wise to use a checklist; an example is given in Table 5.3.

Concerning the technical specifications we should examine both the minicomputer that will reside on the premises and the postprocessing software that will transform the computer's output into meaningful management reports. The flexibility of both the hardware and the software is important; a company's communications use is constantly changing. The equipment should be modular, expandable in both size and features, and easily upgraded from a passive to an active and dynamic system.

We should also be convinced of a supplier's dedication to a continual improvement of his wares, and this includes software.

Estimating Communications Requirements

In this and the following sections we shall concentrate on the voice-grade service. Estimating the requirements of a communications service is not always easy, particularly when a company is large.

First of all we must find out how the existing system is being used, what needs are not being met, and what the future needs will be. Three types of study may be very helpful in this: the executive interview, the employee questionnaire, and an operations-load study.

In the first study the manager of each department is interviewed to determine what his department does, what its future plans are, and how it uses the telephone system.

Several important questions need answers: What is the function of the department? How will the function change in the next five years? Who or what other departments are contacted most often? What are the best and worst features of the existing telephone system? How could the telephone system help the department in the future?

Operations-load studies are vital because they afford an insight into what is happening on a day-to-day basis.

We can determine several factors that are important in assessing the desirability of a PBX service: number of incoming calls in a month, number of outgoing calls in a month, number of operator transfers in a month, percentage of incoming callers who know the name, department, or extension number of the person they wish to speak to, and dates when additional operators, positions of switchboard, or station lines were added. Information available from operators, such as the number of incoming and outgoing calls handled, should be collected periodically and graphed for an analysis and a projection of trends.

When all these studies have been completed, we shall have a pretty good picture of the company's communications requirements now and for the future. The following four items should be given attention.

Number of lines: We should know the company's plans for the next five years and how they will affect the telephone system. Then we can determine the system's growth by projecting the past and present ratios of telephone lines to number of employees into the future.

Number of operators: We can determine the current number of attendant call operations each day and forecast this for at least five years. By relating the forecast to an operator's call-handling capacity we can establish the number of operators that will be required in the future.

Problems with existing system: We should know what the current problems are and what the employees' opinions are on how to improve the system.

Minimal in-dial percentage: We should know the percentage of persons calling in who know whom they wish to speak with and who would dial the extension if they could.

Having now determined the current and future communications requirements, we must decide whether the existing system will meet them and, if not, whether PBX service should be obtained. Some of the factors to consider are the following:

Capacity: Can the system meet the future station line requirements? Is there room for future growth?

Table 5.3
A User's Checklist for a Telephone Monitoring System

A. *Equipment*

---

1. Modular, expandable units: to more lines and trunks, to active or dynamic features, to allow for company expansion and for more sophistication.

2. Connection to line or trunk: has flexibility; can be tailored to user needs; an initially low-cost system can be upgraded later.

3. Wide breadth of line and trunk toll restricting abilities; tailoring of telephone usage to management responsibilities.

4. Proven technology.

5. Enhanced reliability.

6. A minimum of one month of magnetic-tape storage saves necessity to change tapes frequently.

7. On-line diagnostics and on-line reports through teletypewriter: immediate monitoring of points of developing bottlenecks.

8. Rotary or touchtone or both, as input: saves system conversion, enhances flexibility.

B. *Software*

---

9. Ability to capture only the calls required (not local or intracompany calls): saves postprocessing expenses.

10. Ability to capture call records in real time: saves postprocessing, increases capacity of magnetic-tape storage.

11. Complete and wide array of software capability available now: increases breadth of management reports available, enables customizing of reports.

Table 5.3 (cont.)
A User's Checklist for a Telephone Monitoring System

12. Supplier service center facilities available: relieves user of electronic data processing.

13. Service-center programming and data base updated as tariffs change: ensures timeliness and accuracy of management reports.

14. Automatic recommendations on optimized network configurations: enables responsive, rapid configuration.

15. Hourly distribution of call minutes per trunk: pinpoints congestion, enables smoothing of peaks and valleys.

16. Line or trunk correlation: trunk identification for accurate engineering, performance analysis, charge back.

17. Alternative methods of cost distribution such as between Wide Area Telephone Service (WATS) and WATS overflow lines: enables fair allocation of telephone expenses.

18. User data base easily changed: maintains accurate and up-to-date- cost allocation and management reports.

C. *Crucial Factors*

19. Variety of short- or long-term rental or lease programs available, also purchase or lease and purchase: customizes acquisition to meet financial policies.

20. Breadth of maintenance ability: to ensure uptime, to enhance credibility of references available.

Equipment: Can the important existing communications problems be solved? Is the system maintenance-free or old and out of date?

Size: What is the initial number of lines? What is the needed growth capability?

Features: Which are mandatory features? Which are the desirable features?

Maintenance: What is the expected reliability? What are the type and frequency of maintenance required?

Site: Which are the site limitations (floor space, ceiling height, floor loading, power requirements, and environmental conditions)?

Schedule: What is the schedule for starting installation? For cutting over the system?

Cost: What is the cost of equipment? Of the service, installation, maintenance (if extra)? Of the moves and rearrangements?

Objectives: Does the system enhance our corporate objectives? Can it be expanded to meet objectives as requirements develop?

Future costs: How much will it cost to expand or modify the system to meet the company's future needs? How much will additional operators cost? How much is the necessary floor space worth?

It should be understood that this impressive list of questions relates to a PBX, not to a computer and data communications network; the requirements for the latter are much broader.

Calculating Unit Charges

In calculating message unit charges, the following issues are of importance.

Message unit: A measure of telephone service used on station-to-station calls within an area, based on time and distance.

Message-rate service: Every call is message unit or long distance; calls within certain areas are only one message unit, regardless of length of time of call.

Local-area service: A flat rate for a small area, message unit or long distance for others.

Metropolitan service: A flat rate for a large area; message unit or long distance for others.

Flat-rate service: A more expensive flat rate for unlimited calling within a limited area.

Metropolitan-area service: Calls timed within the area, such as WATS.

Foreign-exchange (FX) service: One of the above from another location.

In controlling abuses and misuses in order to lower costs, management must:

Determine the overall problems; find out where calls go and why.

Train the employee in telephone usage.

Study the equipment and line configuration, considering alternative services and removing unused equipment to reduce exposure.

Evaluate the wisdom of restricting individual telephones to cut down on unauthorized calling.

Lock telephones after hours, to prevent unauthorized calls by after-hour personnel.

Employ equipment that can check for proper use and block improperly selected calls; hardware devices monitor and control calls.

Establish exception-reporting and analyze results on a continuing basis.

The common background of the aforementioned points is the need to analyze the costs of communicating on a regular and systematic basis to ensure full value received for each dollar spent.

For a documented cost control (and billing), call records must be consistently kept. They include the authorization number, the number called, the duration of call in minutes and tenths of minutes, the time of initiation of call, the type of long-distance line desired, and the actual type of long-distance line used. This information is the basis for billing the individual users in their departments for their use of the telephone network. It also provides the data for systems usage analysis and reconfiguration.

A cost-control scheme is of fundamental importance if we wish to evaluate the means of communications used so as to ensure that the best available method is being utilized, commensurate with the job at hand. The more limited, and more immediate, object of calculating unit charges is to establish a cost allocation procedure, which would permit the company to take advantage of shared services and produce cost breakdowns that are acceptable and equitable in the various divisions. The findings may be instrumental in defining a number of other issues. For example:

Developing employee education programs designed to encourage good communications habits.

Promoting an awareness and appreciation of communication costs.

Developing a working knowledge of equipment capabilities and limitations.

Optimizing, within the existing tariffs and regulatory changes, the use of the telephone facilities.

Studying the applications of new equipment, systems, and offerings, as they may be profitable and effectively used by the company.

Companies that have studied the cost effectiveness of their current systems have found that they should use the following: data terminals to reduce transaction-recording (clerical) costs, data concentrators to cut the line costs, special common carriers, interfacility private-line costs, an advanced PBX for combinations of voice and data and to reduce operator needs, and the "interconnect" PBX to gain the advantages of industry-specialized design and of lower costs.

Expected Benefits

The control of costs, though absolutely necessary, is not enough. If costs were the only problem, we should not use cars, the telephone computers, or electricity at large. Money is spent to produce a useful product, and the most appreciated benefit of any product is that which materially improves the user's productivity and ultimate profit. The most direct route to the top in any corporate organization is via the management discipline most crucial to success: the enhancement of profits. Industry has seen the marketing "whizz kids" climb to the top in the 1960s and the computer specialists climb to the top in the 1970s; the telecommunications experts may be there in the 1980s.

The reasons behind this new field of interest are structural. They include the growth and concentration of service facilities, the fragmentation of nonstandardized production runs, the growth of marketing organizations, a plethora of government regulations, and an acceleration both in the volume of recording and in time scales.

Corporate personnel are less and less concerned with the actual management techniques and more and more with the recording and monitoring of production, marketing, and finance functions. The information flow becomes the lifeblood of an enterprise. Without adequate supplies of relevant information, management is increasingly unable to reach rational decisions.

Another reason for this field of interest is that information theory has lagged behind the demands placed on it. The layer upon layer of management reporting structures is distorting the information flow.

The combination of computing and telecommunications technology has made itself felt. Banks are an obvious example. No major financial institution today would contemplate running its business without on-line systems that not only serve their clientele more efficiently but also are an invaluable marketing tool. The banks are consolidating credit and credit-card information, offering services to a far wider range of customers than formerly allowed.

Electronic mail is another example, though it is still in the experimental stage.

The airlines, too, have long computerized their reservation systems and their arrival and departure information, so that the traveling public may be better informed on actual flight arrivals and departures.

Through point-of-sale terminals the retail trade is moving toward credit authorization, and almost instant information on the sales of particular products, using that information for rapid reordering, so as to avoid heavy inventory positions.

The potential is hardly scratched. As the price of long-haul communications facilities drops, the size of communications channels widens to suit the information flows, and computing power is focused on the manipulation of the flow of data, voice and image. It is in this way that the full potential of telecommunications begins to emerge.

New Perspectives

To manage communications effectively a firm must look to the future and, in some cases, the far future. Communications today are more manageable than they have ever been, and communications managers have more useful tools available to them to do a better job. Future systems promise a total upset of the present values. Which are the systems that will have far-reaching impact? They are the communications satellites and waveguide transmission, the large-scale terminal-oriented computer systems, the lines that will carry 250,000 telephone calls simultaneously, and the computer-switched telephone exchanges (already here). As they grow, these systems will enable information to be transferred a full order of magnitude more quickly, accurately, and broadly.

Interactive television, allowing one to see as well as hear the other party, and two-way broadband cable (CATV) communications systems are in limited use today. When perfected and accepted widely (probably in the early 1980s) the developments will spark major shifts in marketing techniques, in the deployment of physical facilities, in travel patterns, and in work habits.

The developments are timely, because the current systems and the procedural solutions are both overburdened. There are more than 120 million telephones in the United States and 130 million more in other countries. The telephone exploits a basic electroacoustic technology that is difficult to improve on, given very tight economic bounds; yet, simple as it is, it acquires enormous power by virtue of the network to which it offers access. One of the reasons for exploiting to the fullest degree the potential of a telephone system is its general use. Since it is in almost every home, the telephone reaches many strata of a working population. The network embraces more than 200 countries and territories, making it possible for virtually any pair of telephones among the more than 250 million to be interconnected on command. The new needs (data solutions) extend this perspective.

Facsimile terminals in the home or business office will supplement and, later on, replace the mail carrier. New approaches to Telex communication will aid in this direction. At present most Telex terminals are of the type using 50 bits per second or the 5-bit Baudot code, with 75 bits per second being used in recent years. Since the data transmission capacity of a telephone line, however, can be 9,600 bits per second, the Telex authorities, or users with large numbers of terminals themselves, combine the low-speed data streams and transmit them over a single high-speed facility (time-division multiplexing).

Many areas in the use of telephony are still unexploited. For example, a simple attachment to the telephone handset makes it possible to transmit a patient's heart signals to the office of a physician, where the signals are reproduced on a cardiograph. Other developments, still in the experimental stage, are transmission via optical media, electronic mail, and voice-input recognition. All these will offer strong economic incentives for executives to change some of their basic ways of conducting business. That is why we cannot foretell tomorrow's solutions on the basis of what is available today. New systems are being developed that will revolutionize the current communications services.

6

Space, Frequency, and Time

The four basic design parameters characterizing a data communications network are transmission, switching, storage, and control. In this chapter we shall be concerned with the technology of transmission: space, frequency, and time.

Transmission is the function of the links, or channels. The links may be twisted wire, coaxial cable, waveguides, radio bridges, satellite channels, or other media. They may be arranged in a star or in a loop shape, to interconnect a switching center with other switching centers and with subscribers. As regards the technical aspects of transmission, we must account for electrical characteristics, such as conditioning, synchronization, regeneration, and the frequency spectrum. Across the electromagnetic spectrum even the nomenclature changes. *Discrete frequencies* are used mostly for audio and speech. *Conventional wavelengths* are radio waves through microwaves. *Rays* are heat, light, and molecular-electron emissions (which are also frequency-related phenomena). *Wideband* usually refers to media that allow the handling of any type of signal whatever, including transmission and switching. (In this sense, if one had to transmit only voice and Telex, a 1,200-band line is a wide band. A wideband solution means, essentially, transmission and switching that do not have limits due to band.)

Voice traffic has classically been accomplished with half-duplex links (requiring one pair of wires). In half-duplex it is necessary to invert the line in order to change the direction of transmission. This fits voice requirements, since in person-to-person communications the two stations do not need to transmit at the same time, but it is inadequate for data communications, with the so-called intelligent terminals and computers, which can transmit and receive simultaneously. Simultaneous two-way transmission requires full duplex (two pair of wires).

Another major difference between the lines for voice grade and those for data communications is in the bit error rate (BER), which is the number of bit errors transmitted per, say, one million bits. Bit error rates of 10^{-4} to 10^{-5} are acceptable for voice-grade lines, but they must be upgraded by nearly three orders of magnitude, to 10^{-7}, for data communications.

Two other factors differentiate voice-grade lines from data communications, one being the call-holding time and the other the store-and-forward capability.

The call-holding time in voice-grade communications averages three minutes. The average for data traffic depends on the type of transmission being treated: very large messages may take one or two hours, whereas queries and real-time update will take only a few seconds. But data transmission can be spaced in convenient ways: very large messages are usually sent during the night hours, when traffic is least, so that by helping to fill the slow times an optimal use of the network is made.

Store-and-forward was implemented with message-switching. The receiving node stores a message, if traffic is too great, until it can forward it down the line. Today this process is largely reserved for data traffic, but we may expect changes in the general character of voice traffic due to the evolving requirements, the increasing speed of the lines, and the limited sensitivity of the human communicator to minute interruptions.

Space Division

Information is transmitted over channels so that an end-to-end communication may be established. The search for channel capacity has led to significant developments in switching technology. The process of switching necessitates the activation of some sort of physical connection or path to allow a conversation between two stations, whether they are telephone sets or terminals. The connection may occur by electromechanical means (a relay contact closure) or by electronic means (activation of a diode) without any difference in the basic switching principle. An actual metallic switch point (cross-point) must be there and be available to make the switched connection. Space-division switching is one of the most commonly used in telephone systems (Figure 6.1). The "space" is to the physical metallic path, which always exists for a given switch connection. This kind of switching is done with a multiplicity of individual wires, the talking paths over which the voice or data are carried. All conversational electromechanical telephone switching systems are of this type. Most electronic systems today also use space-division techniques.

Space-division switching is not the only means of connecting two points; time and frequency division are two other approaches, fundamentally different from that of switching, so that there is a total of three different methods. Frequency division and time division differ from space division in that separate physical paths or circuits are not required for each voice or data transmission. One advantage of using frequency and time separation for switching is that the number of elements (cross-points) is reduced and, hence, the cost in the interconnection network.

Figure 6.1
(a) Space-division switching (space = actual metallic physical path);
(b) frequency-division switching

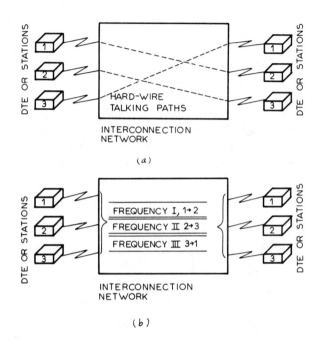

Furthermore, time switching provides an elegant basis for the transmission of voice, data, and image on a single channel.

Frequency and Time Division

If simultaneous conversations that are to be switched are established in different frequency bands with a means at both ends of discriminating and recognizing the assigned frequencies, then we have a switching technique based upon frequency separation. Since voice occupies a bandwidth of only about 4,000 cycles per second, a transmission scheme that has a bandwidth of some multiples of this allows many conversations to be sent over a single piece of wire.

The use of frequency for channel separation is common enough; it is known as frequency-division multiplexing (FDM). It is applied in two major areas: carrier transmission systems and data multiplexers. Transmission systems employing it are used widely by common carriers on computer communications systems. Concentrating low-speed terminals onto a single high-speed line makes use of frequency-division multiplexing.

At present frequency-division multiplexing is not used to any great extent in telephone switching, being limited to applications with relatively few subscribers because of the physical size and cost, but it has specific technical advantages in certain applications.

The use of time for channel separation, like frequency, is becoming common for carrier transmission systems and data multiplexing (Figure 6.2); it is commonly referred to as time-division multiplexing (TDM). It is used chiefly when large numbers of subscribers' lines need to be accommodated.

Time-division multiplexing has the advantage of becoming more economical as the number of lines increases; this makes it eminently suitable as a replacement for space-division switching in telephone applications (data, voice). All subscribers, lines, or channels, share the same portion of the frequency spectrum, as does space-division switching, but they do it in a time-dependent manner. The channels are separated on a selective, sequential basis. Thus both time-division and

Figure 6.2

(a) Time division switching and (b) time-division multiplexing

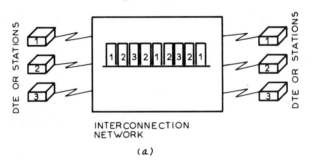

(a)

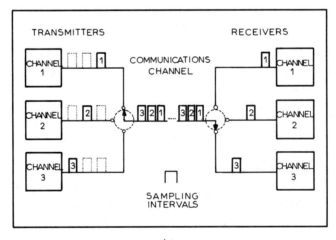

(b)

frequency-division have the ability to multiplex many channels onto a single wire or cable while remaining, as in space-division switching, independent of frequency considerations within a particular system; see Figure 6.3.

In time-division multiplexing all information is represented in a digital format in order to achieve the required time separation between channels and drive the synchronization at both ends of the link. This presents no problem for the transmission of data, but for voice it requires that analog information be converted into digital form. The process by which this is accomplished is called sampling (see the next section).

Long-haul digital transmission is rapidly emerging as the next logical step in the conversion to time-division multiplexing of trunk data communications systems. To accomplish this conversion and to take maximal advantage of existing communications facilities, we need both frequency-division multiplexing and digital processing and modulation techniques; they should make efficient utilization of the existing allocated bandwidths.

Figure 6.3

FREQUENCY–DIVISION MULTIPLEXING (FDM)

AND TIME DIVISION MULTIPLEXING (TDM)

THE CHANNEL DIVISION CAN BE CARRIED OUT
AT BOTH ENDS WITH   FDM

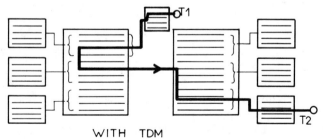

WITH   TDM
THERE IS A CASCADING OF ARRANGEMENTS
WHEREBY TERMINALS COMMUNICATE THROUGH
TIME SLOTS.

Let us recapitulate. To connect one point with another for the transmission of information we need a link, that is, a communications channel. The link may be created by pulling from point 1 to point 2 a twisted wire (which we really would not do), or by putting a coaxial cable or a private radio bridge between them or by getting the telephone company to provide the line. The information will travel over the line by means of multiplexing with space, frequency, or time division.

Code Conversion

In the preceding section we spoke of the process of sampling, the conversion of analog information to digital. There are both economic and technical advantages in converting voice and image signals into digital forms (Figure 6.4). This calls for a code-conversion procedure, of which there are three types: pulse code modulation (PCM), differential pulse code modulation (DPCM), and delta modulation (DM). Pulse code modulation has been traditionally used for the digitization of voice and it still constitutes the standard form, but delta modulation is the simplest and most economic of the three.

As Figure 2.3 shows, voice-encoding involves sequential steps. First an analog input signal is band-limited by a low-pass filter to the cycles per second (Hertz) corresponding to the frequency band of speech, 3,000 to 4,000 Hertz. Then the signal is sampled at a frequency rate greater than the frequency band. Thus, for voice a sampling base of 8,000 times per second is used. The sampled signal is held in a sample-and-hold device during the period between two sampling intervals. Then it is quantized into one of 2^n levels (if the coder is designed to produce n-bit words per sample). The larger the n, the more accurate the representation. To code, for instance, the signals in Figure 6.3 we need at least $n = 5$. American telephone-quality standards require $n = 13$ to encode low-level signals. Next is needed a linear coder with uniform quantizing step sizes; this produces linear pulse code modulation (LPCM). This then reduces excessive bandwidth requirements by compressing words in linear pulse code modulation according to standard algorithmic methods; this is called compressed pulse code modulation (CPCM). The functions of equalization and compression are often combined. In decoding, the 8-bit compressed pulse is converted into amplitude level, and the pulse samples are low-pass filtered at the original bandwidths.

The delta modulation principle is quite different in several ways. The band-limited input signal is compared with a "prediction" of the input derived from the encoder's digital output. All intervals are controlled by clock. The output of the error signal is quantized into 1-bit words. Finally, if the error signal is positive, the quantizer's output is 1; if negative, it is 0.

The code structure of delta modulation is inherently simpler than that of pulse code modulation. Its clock rate is much higher. This suggests the use of much simpler band-limiting filters. Furthermore, the feedback network is designed so as to allow the output to be a close approximation (estimate) of the input signal at the

Figure 6.4
(PAM, pulse amplitude modulation)

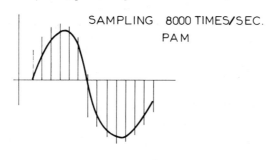

SAMPLING 8000 TIMES/SEC.
PAM

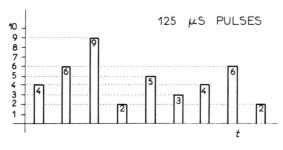

125   μS SAMPLES

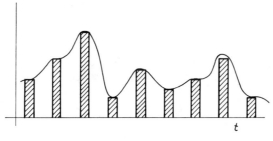

125   μS   PULSES

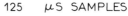

SIGNALS TO BE CODIFIED

next clock pulse. And improvements can be applied, such as adaptive delta modulation (ADM).

Time Slots and Alohanet

Though frequency and time division may be used equally well with voice and with data communications, the fast-growing demand for data and image transmission underlines the need for new techniques or else the generalization of old ones that are so far quite specialized. A different way of saying this is to say that the growing use of distributed information systems and the increasing intelligence of terminals make imperative better solutions to the problems of communications from computer to computer, from computer to terminal, and from terminal to terminal. One may say that the real need is for a communications system with the following characteristics.

A large number of terminals transmitting data in a very "bursty" or "low-duty-cycle" fashion.

A small number of nodes (hosts) transmitting data at a "high-duty-cycle."

A medium number of devices exchanging synchronous data, e.g., facsimiles.

A medium number of devices with asynchronous data concentrated in clusters. (*Asynchronous* means start-stop, or character by character; each character is preceded by a start bit, the zero condition, and followed by one or more stop bits.)

A high priority on full connectivity for a large number of subscribers. Full connectivity means that ability of any subscriber to communicate with any other subscriber or group of subscribers simultaneously.

One solution is time-division multiple-access (TDMA) bus, or satellite broadcast; in this system time is divided into intervals called slots, which are combined into larger intervals called frames.

The pioneering effort in this field was made in Hawaii, where the Alohanet was developed. The system uses small radio transceivers connected to interactive terminals, to provide communication between these terminals, which are scattered throughout the Hawaiian islands, and a central computer. Each terminal buffers several characters and then forms a message with an address and a checksum; it then attempts to transmit this message to the central computer. If it accepts the message correctly, the central computer sends back an acknowledgment. If the transmission is in error (for instance, when there is competition between that message and another terminal's message), no acknowledgment is returned, in which case the terminal waits for a given amount of time and retransmits the message. Transmissions from the central computer to the terminals, on the other hand, do not suffer from "contention" since there is only one source of traffic in that direction.

A project that, like Arpanet, is sponsored by the Department of Defense, is Satnet. Among its features are the following.

A number of satellite nodes, called interface message processors (IMP), are connected to satellite earth stations and share a broadcast satellite channel.

The same principles as in the Alohanet hold here, with a few exceptions.

All the interface message processors act as sources of traffic as well as receivers, so there is contention in both directions.

The traffic over the channel consists of long file transfers as well as interactive traffic.

The speed of the channel is very high, for instance, speeds of 50 kilobits per second have been tested, and speeds of 1.5 megabits per second are intended for the future.

Such are the factors that have influenced the designers of satellite contention systems to provide for more efficient mechanisms than so-called random Aloha.

The simple expedient of synchronizing all interface message processors so that packets fit into time slots leads to only half as many "collisions." Further refinements, including advance reservations of time slots, are also possible.

Another system using contention is Ethernet, developed by the Xerox Corporation for local network connection. A number of subsequent developments in this field have also begun, such as the Network System Corporation's Hyperbus and various projects around the country at, for instance, the Massachusetts Institute of Technology.

These systems have in common a coaxial cable as transmission medium, with cable adaptors connecting the various computers and terminals in a local area to this cable. The typical transmission speeds are in the range of 1 to 10 megabits per second. Contention for transmission over the cable happens in exactly the same manner as over a radio or satellite system. Messages are addressed and carry checksums. Collisions between messages can be noted by the senders.

The cable-based systems are often implemented in such a way that it is possible for a potential sender to sense the carrier on the cable before initiating its own transmission; if the system is already busy, it can wait until the cable is free before transmitting. This is impossible in satellite systems because of the long propagation times, but it is not impossible in radio systems such as Alohanet. Thus, the collisions in a cable-based system can be much fewer than those in transmission systems with long delays, such as satellite channels. The basic principle underlying transmission with and without slots is shown in Figure 6.5.

Time Assignment Speech Interpolation

Costly communication links can justify extraordinary signal-processing at the terminal if their traffic capacity can be materially increased. One such signal-processing adjunct is the time-assignment speech interpolation (TASI). It was developed for the very expensive transatlantic cable (for voice transmission). The method is a concentration by what is called stuffing. It differs from multiplexing, in which different voice paths require their own discrete time slot on a frequency-division channel. It takes advantage of the brief silences in normal conversation to achieve channel savings of more than 2 to 1. The silences are simply not transmitted. When the speaker pauses, the channel is taken away from him and assigned to an active speaker. With this strategem 96 overseas telephone channels can carry 235 simultaneous conversations spread over different trunk lines.

Figure 6.5

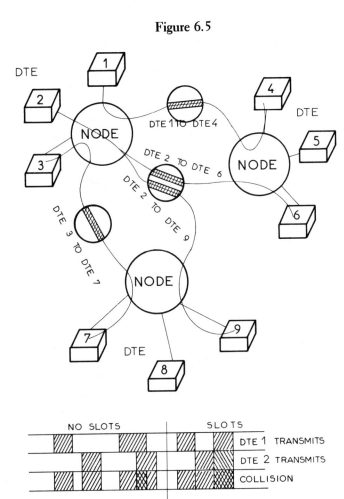

The procedure is based on a characteristic of normal conversation, which is that there are many short pauses between words and phrases and very lengthy pauses when one person is listening or searching around the telephone for a pencil or some such. In a two-way conversation the average speaker is actually talking somewhat less than 40 percent of the time. The TASI monitors each speaker's time and compares its signal 25,000 times per second against five distinct reference levels. The speaker is assigned a channel only when he is judged to be active. In general, a speaker will retain a channel for the second or so taken up by a word or group of syllables. Only after a pause of a fourth of a second is the channel taken away from him. When he resumes speaking, he is likely to be assigned a different channel.

This is an excellent example of a technology that fits perfectly into a data communications environment. Let us see why.

Data terminal equipment—a computer, minicomputer, or terminal—may be linked to a network via single physical circuits and employ packet-interleaved asynchronous time-division multiplexing (ATDM), which is a hybrid of multiplexing and concentration. This type of multiplexing differs from other time-division multiplexing in that a dedicated time slot is not provided for each circuit being multiplexed. It exploits the fact that a typical circuit to remote data terminal equipment may actually be carrying data only a small percentage of the time. It dynamically allocates the bandwidth to an active circuit, thereby increasing the overall utilization of the line and decreasing the bandwidth needed by the circuit connecting the terminal equipment to the network node. The bandwidth of the physical circuit must be based on queueing delays for handling the average busy-period loads for the virtual circuits being multiplexed.

This can be said in summary: the transmission of data, by means of logical solutions, on the same physical facility, have developed in the way in which voice transmission disciplines have developed with the telephone lines since the 1950s. Without such fundamental evolutionary steps it would not have been possible to talk today of the multiplexing of voice, data, and image nor of the exciting new perspectives in data communications.

Intelligent TDM

More demands for services and better capabilities produce better tools. Such is true of the recently developed "intelligent" time-division multiplexers. The immediate attraction of the new TDMs is the significant improvements in network utilization that they offer. They provide the network with the efficiencies of a concentrator and the network transparency of a hard-wired TDM, at a cost only slightly higher. They accomplish greater network efficiencies by taking advantage of network statistics. If we regard a circuit as the path between a terminal and the port of a central processing unit (CPU) we can view its use from three statistical aspects.

The statistics of circuit use: The dimensions of the periods of complete connection between a terminal and its port vary from the occasionally used terminal, such as in time-sharing applications, to the full-period dedicated terminal.

The statistics of data activity: The periodicities of data transmission on a connected circuit vary. Keyboard entry is at the low end of the activity range, and devices that transmit data without interruption, such as the high-speed aggregate of the TDM itself, are at the high end.

The statistics of language use: Individual characters within a set vary in the frequency with which they are used. Morse code, for instance, has a set twenty-six letters, ten numbers, fourteen punctuation marks, and some operational characters. The length of each coded character is inversely proportional to its frequency of use in the language. In English, for example, the code symbols for the letters E and T have one signaling element each, whereas the code symbols for punctuation marks have six.

Different multiplexing techniques are used, each with its own characteristic advantages and disadvantages, but all are statistical in nature, and the term *statistical multiplexing* has come to mean those techniques that are based on the statistics of data activity.

On a typical active circuit there are periods when no data are being transmitted, such as between keystrokes in a manual-entry circuit or between ACK and NAK transmissions on the return path of a bisynchronous circuit. In statistical multiplexing only active data are transmitted. They are formed into packets, together with channel-address information and error-protection coding. The packet length varies from system to system and depends very much on the applications. For instance, when propagation delay is important, the packets are kept relatively short, perhaps 32 characters or bytes. There may be also the requirement to transmit "short packets," such as the last few characters of a typed line. The intelligent TDM must therefore monitor all the transmissions in search of packet-terminating characters.

Statistical multiplexers are transparent to the standard code sets, but their use is limited in random-pattern transmissions because packet-terminating characters are generally unidentifiable. Since the packets consist of channel-addressing information and error-protection coding besides data, the proportion of the high-speed aggregate data stream occupied is somewhat greater than the circuit data rate, the actual proportion being determined by packet length.

The network traffic statistics must be monitored very closely when statistical multiplexing is used. If traffic forces a channel to wait for "space" on the high-speed aggregate data stream for a period longer than the buffer length assigned to the channel, then subsequent data are lost. This potential blocking may be reduced by extending the channel buffer lengths, by increasing the high-speed aggregate data rate, or by reducing the number of circuits that have access to the statistical multiplexer.

Data-compaction multiplexers gain their efficiency through the statistics of language use. This technique can be very efficient for a very specific language application, since the more frequent characters are assigned few signaling elements, and the less frequent characters are assigned to code words, the number of signaling elements being roughly in inverse proportion to their frequency of use.

The same characteristic that makes a code set very efficient for a specific language application can make it very inefficient for some other application. For instance, a code set intended for the transmission of an English-language text can be very inefficient for the transmission of numerical data (as in the case of Morse code). For maintaining a high level of efficiency the terminal code set, such as ASCII, is abbreviated when converted to the data-compaction code set for transmission. The efficiency is therefore obtained at the sacrifice of data transparency.

The data-compaction characters define, in their bit sequence, their own termination. This is necessary for determining whether a sequence of, say, 10 bits represents one 10-bit character from one channel, two 5-bit characters from two different channels, or perhaps two 3-bit characters and one 4-bit character from three different channels. This being the case, a bit error in a data-compaction character destroys the identity of its termination. This loss of character synchronization permeates the succeeding characters of other channels, although eventually a true character ending is recognized, and character synchronization is restored. This error-multiplying characteristic means that data-compaction multiplexers must operate with a sophisticated error-protection scheme.

The data-compaction channels will, when the code is properly matched to the language, utilize a proportion of the high-speed aggregate data stream that is, on the average, less than the overall circuit data rate. The instantaneous proportion will vary above and below this average, depending on the specific character transmitted. The minimal bandwidth is utilized when there are no data on the channel and only the terminator for that channel is transmitted. By the same token, data compaction will, like statistical multiplexing, exhibit variable propagation delays during periods of high network activity. It is also susceptible to blockage if the data activity of its channels exceeds the capability of its buffers to bridge the transmission delays encountered.

With the intelligent time-division multiplexers we have techniques that all offer significantly higher levels of network utilization than are possible with the hardwired kind.

The Problem of Vocabulary

Before closing this discussion of the fundamentals of our subject, we must speak of definitions. One of the psychological barriers in data communications is the technical jargon. The following is a discussion of the most basic terms.

The first subject is *signals*. There are three basic functions of signals: control, clocking, and data transfer. *Control* constitutes the *conversion* that takes place between terminal and modem; equipment are "on" or "off." *Clocking* regulates the speed of the data transfers. *Data* are transferred in a *serial* manner; they may be converted (by the modem) into an analog form or carried through the network in a digital form.

The difference between a *baud* and a bit per second is important.

A *baud* (the word is a derivative of *Baudot*, a telegraphy code) is (1) a unit of signaling speed in data transmission, (2) a function of bandwidth, (3) a figure indicating the number of times per second that a signal changes, and (4), in an equal-length code, a rate of one signal element per second; (for example, with a duration of a signal element of 20 milliseconds the modulation rate is 50 baud).

Modulation is counted in Hertz (one Hertz being one cycle per second). A sine-wave signal repeating itself once every second travels at 1 Hertz; if it repeats itself once every millisecond (1/1,000 sec) at 1,000 Hertz, each repetition of a signal is called a cycle.

A *bit per second* is not exactly the same as a baud. Bits per second are (1) a function of transmission (quality of equipment, lines, modems) and of noise, and (2) the measure of the true bit data transfer rate. Further, the *levels* at which a modem operates may be measured in *dibits* or *tribits*; for example, a 2,400-baud modem operating on dibits works at 4,800 bits per second (two bits in one baud), and a 3,400-baud modem operating on tribits works at 9,600 bits per second (three bits in one baud). To operate in this way we must *pack* and *unpack*.

The maximum capacity of channel is C (in bit/sec) = bandwidth (in Hz) × $\log_2 (1 + (\text{signal/random noise}))$. Hence, bits per second are a function of the means with which the communication is done. Bandwidth is bits per second; it is the difference expressed in cycles per second (Hertz) between the highest and the lowest frequencies of a band.

A *wideband* is a bandwidth greater than that required for a voice channel; in a wideband the capacity to modulate is critical.

A *carrier* is an electrical signal chosen because of its ability to travel through the transmission medium utilized; hence, "to carry the data." In data communications the medium is the telephone line. The presence or absence of a carrier refers to the presence or absence of transmitted energy.

Broadcast is the dissemination of information to a number of stations simultaneously.

Information that is transmitted over lines is, at its origin, in the form either of analog signals or of digital signals. *Analog signals* represent voice, music, television, images (charts, drawings, frame freeze, picturephones). *Digital signals* are telegraphy, Telex, data, and facsimile.

The following are the transmission alternatives available today for data communications purposes. The first three are for the low-speed transmission of binary signals; the networks are direct current with voltages of 40 to 120. *Telegraphy* was the earliest transmission medium (transmission of binary signals or pulses). *Telex* is a dial-up message-switching network for the transmission of binary signals at not more than 50 baud (originally). *Datex* is a dial-up network for the transmission of binary signals at 200 baud and more. *Telephones* are line-switching voice-grade lines operating at 300 to 400 Hertz and 48 volts. *Broadband* is lines with an extended frequency range (better than 4,000 Hertz). *Dial-up circuit* is a switched public network, generally of low quality with noise interference. *Leased circuit* is a dedicated line; it allows specification of the quality required (*conditioning*); it operates at higher speeds for a given transmission error rate than in a dial-up connection; it is very costly.

7

Switching Technology and the PBX

Telecommunications account for just over 10 percent of the nearly $700 billion a year that AT&T estimates U.S. business spends on communications. The telephone is a basic criterion of how advanced a country is in terms of providing basic services and the resulting competitiveness of its business and industry.

In the U.S. there are about 73 telephones for every 100 people. The reason is simple: If a country does not have telecommunications of good capacity and up-to-date technology, it cannot function as an efficient economy. With efficient communications we can save energy and even promote a cultural identity.

Telecommunications equipment of all types—from switching to transmission—is a very competitive market. The economics of the communications equipment industry dictate a quest for world markets. The cost of developing competitive new products, such as digital switches, will simply not repay investment within a single domestic market, no matter how well protected. Any industry that refuses to enter the global race runs a real risk of being preempted from the vast new markets that will arise.

Four basic design parameters characterize a switched network: transmission, switching, storage and control. These are the basic issues around which revolve the concepts and devices of a communications mechanism.

Many problems in the field of telecommunications relate to and derive from the voice-grade network. Others are proper to the origin and evolution of the data communications discipline.

The evolution of data communications has long been based on the technology and capital connected to voice-grade lines. One of the issues facing specialists is, "How are we to integrate computer-based requirements with the existing telco (telephone company) voice-grade networks: extend? overlay? separate?"

There are advantages and disadvantages with each alternative. Systems questions are also to be considered: Is it rational to put horizontal (user) solutions on basically star telco networks? How radically will current network concepts be altered by the coming "user" requirements of 10,000, 20,000, or even more terminals? How can we protect our investments while keeping the door open to the steady stream of technological advancements?

Switching Functions

The technical problems with telecommunications start with transmission. The choices of media, speed, and quality play a major role in this regard.

We have stated that a basic design of a network is switching. This is the key to distribution. Signals have a destination; they must be channeled from sender to receiver(s). The mission of a telephone exchange is to answer the distribution responsibility. The distribution can be two-way (bidirectional) or one-way. The needs of a two-way distribution brought about the the development of switching mechanisms (step-by-step, crossbar, electronic switches). Two-way solutions are necessary for interactivity (conversational). The one-way solution (telegraphy) was the earliest to be used. Some processes do not require bidirectional switching, such as televisions, telegraphs, and (to some extent) facsimiles (given current slow speed).

In general, present-day networks are *not* able to transmit and distribute in a homogeneous manner the different types of information with which we deal. Such technology has other limitations. For instance, the switching centers (telco) are *not* made for the transmission of TV signals; they are made for voice—about 4 KHz, whereas TV needs 6 MHz. If signal switching for image handling is wanted, then wideband should be used to allow the different types of signals to travel.

The mechanics work as follows. When we dial a telephone number to a telephone station, we are sending dialing signals to a local central office (CO). This office receives the signals and acts on them, sending an interoffice tone form to direct intervening connections. There are two kinds of telephone signals: dial pulse and multiple signals. Rotary dial phones produce dial pulse signals. They are created by opening the telephone circuit the number of times corresponding to the number dialed. Dialing "3" creates 3 open/close sequences, while dialing "7" creates 7 open/close sequences. Each open/close sequence makes a sound that can be heard at the caller's telephone. Dial pulse signals are registered at the local CO, but are not sent beyond that point. Multiple tone signals are transmitted beyond the first CO.

Pushbutton (touch tone) phones generally produce multiple tone signals the dual tone multiple frequency (DTMF). Each button pressed on the keypad creates two frequencies which make up a multiple tone signal. When the CO receives these two frequencies, it identifies the number pressed on the dial. However, some pushbutton phones do not produce DTMF signals. Instead, they generate dial pulse signals even though the user enters a phone number with a pushbutton keypad. When dial pulse signals are generated, telephone stations cannot be used to enter commands to a remote computer. A separate keypad is therefore necessary, as is the case with many European offerings of videotex.

Thus, computers can be programmed to recognize dialing signals as commands. The latter can be used for identification, for instructions to access specific information, or for response to queries. Telephone commands enable remote access to computer information using the phone as a station terminal.

Switching is the cornerstone of the modular construction of networks, their interconnections, and their steady growths. Switches provide a simple method for increasing the size of the network, its expansion rate, its flexibility, but also constitute points of congestion and delay. A little-noticed fact with switches is that they remained unchanged for almost a hundred years, hence restricting capability and increasing the cost of communications systems. This is now rated for a radical change.

A switch can work in successive stages (the Strowger principle of 1889), can be of a crossbar type (1919), or can work with the latest technological advancements. During the last 20 years, the tendency has been to convert the basic design principles used with electro-mechanical media to modern devices such as semiconductors. But keeping the design principles the same has slowed the impact of technology. Only recently is a determined effort being done to modernize circuit switching principles. The time-space-time (TST) solution is an example.

Both step-by-step and common control are characterized by 12 quite similar objectives:

1. Recognize a communications request.
2. Determine the identity of a DTE.
3. Connect the requesting terminal to the switching facility.
4. Decode the address and signal the destination terminal.
5. Terminate the status of the destination terminal.
6. Arbitrate among DTE contending for the use of facilities.
7. Select and allocate a communications path.
8. Establish the connection.
9. Monitor the session.
10. Assure recovery procedures in the event of errors.
11. Disconnect when the session is completed.
12. Guarantee quality of service, providing the needed data for error detection and correction.

In a step-by-step solution, a single mechanism combines contact switching action and address coding. An incoming line is connected to several line finders. One of them will be used on a given call. This solution is also called "progressive control," as successive digits of the address are directly employed by the operation, correspondingly defining successive switch stages.

Fundamentally, switching allows communication to be established between terminals (or stations, in voice networks) temporarily connected in a point-to-point fashion. Since the late 19th century, the goals of switching have not changed, but modern design aims to eliminate the switching machine with its bulky electro-mechanical devices that are located in large, costly spaces.

The two basic switching disciplines are step-by-step (the older one) and common control. The latter evolved through a number of phases; the eldest is crossbar switching—a hard-wired mesh where the switching process is effected by means of relay contact. The newest is computer-based where switching is assured through software support. Common control comes in different levels of sophistication, but all involve logical operations to generate control signals. Decoders, senders, markers are necessary and their management can be accomplished through hard-wired logic (as with crossbar solutions) or by stored programs (the computer-based alternative).

Quality Service and the Erlang Algorithm

Quality service is enhanced through computer-based control activity. If nothing else, the growth rate in communications and dropping computer prices impose:

the use of statistics and failure rates,

the optimal allocation of expensive equipment,

the minimization of set-up time,

and the control of delays

Such problems must be solved automatically—not manually—both for reasons of efficiency and cost.

Furthermore, to sustain substantial voice and data loads, switching units must be designed for unattended operation. They must allow remote monitoring, fault location, and on-line maintenance. Switching centers should provide (through software) the implementation of efficient resource allocation and routing algorithms—which leads from the notion of the simple switch to that of the intelligent switch, or node. (Intelligence means memory: both data and program storage.) Message and packet switching capabilities have developed out of this simple fact.

The use of storage elements is changing the entire area of switching. It influences the flow of traffic, speed, error rates, delays, and the cost and quality of service. Most importantly, there is an interrelationship between storage, transmission and switching—and storage is the connecting link.

Storage capabilities help in terms of quality service because they allow for value-added facilities, as we will see in a subsequent chapter. Switching centers with programmable features can improve on the bit error rate (BER) of the transmission lines. Typically, for voice quality circuits the BER is 10^{-5}. Poor quality voice lines support 10^{-3}. High quality circuits particularly made for data communications feature a BER of 10^{-7} or better.

Switches need to be redesigned both for quality service (low BER) and with data, text, voice and image handling in mind. Presently available switches have been classically projected for voice only and hold traffic for 3 to 4 minutes. What we really need are call processors which are fast, modular, and short-interval oriented. These are projected for 56 KBPS to 200 MBPS transmission lines.

Furthermore, the inclusion of a storage capability enlarges the concept of control. In communications, control means monitoring, logical functions, traffic analysis, testing, reconfiguration, deferred traffic, and reporting for management purposes. (We will return to these subjects when we talk of communications software.)

Quality is needed for software-controlled intelligent equipment that interprets dialing pulses and makes the proper logical connection between two telephone stations through carrier services. The local central office; remote (foreign exchange, or FX) central office; the nationwide dialing network; special tariffed services such as WATS; off-site tie lines; and the private branch exchange (PBX) work on these principles. The same reference can be made for connections between terminals and local or remote processors such as word and data processors, electronic mail, timesharing, and other digital computer services. In all these examples, the intelligent switch consists of a digital computer, software, storage device, and some racks of speciality hardware to perform the actual connections.

Operations-wise, the intelligent switch samples an incoming line, reads the digital code, and transmits this coded signal to the device that appears in the connection table entry that was created when the call/session was set up. The capacity of a centralized switch in regard to the number of calls/sessions that can be processed simultaneously can be determined by dividing the number of available time slots according to a built-in algorithm. This gives the percentage of devices that can be simultaneously active.

Capacity bottlenecks can occur in the interconnecting circuits or buffers. We have lived with switches that become saturated when 15 percent to 20 percent of the devices are simultaneously active. A switch can run out of capacity because

the processor runs out of computing cycles,

there is insufficient memory to hold the queues and control tables,

the hardware connection matrix limits the number of simultaneous logic circuits, or

the machine runs out of time slots.

The principal objective of the research on telephone traffic is to find norms to dimension the switching exchanges. Such research is based on the observation of the nature of traffic, including the behavior of the telephone users.

The first important contributions to traffic research came in 1910, though the first international congress was held in Copenhagen in 1955 under the auspices of the local telephone company (KTAS). This was also natural, as A.K. Erlang, the founder of traffic research, worked at KTAS. The main interest of this first congress regarded the traffic capacity of the different switching circuits.

The Erlang algorithm, published in 1917, is:

$$E_{1,n}(A) = 1 + A + \frac{A2}{2!} + \ldots + \frac{An}{n!}$$

where $E_n(A)$ is the probability of congestion with the available devices
   n is the number of the available devices, and
   A is the traffic in Erlang.

Erlang reflects the capacity of a communications system. It is a unit of traffic intensity, it has no dimension, and is employed to express the average number of connections under way—or the average number of devices used on a line. Traffic in Erlang is the sum of holding the time of paths divided by the measurement period. One Erlang expresses the continuous occupancy of a traffic path.

Solutions relative to dimensioning problems demonstrated that the controlling factor is principally economical, rather than technical, and purely concerns transport capacity and congestion—with investments and operating costs being the principal parameters. Planning systems must account for this factor.

Another important element is the human component. User behavior in different situations is a function of prevailing telephone habits. Hence, a direct interest for researchers is the observance of effects of human behavior on telephone traffic.

Tariffs are among the factors which influence usage growth. Yet, statistics tend to demonstrate that once a usage pattern has been established, tariff changes (including increases) tend to have a limited and temporary effect on telephone traffic. It is only in the longer run that tariffs have a decisive effect on traffic volume. For example, studies have revealed a distinct shift between night traffic and day traffic after different tariffs have been implemented.

The computer has revolutionized research on traffic. Computers can allow for calculations which formerly were inconceivable because of the volume of work. They also helped create a traffic methodology with wide applications.

There are three basic functions which affect exchanges and telephone channels: channel technology, channel administration, and immediate channel management. The first estimates where and when to introduce new devices in a way to satisfy the objectives of the service. The second optimally assigns existing resources. The third works short-range on the basis of traffic variations and attempts to optimize available resources.

At the same time, computer optimization studies done by the user organization bring under perspective ways and means for implementing economic solutions for users. The computer plays a major role in terms of managerial decisions as well as in helping the exchanges become intelligent.

Evidently, computer usage in business, financial and industrial environments—and the resulting data communications needs—provide work for the exchanges. Yet, forecasts made 20 to 25 years ago have not been fulfilled. When data transmission started in the late 1950s, the opinion of the telco was that datacomm traffic volume would reach and exceed that of the telephone. Experience has, however, revealed this as an exaggeration. Today, the traffic volume for datacomm purposes reaches only 10 percent to 12 percent of total telephone usage, the balance being voice exchange.

Analog and Digital Private Branch Exchanges

Private branch exchanges (PBX) are composed of four basic parts: switching, trunks, control, and user stations. The switching circuitry (or matrix), line and trunks are the heart of the equipment. In addition, there are service circuits for ringing, call progress tones, and other signaling information.

PBXs have a central role to play in office automation and in the management of all types of messages: voice, data, text, and image. Like the switching features for CO we have discussed, the PBX ties telephones, data and word processing, facsimile, and even slow-scan video equipment into private or public networks. Electronic PBXs have been available since the 1960s, but only recently have computer-based units attracted the market's attention.

By using the PBX as the hub, circuit switches can be arranged to interconnect sets of nodes. The major components include communication circuits, ports of various devices, and multiplexer switches to interconnect these devices.

On the DP/WP side, each attached processor can be a complete computer with its own memory, peripheral devices, and mapping function. Each processor can evoke a certain range of activities on any collection of other processors through a mechanism provided by the PBX.

The PBX switch is generally transparent to the sending and receiving computers and appears to be a direct wire connection. It can, in fact, be replaced by such a connection. Its switch matrix will generally consist of two essential components—a circuit switch and a link controller. The circuit switch is a multiple link switch used to connect pairs of computers together. The number of simultaneous connections is limited by the number of links provided in a given system. The link controller's logic selects, connects, and disconnects links between ports on the switch matrix. Selection is based on the next available free link, the status of which is maintained by the link control. (Connection is based on a coded order from the prescanner, and disconnection on the link control detecting traffic cessation.) This can be augmented by a diagnostic unit and an equipment switchover unit for on-line testing and equipment restoral. The lack of overt supervision allows the switch to be transparent to the subscriber, both electrically and logically.

PBXs have been introduced in several generations, and their technology largely followed that available for central exchanges.

The first generation was of the classical manual switchboard variety and lasted till roughly the late 1960s when a torrent of new product introductions with automatic features hit the market. (This was often misnamed PABX, for private automatic branch exchange.) In the second generation, the PBX and associated equipment consisted of a software-controlled device managing switching circuits through which were handled analog signals. The recently introduced third generation features PBX equipment consisting of software control (hence computer-based), but handling digital signals. Some third-generation architectures are distributed, others are centralized.

Technology propels the digital PBX, and though telcos argue that "It doesn't make much difference whether the PBX is analog or digital, as long as the system provides the features needed," to avoid obsolescence in five years, it may be worth it to pay more for digital solutions.

PBXs can be broadly classified into two large groups—analog and digital. In an analog system, the signal retains the same form in which it passed through the telephone line. This signal is represented by variations in voltage reflecting the changes in the human voice or in the data signal. (Analog transmission means that the signal transmitted is a direct analog of the actual signal. Analog signals must be amplified and are also subject to noise.)

An analog PBX passes the signal through in analog form. From their invention to about 1974, all PBXs were analog. Some newer analog PBX operate on the voice signals and transform them into pulses whose amplitudes vary at sampled signal variations. This process is known as pulse amplitude modulation (PAM). It uses time-division multiplexing (TDM) for switching efficiency. Hence, an analog PBX can be TDM, solid-state, and computer-controlled.

Analog PBXs typically use space division switching. Each connection can be traced through an acutal physical space or circuit established by the connection of points within the switching domain. With the call terminated, the connecting points on the circuit are released and made available for other connections.

In a digital PBX, the signal is converted through modulation into binary form. The signal passes through the PBX in this form and is converted back to analog for transmission over the public switched network, which is mainly analog. (The newer copper cables (T1 carrier) and optical fibers can accept the output of a digital PBX, so conversion to analog is therefore no longer necessary.) In this sense, digital vs. analog refers to the way the switching matrix operates. It has little to do with the control equipment.

The characteristic of digital modulation techniques is that all of the pulses are the same in amplitude and width, but the PBX must determine whether a pulse is present or not. A series of pulses in successive time intervals defines the amplitude of a voice.

A digital signal takes on one of a finite number of values at any instant. It does not have to be amplified, but it must be measured, its value determined, and a new signal made just like the old one getting rid of the noise.

The first series of PBX was introduced in 1973/74; the equipment was primarily intended to handle voice switching rather than data (though such equipment could handle data as a secondary function).

The second series (1980/81) supported heavy data switching and has been used primarily to handle heavy data traffic. It also features integrated voice and data capabilities.

A digital PBX design includes sampling (and hence PAM), but works on a digitization process converting each analog signal pulse into a number of binary digits. The resulting pulses are digital.

Digital PBX should not be confused with Data PBX. These are special-purpose digital switches which handle digital data only, no voice. There are no analog signals and, hence, no digitization process. A digital PBX can do everything an analog can—and much more. Above all, it holds the promise of switching any kind of digital signal initially up to 56 KBPS data and 64 KBPS voice including word processing, electronic mail, videotex, slow-scan video, teleconferencing, etc.

Digitizing voice at the station level enables a user to integrate voice, data and image immediately. Voice and other signals can be encrypted. Protocols, codes, and speed conversion capabilities are being developed.

With a digital network served by digital switches handling digital user stations, voice, text, data, and image can be mixed for transport purposes. Nonvoice communications are easy to handle and can make effective use of advanced technology.

The key factor in a telephone switching exchange—whether analog or digital—is the switching matrix. In years past, this matrix was made up of mechanical crossbars, relays, and so on, but these are now being replaced with more versatile computer-based, programmable solutions. Computer control offers the ease with which new features can be installed, the ability to improve services, and upgrading through changes in the course of regular activity. The processor inspects all lines, trunks, service circuits, and other portions of the system for supervision and for any additional information that may be needed (maintenance or other control data).

It should be possible to troubleshoot from a remote site, usually a vendor location. Self-diagnostic and maintenance features are helpful to any PBX system. Software should be modular for distributed control.

Some PBX provide for multiple redundancy down to the lowest level of the system. There are regular and standby test buses for remote and on-site diagnostics. For fail-soft purposes, if a critical circuit fails within a system, the total load will be supported by the remaining equipment.

Cost Control and Service Features with the PBX

A PBX can cut costs by optimizing phone usage. Calls can be restricted to non-busy periods and/or lowest tariff lines. The cheapest pathway for the call can be utilized, and the length of calls can be controlled. Complete reports on phone usage, showing just who is calling where, at what time, and for how long, are produced by some PBX.

An effective way to cut monthly phone charges for all categories of calls is to install the various active and passive control systems. Active control systems route long-distance calls over the least-cost path, as determined by computer programming, and keep track of who placed the calls and when. Passive control systems merely keep track of who placed the calls (local or long distance) by identifying the code of the originating station.

With *usage-sensitive* pricing, charges are based on the length of the phone call and the time of day it was made. Auditing of computer-kept records on calls, called number, length of time, and type of usage, helps cut down telephone expenses.

Problems with telephone service and tariffs are not new. Back in 1907, letters to New York's *Herald Tribune* complained of excessive rates and poor service in connection with local telephones. The newspaper's comment was as follows:

> "The telephone is not a luxury; it has become a necessity in most households and business offices.
> "The telephone franchise, a tremendously valuable one, was not accorded for the benefit alone of the company, but carries with it the proviso of an adequate public service at a reasonable charge to those served."

In regard to tariffs, the trend during the last few years has been to pay on usage rather than a flat rate. This makes computer-based communications systems much more attractive. For instance, WATS lines have been charged for many years on a flat rate basis or a mixed flat rate and low cost usage. But now we pay for every call made on WATS, and the longer the call, the more it costs. (The new tariff structure for WATS is in a way influenced by the AT&T split into long lines and local service companies, which leads to the fact that the telco cannot anymore charge a high long haul rate to subsidize local companies, or offer other service plans which might infringe the local companies' rights. The coming years will bring dramatic changes in tariff structures, and the computer-based PBX can help in optimization.)

Least cost routing enables the PBX to know the costs associated with various local area and long distance telephone services. It can therefore select the cheapest service that is not busy, or queue calls for busy circuits provided the caller can afford the delay. The PBX will also contribute to supported services. For example, callback queueing allows the switch to maintain a list of callers who have requested a busy line, and to call them back automatically when the line is available—for, among other things, cost optimization. Automatic callback may have one or more callers waiting for an existing call to be completed so that the system can call them back.

Another PBX service, speed dialing, provides a little table for each telephone extension. Hence, the person at that extension can dial a two-digit code while the switch references the associated list to find the function (full digit string) desired and dials it.

A call encountering callback at the terminating line will be dealing with several levels of busy signals to contend with. Hence, a simple test to see if the line is busy is no longer sufficient.

An outgoing call starts off the same way as an extension-to-extension call in the PBX. The control can complete its part of the job by connecting to any one of several trunks to the local CO, and it can do so before the caller has finished dialing.

Call forwarding is a way to temporarily route the calls from our extension to some other extension within the system covered by the PBX. This way, we can transfer all our calls to a secretary, or if we are going to be working in a conference room, automatically switch all calls there until we return to our office and reset the transfer condition.

A simple PBX feature that causes the equipment to remember the last number dialed so it can be automatically called by the simple actuation of a feature button is *redial*. This can help save the trouble of creating that character string again.

Advanced features will be the order of the day with new PBX. They will integrate services which are offered in the community by the telco and hook up to the telco network for these services—in a way totally transparent to the user. An example is the cellular radio.

Cellular radio was first proposed by Bell Labs in the late 1940s. Now, advances in computer technology are making it work. Among others, AT&T has run a highly successful commercial test system in the Chicago area for over four years prior to offering steady service in that city.

Cellular radio is the mobile telephone of the future, a highly advanced form of car telephone (though it will not be long before we see fully portable cellular telephones). Mobile phones have shortcomings, and are difficult to obtain. In some states, the prospective user has to wait years to get a car phone. Available channels are jammed, particularly in large cities.

Cellular radio changes this by providing virtually unlimited mobile telephone service accomplished by dividing a city into small sections: the cells. Each cell contains a low-powered transmitter/receiver. The cells cover an entire city and are computer-controlled. As one moves from cell to cell, the central controller continuously monitors the strength of the signal. When it grows weaker in one cell and stronger in another, the controller automatically hands the signal from the first cell to the other. This happens so quickly that it does not interrupt the conversation.

The cell-site transmitter is low-powered. Hence, the cellular system is able to reuse the same frequencies in other cells within the city. This concept of frequency re-use gives cellular service a virtually unlimited number of available channels and makes it technologically possible to spread the service city-wide. The first cellular phones will cost over $2,000, but prices are expected to drop to about $500 within a few years.

While the cellular radio is a coming development, facsimile is a current service. Let's review the fundamentals:

Group 1: Four and 6-minute analog fax machines, including many of the early units built before the establishment of the CCITT standards.

Group 2: Two and 3-minute analog fax machines, built to conform to this standard since 1978.

Group 3: Digital fax machines operating at one minute or less over conventional, voice-grade phone lines.

Group 4: Digital fax machines operating very fast (in seconds) over digital communications links. This standard is not yet agreed upon.

Several modern offerings present units which can alternatively work as Group 1, 2, or 3 depending on line conditions and tariff optimization.

Group 4 machines are a large issue. There are a variety of choices, each being pushed by a different vendor. Whether the resolution will be 240-by-240 lines per inch, 300-by-300, or 400-by-400 has yet to be resolved. Most major vendors have Group 4 units under development but are awaiting the resolution of the standard issues. At least some manufacturers have built a unit which permits store-and-forward fax based around advanced switching principles.

Some organizations, particularly larger ones, also want links through PBX video equipment—monitors, cameras, and record/playback devices for security, teleconferencing, and educational applications.

There are three popular technologies being used by organizations to implement local area networks for interconnecting different varieties of equipment and exchanging different forms of information: PBX, broadband, and baseband. Each of these has a unique set of characteristics and, by and large, each is optimized for certain applications.

The local area network and the PBX are compatible, and both have the aim that every user can still reach any information or other user no matter how he is connected. A LAN and PBX can form one totally integrated system, or stand alone. We can start with whichever system we need *now*, and add the other later.

The PBX will play a major role in the future of office automation and data communications. It will be the office's nerve center, and the more self-maintenance features it includes the better will be its employment.

A major issue, however, with any computer-controlled system is the maturity of the software. Most PBX failures are software-related, and the failure rate varies with how well the software is written and checked out. Computer-based solutions are welcome, but attention should also be paid to the quality of the software and hardware service one buys.

8

Transmission Media: from Coaxial to Satellites

We have spoken of space, frequency, and time division multiplexing and of switching technology. We will now devote interest to modern transmission media at our disposition—voice, data, text and image.

The prospective network user is well advised to carefully analyze what technology offers in terms of cost/effective solutions *now* and how those solutions will seem in five or ten years. (The time period will depend on a number of factors, such as accounting depreciation practices.) Both current and future possibilities should be examined. Ten years ago it would have been senseless to suggest high capacity pumping through satellites. Today, for long haul datacomm networks it has become a most advisable alternative.

Just the same, mainly because of difficulty in multitapping and the lack of specially designed terminals, modems, and computers, optical fiber technology—as one example—is not yet mature. Present-day choices suggest the coaxial cable for medium and short haul communications, and microwave links for connections over longer distances.

Coaxial cable has become a popular broadband medium in local area networks because of its capacity, low error rates, and configuration flexibility. Something similar can be said of twisted wire for baseband solutions. (Broadband and baseband are signaling techniques which are independent of the physical medium. These names have, however, been tagged onto the most commonly used varieties of coaxial cable for the two signaling techniques in reference.)

The (prospective) user should also evaluate each vendor's suitability as a supplier for his company. If the user's network will extend from coast to coast, the vendor should have a comparable service capability. If the user's company is a $1

99

billion-a-year business, he may not want to do business with a $20 million-a-year vendor.

Fault-free performance is another consideration in network selections. Though it may be taken to be independent of the transmission medium per se—and in a certain sense it is—some media are better for supporting intelligent lines.

Coaxial Cable Installations

Since the early 1970s, coaxial cable systems have increasingly been used as transmission media. Since the coaxial cable is a multiservice medium, organizations of many types began using its wide bandwidth for supporting television distribution, local area networks, security systems, video conferencing, and audio distribution. During the last 10 years several manufacturers began developing and perfecting the RF data modem to the point that they are reliable as well as inexpensive, and can support low to medium speed data processing equipment.

By wiring their assembly plants and office complexes, companies have been able to solve not only datacomm requirements, but also several other communication needs on one single, easy-to-maintain system.

Coaxial cable networks can support both baseband and broadband. The answer to the question, "How *broad* is broadband?" can vary as a function of time, technology and of our own requirements. An easy, though not technically precise answer is that broadband means a greater frequency range than our *current* requirements call for. In technical terms, a different answer should, however, be given.

Let's take as an exampale coaxial cable transmission within the perspective of a local area network (LAN) implementation. We speak of *baseband* solutions when the channel capacity is in the range between zero and 10 MBPS; of *broadband* when the usable range varies from, say, 5 MBPS to 400 MBPS. Satellite transponders work broadband. Television channels require a high amount of bandwidth—typically 6 Megahertz for a color TV signal.

A variety of taps, controllers, splitters, couplers, and repeaters are available that enable the cable to be easily extended and branched off to reach user locations for connection of user devices. The capacity of the coaxial cable is used in baseband local area networks primarily to transmit a single baseband signal at very high data rates, in the area of 10 or 12 MBPS.

In broadband local area networks, the capacity is used to create a large number of frequency subchannels from the one physical channel. Coaxial cable commonly used for CATV (and broadband local area networks) has available bandwidths in the range of 300-400 MHz. This translates into enough capacity to carry over 50 standard 6 MHz color TV channels of thousands of voice-grade and low-speed data signals (for example, 9.6, 19.2, or 56 KBPS). Correspondingly, currently available optical fibers have usable bandwidths of up to 3.3 billion Hz (GHz, gigahertz,

10^9Hz) compared with the upper limit of 500 MHz for coaxial cable. With such capacity, data rates of over one GBPS (10^9 bits per second) can be supported.

Though we don't *yet* have the need for such capacity, a point of attraction is the very low BER of optical fiber technology. Error rates gravitate at around one bit error per 10^9 bits, with the result that most error detection and retransmission overhead can be eliminated. By way of contrast, coaxial cable assures a BER of 10^{-8}.

The use of coaxial cable is, however, a mature technology. In 1949, when the first Community Antenna TC (CATV, or cable TV) systems appeared on the scene, the operator was satisfied if he could receive, amplify, and deliver a signal to locations where the signal could not be picked up directly. This simple technical approach is no longer adequate when CATV systems support:

two-way communications,

customer response,

transmissions addressed to selected receivers,

central databasing and retrieval,

utilities such as meter reading, and

intrusion protection.

(Since then, the CATV industry has grown dramatically and currently reaches 21 million subscribers in the U.S. alone. It is predicted that by the end of the decade this figure will rise to 65 million.)

There are two areas where advanced design concepts and techniques must be involved: the cable system as a network and the circuit design of the components used in the network. Many of the component and circuit-theory problems have been solved successfully throughout the industry, resulting in highly reliable components offered at very low prices. Massive competition for the coaxial cable market has resulted in improvements in designs and in component level advancements, which is not the case with optical fibers.

The choice of cable type and its installation can be classified by distinguishing first the *grounded coaxial*. It can pass high information rates but is subjected to ground loops and radiated noise. The *ungrounded coaxial* presents similarities to the preceding example but lowers the ground loop interference.

Whichever carrier design is chosen, a CATV network will typically feature a headend with forward and return bands or, alternatively, dedicated wires. In a dual cable system, the entire bandwidth of the cable is available for message transmission in both directions, allowing a great deal more capacity for network channels and nodes. The coaxial cable is simply looped around the headend of the network, passing each node twice. Nodes send on half of the cable and receive on the other half, with both signals occurring at the same frequency.

Cable costs will be higher, as will the cost of taps, since each node must connect both "halves" of the cable. However, these costs would most probably be offset by the gain in capacity over a mid-split single cable system.

The headend, or central retransmission facility (CRF), is a device that consists of amplifiers, filters, and signal modulators. All messages must travel to the headend from source nodes and from the headend to destination nodes. The CRF designates and explains the course that messages take when traveling to and from nodes. This is worth noting, since transmissions in single-cable systems for cable TV and LAN are commonly discussed in these terms.

Source nodes transmit (send) messages upcable on the reverse or return channels to the CRF, typically at lower frequencies (say, 10 to 110 MHz). The CRF amplifies and modulates these signals to higher frequencies (say, 175 to 310 MHz) and transmits them downcable on the forward channels to destination (receiving) nodes.

In a cabled environment, the most common cause of system failure are physical breaks in the cable introduced by natural and man-made reasons, power interruptions, processing equipment failures, and device failures. Networks contained in buildings usually have fewer breakdowns. The reliability of CATV equipment can be expressed in mean time between failures (MTBF).

The typical life cycle expectancy of passive equipment properly installed can be 35 years. Passive components perform no active function, and maintenance is not required in the terms we usually understand, but basic physical and signal performance checks should be done once a year.

The MTBF of the active amplifiers is 18 years, giving an average system MTBF of some 25 years. Theoretically, once the active components are adjusted for signal level, equalization, and voltage inputs, no further adjustment should be necessary. It is good practice, however, to check system levels at the amplifiers once a year.

To reduce the impact of a potential failure, redundant cable networks and standby equipment can be implemented. Redundancy applies to processing equipment, data translators, amplifiers, and power supplies. Remotely controlled coaxial switches can be implemented to link the primary system to the secondary. In general, however, properly laid out cable systems will not crash unless the headend is disabled.

Experiences with Cable Television

In the 1970s, data communications requirements grew at rates beyond the capabilities of existing telephone, twisted pair, and similar type communication solutions. Advancements in data processing, interactive terminals and networking concepts now impose operational strains on conventional schemes.

Star-type twisted pairs become unreliable and cumbersome to use when the system requires constant expansion and reconfiguration; demand complex central intelligence; limit device placements and data flow; and are unable to provide high quality information transfer necessary for video conferencing and security applications.

Current technology, however, permits an integrated multimode communications network by using a single communications medium to satisfy these requirements. As stated in the preceding section, the CATV industry led the development of broadband distribution techniques which provide reliable, inexpensive communications over coaxial cable.

Coaxial cable networks are composed of several types suitable to numerous environmental conditions. If damaged or broken, the line can be spliced or short sections can be replaced in a matter of minutes by personnel using simple tools.

Fault isolation in a coaxial network is relatively easy using a variety of test equipment, and can be enhanced through the use of statistical recall systems, status monitoring facilities, and programmable spectrum analyzer/signal generators. Furthermore, network services can be easily relocated without incurring undue cost. Buildings of any size can be prewired with coaxial cable at a fraction of the cost of conventional wiring schemes. Connection to the network is done through simple units which allow users to connect or disconnect communication devices.

The implementation of CATV technology inside and outside the field of television distribution has given rise to a need for further advancements, some of which appear below.

Addressable converters take advantage of a video channel's unused scan lines. Some use four lines, each containing 26 bits of digital information, which is enough to hold about a million subscriber addresses within each of two thousand market categories. Addressability in cable systems permits control over signal reception. The operator can change paychannel services, set up special pay-per-view events, and shut off the subscriber's service when a bill is not paid.

Two-way communications are more important to video implementation but can also help in television broadcasting. The Federal Communications Commission required this capability of cable operators until 1979, when the Supreme Court severely restricted the FCC's cable-regulating powers. (Cable operators seeking the profits of impulse pay-per-view often install a two-way capacity.) *Limited two-way communications* means that the subscriber can send only narrowband signals (voice and data) to the cable operator. QUBE, of Columbus, Ohio, is the best-known example of a limited two-way system.

Scrambling can be done through two methods:

1. By reducing the amplitude of the synchronization pulses which cue the TV set to start a new line or frame. The descrambler can identify or restore the pulse even when it is buried within the amplitude range of the video picture signal.
2. By reversing the picture signal, so black becomes white and vice versa. The descrambler thus reinverts the signal.

Some systems can switch randomly between these scrambling methods, or use both at once. This enables cable operators to alternate between scrambling modes on the basis of dynamic algorithms that constantly monitor the video signal.

This short list of features can be enriched by focusing attention on technical characteristics to be considered, including impedances, control of reflections, signal levels, noise levels, and amplification.

Cable outlets should be terminated with a 75 ohm characteristic *impedance* to prevent undesired reflections when a user device is not connected. This can be done by inserting an appropriate terminating connector, or through the use of self-terminating outlets. (The terminator's function is to convert RF energy to thermo-electric energy to minimize reflections.)

Reflections, or echoes, are clones of existing carriers on the system and of discontinuities caused by irregularities. Bends in the cable, connectors, taps, and improper terminations help create such irregularities which, when encountered by RF energy, reflect part of the signal. Reflections do not become a problem until their amplitude reaches a state interacting with the desired signals. The use of high quality drop cables and the assurance that each unused port outlet is terminated help minimize reflections.

Signal Levels are an important factor. Modems require less signal-to-noise ratios than do television signals. Since data levels are of less amplitude, this lowers the overall intermodulation distortion on the network. The same is true of inbound transmissions to the headend. The difference in signal levels for data depend upon the amount of bandwidth each unit occupies in a 6 MHz TV-quality channel.

Noise, being any unwanted input, it should be given careful consideration in any CATV system. Design considerations should ensure that all attached devices corresponding to a given service (data, voice, image) have input and output levels within 6 dB (decibel). Electrical and thermal noise make negative contributions.

As for *amplification*, noise is generated by any active device; its amount of noise is a function of bandwidth and temperature. Each amplifier has a noise figure which is the amount of thermal noise contributed to the signals passing from its input to its output.

These variables are not changeable by the user during alignment or maintenance processes; they are built at the drawing board. So, design perspectives must be carefully outlined, the more so as CATV is in a steady state of evolution.

The steady growth of supported facilities is propelled for entertainment and datacomm reasons. The household with several TV sets has become a norm. At the same time, the projected spread of videorecorders* stands at 55 percent to 60 percent of households. (In England, the present rate is about 12 percent, possibly the highest in the world.) Work at home through PCs, computer-aided instruction and the use of home computers with a multitude of videogames and software programs has taken hold in the U.S. and is invading European households.

From American experiences we can learn what programming offered by cable television is most popular. The four most successful cable channels are Home Box Office, Showtime, Cinemax, and The Movie Channel. All four offer movies as pay-TV without advertising interruptions. Sports and news channels are also popular. (In Europe, with an estimated cable density of 25 percent by the mid-1990s,

---

*In the U.S., Western Europe, and Japan.

advertisers will not soon advertise on cable TV due to its lack of popular offerings.) Satellite TV may become a carrier for advertising given its wide area coverage.

Presently, Netherlands—followed by Belgium and Switzerland—is the most cabled European country. More than 60 percent of all houses (over 80 percent in the large cities) are connected through CATV.

The emphasis today is on interactive installations which can not only distribute television and radio program but also videotex, telealarm and telecontrol. A major experiment is under way in the south Limburg area (in the triangle of the cities Kerkrade, Maastricht and Sittard). The financing of this system is assured through private and governmental participation with the objective to link together (as a first phase) an estimated 250,000 homes.

As large areas, particularly metropolitan, are cabled, CATV will help accelerate the horizontal as well as vertical concentration in the media field on a national level. There are, however, financial risks involved in hardware and software, as obsolescence may be faster than generally expected.

At the same time, national plans will interfere with CATV developments. For instance, the French Government has taken a very active role in the development of a television network through the "plan cablage" (cabling plan). In the 1983-1985 timeframe, investments of 12 billion Francs ($1.6 billion) are being projected, with nearly 60 percent to be carried by the government. Government experts have opted for optical fibers rather than coaxial; the cable will carry 32 different channels, of which 26 will be of TV bandwidth; and the monthly charges are projected at about 50 Fr. (roughly $7) including the cost of the subscription and decoder. The decoder currently costs 1,200 Fr. ($160), but it is foreseen that in less than 2 years this price will be more than halved.

Optical Fibers Technology

Developments at AT&T and other companies involved in fiber optics—Corning Glass, ITT, GTE, NEC, Siemens and Philips—are concentrating on better methods of fiber-making to cut costs and to reduce the losses and dispersions of light signals.

Fiber optics have well-known advantages. Transmission is not affected by electrical or electromagnetic interference, nor does it emit noise, thus making the carrier inherently secure. Optical fibers are very small and light, allowing space and weight savings, but the implementation technology is not yet sufficiently mature. The lack of efficient physical interfaces and of new design equipment to be connected are two reasons for the lack of fiber implementation.

Fiber optics depends upon a light source and the cable. A laser is a light source producing a highly concentrated directional light.

The first step in manufacturing the cables involves making a glass tube—called a preform—from which the hairthin fibers are later drawn. A gas torch is used to deposit various chemicals on the preform to allow the light to travel efficiently along the optical fiber by altering the refractive index of the glass. (Light does not run straight along the cable but bounces from side to side, and the need is to prevent it from bouncing off the cable, especially at the longer wavelengths being contemplated.)

The leading approach for depositing chemicals on the glass tube is modified chemical-vapour deposition (MCVD). Its advantage is that it minimizes the risk of water contamination. Water in the fiber weakens its transmission ability. Several vendors have come up with solutions to MCVD that speed up chemical deposition to effect cheaper production. AT&T adds fluorine to the chemical dopants being added to the glass. Its latest optical fiber is made of a germanium/silicon core, with a cladding comprising a meld of flourine, phosphorus and silicon. The flourine cuts the dispersion of lightwaves at any wavelength. This allows use of a 1.5-micron wavelength, offering a better mix of speed and capacity than other fiber optic links.

Laser actuated optical fibers is not the only technological implementation. Databasing, video and audio storage devices are also promising areas.

Since 1979 when the first read-only videodisc recording came to the market, the introduction of databasing engines for business applications has been forecast almost annually. It does not yet seem to be around the corner, particularly because of the high BER of the process, currently rumored to stand between 10^{-2} and 10^{-3}.

Much more successful has been the videodisc implementation with entertainment electronics. The audio compact disc (CD) is 120 mm in diameter and plays for an hour without turning over. A single unit contains 5 billion digital sound bits, plus extra bits used for such tasks as speed control, error correction, and visual display. The speed of the disc is controlled by coded information on the disc itself. Each bit is either a flat surface, representing 1, or a microscopic pit, representing 0. They are laid out in a helical track, and one unit of sound information (word) consists of 16 bits. The 16-bit word serves the PCM (Pulse Code Modulation) discipline. Each PCM word is read in under 10 microseconds at a constant rate.

The read mechanism rests on a laser source and a battery of mirrors.* For read-only, the power in the beam is of minor importance—a low output 1.5 mW unit surface. But a very sharp focus point is essential, for the pits in an optical disc track are no more than 0.4 microns wide and 0.1 micron deep, and the spacing between tracks is as little as 1.6 microns.** The laser beam focus point is 0.9 microns in diameter at the half-intensity points. As it has no weight either, it is easy to deflect and control, with instant response and accuracy.

Timing is important, and this calls for accurate turntable motor speed control. The laser beam doesn't wear out the disc, and focusing is automatic; any unevenness or warpage in the disc has no effect on the accuracy of the readout.

Accompanying the main beam are two pilot beams which seek out track edges and thus keep the main beam aimed directly at the track center. If the track wavers

*The mirror system is being made by Olympus and employed by Discovision Associates (IBM/MCA), Philips/Magnavox, Sony, and others. Alternative solutions are by RCA and Pioneer.

**One micron is equal to one-thousandth of a millimeter.

because the disc is eccentric, the beam follows it automatically. The beam can be advanced or retarded on the track to compensate for even the smallest timing irregularities in the disc arising, for instance, from slight eccentricity. Beam timing control provides the extra timing accuracy necessary for the reproduction of a top quality visual signal.

The laser beams through a surface of transparent plastic that protects the information track and focuses directly onto the reflective information layer beyond. Hence, any fingerprints, dust or minor scratches on the disc surface are out of focus; they practically have no effect on playback quality.

As technology advances and current flows are corrected, the use of the optical disc in financial and industrial environments will open new horizons, substituting other processes such as COM (computer output to microfilm).

Communications by Satellite

The first earth satellite was Sputnik 1, launched in October 1957, beating Explorer 1 by four months. Now we have telecommunications satellite support. Half of all telephone calls between the U.S. and Europe now travel via Intelsat V. In 1965 satellites could handle 240 telephone calls at a time across the Atlantic; today the number is above 20,000. By 1993 it is expected to reach 130,000.

Ships and planes establish their locations by sighting not the sun but satellites. The IUE (International Ultraviolet Explorer) help astronomers study distant stars above the earth's veil of obscuring air, and satellites give multinational corporations easy access to their operations. The availability of cost/effective satellite communications creates the possibility for improvements in productivity for organizations needing to transfer data among dispersed locations.

Around 1986, Intelsat VI, built for the International Telecommunications Satellite Organization, will become the world's most sophisticated commercial communications satellite. This drum-shaped, spin-stabilized unit will have twice the capacity of Intelsat V. It will be able to carry 33,000 telephone calls and four TV channels simultaneously. It will weigh about 4 tons at launch and measure 4 meters in diameter.

More than 1,300 operational satellites are presently around the earth, while another 1,620 have fallen silent. Not only do these satellites perform a variety of tasks but they come in numerous shapes, sizes and "nationalities." The Intelsat global satellite system provides the equivalent of over 20,000 two-way voice-grade circuits among 90 nations for long haul overseas voice and data traffic and television distribution.

Satellites are sent up at the rate of about 170 a year. In the next decade, the space shuttles are slated to carry some 200 satellites aloft. Hundreds of others will make the trip in conventional rockets like the Ariane launcher and the Soyuz system.

International satellite services may loosen the grip of government PTT ministries in Europe and Japan. Satellite Business Systems has reached operating agreements with British and Italian authorities to provide high-speed digital private line data and videoconferencing services, thereby entirely bypassing traditional public switched networks.

As the impact of satellite supported communications services grows, we will experience better facilities at a lower cost per unit of transmission with more broadband channels. But we are also going to encounter technical problems, the more so if we keep working with protocols established for a different form of supports.

As of January 1982, for instance, AT&T began freely intermixing satellite and terrestrial communications paths in its long lines operations. This delay can affect bisynchronous and other ARQ (automatic request repeat) transmissions, affecting both users of the dial-up network and those of leased lines. As a consequence of this change in policy, users employing bisynchronous and other protocols will need a software upgrade or else experience a significant degradation in efficiency of datacomm throughput. (It takes approximately half a second for data to be beamed from the earth to a communications satellite and then relayed back to earth.)

Such a delay results in two types of problems for datacomm users. One problem are the echo suppressors for telephone connections more than 1,500 miles long. They would interfere with the transmission of data over the circuit as they include disablers which are activated by a special signal from the transmitting modem.

A second and bigger problem concerns the transmission acknowledgements needed by the bisynchronous or other protocols frequently required by remote job entry terminals. These terminals must receive a signal acknowledging that one block of data has been received before sending the next block. A half-second holdup every time this procedure occurs would chop the net throughput of terminals operating at 4.8 KBPS down to 400 BPS.

A solution is to provide a unit that emulates computer acknowledgement for received data. American Satellite, for instance, offers a Satellite Delay Compensation Unit (SDCU) which is given as part of its data service offering. ASC suggests that the SDCU on satellite links can offer the user a 95 percent throughput.

Another option is a rather extensive software change with packet switching protocols like High Level Data Link Control (HLDLC) and Synchronous Data Link Control (SDLC). These require fewer acknowledgements and transmit larger blocks of data. Hence, they can reduce problems resulting from the usage of BSC (Binary Synchronous Communication).

With packet switching a large block of data is transmitted before an acknowledgement is sent. The larger the block size, the fewer acknowledgements need to be transmitted back to the host, and therefore the lesser is the impact of the transmission delay inherent in satellite based communications.

Other developments not necessarily in communications are still on the drawing boards. For instance, NASA and the U.S. Department of Energy have invested more than $25 million to study the idea of a solar-powered satellite. What they envision is a spherical antenna half a mile long connected to prodigious metal wings. The wings would contain billions of solar cells which would convert the sun's light directly into electricity. The electricity would then be converted into microwaves beamed to a field of antennae on earth. The satellite would be built completely in space from a factory ship. Astronauts would piece the massive grid of aluminum beams together using special mechanical pins. That task completed, they would unroll thousands of thin sheets containing the solar cells, stretch them across the aluminum structure and attach them to the beams by clips and springs.

When finished, the giant structure could be 30 miles wide and 60 miles long and could generate five billion watts of power—more than half the power demand of New York City—at an estimated cost of $90 billion.

Coaxial vs. Satellite Transmission

As cable TV competes with television stations for viewers and vies for advertisers, new technologies are challenging cable before it is fully entrenched. The alternate technologies range from subscription television, a single-channel offering, to satellite master antenna television (SMATV) which theoretically can deliver as many channels as any cable system. Cable experts do not believe that any single alternate delivery system represents a potential replacement for existing cable TV since none offers all the capabilities of multichannel cable. Yet, alternate delivery systems will grab a share of the market and could ultimately claim 10 percent or more of the cable market. (There are presently in the U.S. alone about 30 million subscribers.)

With SMATV, an operator simply puts an earth station (receiving dish) on top of an apartment building. The earth station picks up programming services from a satellite, and the programming is then delivered from the earth stations to apartments through wires. But microwave transmission generally demands a line of sight which limits service to buildings tall enough that an antenna mounted at the top can "see" the transmitter. Table 8.1 presents in a nutshell competitive technologies and their features.

Business applications of satellite links are a logical follow-up. Vitalink, a Silicon Valley firm, has begun marketing satellite-based private data networks. Its DualTrac data networks consist of two primary elements: the DataTrac earth station and DualTrac network services. This company focuses on selling the earth stations and leasing the satellite transmission capability as part of the DualTrac service package. The approach provides users with the benefits of earth station control and ownership without requiring them to assume responsibility for operating the satellite transmission link.

Applications for the DualTrac network include:

electronic mail,

distributed data processing,

word processing,

Table 8.1.
Competitive TV Broadcasting Technologies

Offered by	Type of Service	Potential Channel Capacity
1. Oak Industries, Golden West Broadcasters, Wometco Enterprises, Time	Subscription Television (STV)	1 channel per station; can offer multiple stations in same markets
2. Communications & Cable, Campbell Management, Mehl Cable Systems, Private Satellite TV	Satellite master antenna television (SMATV)	3 to 5 channels but now has all-channel capability
3. Tymshare, Contemporary Communications, Tekkom	Multipoint distribution service (MDS)	2 per city now, expansion to 28 channels possible
4. Communications Satellite (Comsat), Western Union, RCA, CBS	Direct broadcast satellite (DBS)	3 to 6 per satellite

file transfer,

remote job entry,

remote data entry, and

video teleconferencing.

To take advantage of Vitalink's DataTrac satellite earth stations, DualTrac networks make satellite communications a valid alternative to private terrestrial data communications, creating improvements in corporate productivity for organizations needing to transfer data among dispersed locations.

This data network establishes separate parallel data paths linking from 2 to 8 earth stations, each having a throughput range from 9.6 KBPS to 3 MBPS. By providing two independent transmission paths at the earth station and the satellite, the DualTrac network assures users reasonable efficiency, reliability, and system availability.

Another alternative of the Access System from Western Union, offers various networking capabilities; a business can choose between several priorities of delivery times. The user can now connect his own terminals: Telex, TWX, or any small computer with store-and-forward capability into the WU network and move messages such as telegrams, cablegrams, Mailgrams, and electronic mail. He is billed on a per-message basis.

The Access System takes advantage of computer-based switches at various locations in the U.S. that help convert information from one protocol to another. A connected terminal must have five characteristics:

offline storage,

asynchronous transmission mode,

even parity ASCII code,

at least one of four designated transmission speeds, and

an acoustic coupler to modem.

Satellites are evidently playing a key role in intercontinental communications. A 500-pound satellite can outperform the message-carrying capacity, transmission fidelity and energy requirements of the previously-used 175,000 tons of transatlantic cable. Yet, it would be imprudent to totally substitute submarine cables with satellites. For TV and multidestination traffic the seabed cable cannot compete with the satellite, yet on high traffic density point-to-point links cable is cheaper and may offer superior performance.

For short distance traffic the circuit noise of the satellite and the transmission delay time inherent with a geostationary orbit are not acceptable for some services. Circuit routings which involve the tandem connection of two satellite links are generally unacceptable because of the transmission delays (0.24 seconds one way), and there is always present the issue of satellite vulnerability in case of war.

As satellites provide a 400 or more MHz broadband (vs. the 45 MHz of submarine cable technology), one might think that the days of the seabed cable have ended. But submarine cables and satellites are, and for some time are likely to remain, complementary. Each has its own characteristics that can be exploited to advantage.

Hence, rather than thinking of an outright substitution of one process by another, it is more rational to project in terms of partial integration. A good example is given by a British experience involving LAN and satellite implementation.

The British Universe network consists partly of a orbital test satellite (OTS), terrestrial local networks, and low-speed backup communications via X.25 networks. The design and construction phase of the project was largely completed in early 1983, followed by an experimental program. Most of the local networks are Cambridge Rings providing a data rate of 1 MBPS with a BER better than 10^{-9}. Since the satellite channel is only available to the project for about 3 hours per day, gateways are provided to X.25 networks.

Satellites and LAN differ markedly in transit delay. The rings take about 20 milliseconds to deliver the longest block (2 KB) compared with the satellite's 250 milliseconds.

The Universe network is designed to facilitate the use of *lightweight protocols*. A datagram structure is shown in Figure 8.1.

One aim of this project is to understand how its component parts perform in

Figure 8.1. A lightweight protocol. There is no CRC on the assumption of a very low BER: 10^{-9} or better.

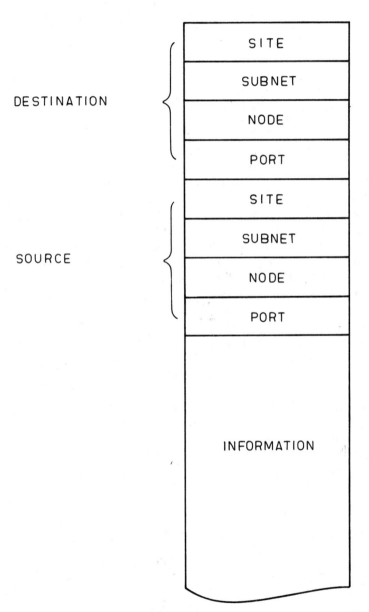

A LIGHTWEIGHT PROTOCOL

THERE IS NO CRC ON THE ASSUMPTION OF VERY LOW BER: 10^{-9} OR BETTER

different environments with respect to data rates (if interworking is done with standard protocols). By contrast, lightweight protocols take advantage of the characteristics of local area networks to provide simple, high-performance communications. Since such protocols lack CRC (cyclic redundancy check), basic assumptions in their usage are very low error rates, very low latency, and no misordering of data blocks. With these conditions, very simple protocol implementations can be built.

Some of the participating sites have more than one ring, and high-speed bridges based on a pair of Motorola 6809 and 68000 microprocessors have been developed at Cambridge University to link them. These bridges are able to provide throughput comparable with the ring and virtually no delay under light loads.

An important component of the Universe network is the *name server* which provides mapping between symbolic names and numerical addresses on the network and sets up paths through bridges. Name servers are simple Z80 processors with 64 KB of RAM at a known address on each ring.

To provide experiments with good flexibility, no stream protocol needs to be "understood" by network bridges. Instead, *byte stream protocol* is used for file transfer, terminal traffic, and so on. The network components "know" the mechanisms for setting up such streams but do not cover flow control. This is consistent with an assumption made in network design: Components are lightly loaded with respect to their buffering, and when congestion occurs an acceptable policy is to throw away data.

Large buffers in a bridge ensure that such incidents are rare. Three low-level protocols are provided in the network:

1. An initial connection protocol (OPEN) which enables a pair of contraflow paths between two processes.
2. A single-shot protocol (SSP) which establishes a reverse flow path through the network.
3. A datagram which allows delivery of a self-contained block of information.

The normal streams built on the OPEN protocol are medium-weight to provide delivery of files. They also support windowing to allow for efficient operation over the satellite.

Applications such as bootstrapping—where code compactness and simplicity are important—have been given due consideration. The SSP protocol is used for simple transactions. In such cases, the request passes through bridges, setting up a reverse path as it goes. The reply then follows that path. Datagrams contain the full address of sender and recipient, and hence leave no state information as they pass through bridges.

The satellite packet protocol divides the available channel time between sites. It is not directly accessible to network users, but does affect the performance seen by users. The satellite channel is divided into time frames of about 125 milliseconds each. Each time frame contains a number of HDLC frames. The first—called the "reference burst"—is always sent by the master station. The master for a session is determined when the satellite session starts. A software-based arbiter aportions time within the time frame.

Each reference burst contains a map of how the remainder of the frame is to be used and during which periods specific sites can transmit.

A site wishing to transmit makes a request indicating the minimum acceptable size together with the actual requirement. If all requirements can be allocated in a single time frame the reference burst indicates the time slot given to each site relative to the start of the frame. If not, the requests are scaled down to fit in the time frame.

In case the scaling down reduces some allocations below their minimum level, the time frame can be widened to a maximum of 260 milliseconds. Mechanisms are included to allow sites to inform the master of their load so that more channel capacity can be allocated to the most needy. In the absence of such indications, the time available is divided fairly among all requesting sites. A quality of service parameter is included in allocation requests indicating normal, priority or bulk services.

Bulk services are expected to be used for allocation of a fixed bandwidth channel through the satellite, and are used for transferring realtime data such as slow-scan TV images or voice.

9

Terminals

Terminals are typical components of a communications system, which consists of a chain of several terminals and channels. A terminal converts a signal appropriate to one channel to a signal appropriate to the next channel, while preserving the signal's information content. For example, a message may originate in a human brain, be transmitted to the fingers, pass into a teletypewriter, travel over a wire line to a radio transmitter, journey through space to a radio receiver, be typed out onto a sheet of paper, be scanned by a pair of eyes, and, finally, enter another human brain.

The communications engineer often regards a terminal as any apparatus at either end of a discrete electromagnetic channel. More commonly, however, a terminal is viewed as an apparatus for converting a visual, acoustic, or tactile signal into an electrical signal, or vice versa. This is a basic definition, a good one to be kept in mind. Telephone sets and their logical extension into data communications are the most common terminal devices, and they are the least expensive.

Telephone sets, unintelligent or intelligent terminals, computers—that is DTEs in general—are built with certain blocks; the electronic components, such as the microprocessor, the memory, the decode and control, and the peripheral interface adapter, are nowadays made of semiconductors.* The most striking feature of the semiconductor industry is its continuous and rapid change. During the last five years many opportunities have presented themselves as a result of investments made in research and development and in manufacturing engineering.

---

*A substance, as germanium or silicon, whose conductivity is poor at low temperatures but is improved by minute addition of certain substances or by the application of heat, light, or voltage; used in transistors, rectifiers, etc.

The user of a computer and data communications service can now have his own DTE at very low cost. Right after World War I the radio became a household item. A third of a century after World War II the same has happened to the computer.

Such developments require time to mature. The circuitry had to be simplified and controls had to be redesigned to make their function as obvious as possible and the chances of a mistake in operation as minimal as possible. More importantly the prices had to be brought down to a level appealing to the users' market.

These developments have come to maturity. The products available in the market now and in the years ahead make the microcomputer necessary to the consumer, just as are the telephone, the radio, and the automobile. That is why this decade is so exciting in the computing field.

The Use of Terminals

Terminals capture, buffer, transmit, and receive data. They fall into two categories: the inexpensive, passive units, and the intelligent units.

The first has limited functions that serve the basic needs of sending and receiving messages. The transaction telephone, for instance, performs those functions from the customer's card and manual entry and then transmits the data from memory when an answering signal is received. This data terminating equipment is new. It has a number repertory for repeated calls to the same number, it can dial out from a private branch exchange or on a foreign-exchange line, it automatically tests proper operation, and it may be equipped with an auxiliary manual-entry card so that the customer at a bank or store can enter a personal identification number (PIN) if necessary.

The second category, intelligent terminals, have expanded capabilities and functions, processing message data before they are transmitted and after they are received. To do this they require self-contained storage and local data-handling facilities. This means they are programmable. The user would have hands-on experience with such terminals and could obtain both hard copy and soft copy (CRT). Figure 9.1 presents the output alternatives.

An intelligent terminal usually will be programmed to check that the data received are accurate and in correct sequence, so that the computer does not find errors at processing time. If errors are found, the terminals will inform the operator accordingly (for example, through a video screen or in printed form), so that corrective action may be taken (probably canceling the information just entered and repeating the input).

Data clearance at the point of origin is important because it permits the operator to know at once whether the input has been accepted, prior to the next batch of data. This requires a set of instructions. An unintelligent terminal will be instructed what to do by the computer (or minicomputer) with which it operates on-line; an intelligent terminal will have its own programs to perform.

Figure 9.1

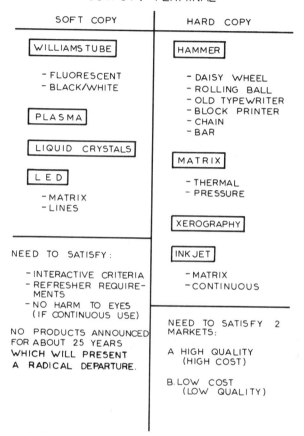

OUTPUT / TERMINAL

SOFT COPY	HARD COPY

WILLIAMS TUBE

- FLUORESCENT
- BLACK/WHITE

PLASMA

LIQUID CRYSTALS

LED

- MATRIX
- LINES

HAMMER

- DAISY WHEEL
- ROLLING BALL
- OLD TYPEWRITER
- BLOCK PRINTER
- CHAIN
- BAR

MATRIX

- THERMAL
- PRESSURE

XEROGRAPHY

INK JET

- MATRIX
- CONTINUOUS

NEED TO SATISFY:

- INTERACTIVE CRITERIA
- REFRESHER REQUIRE-
  MENTS
- NO HARM TO EYES
  (IF CONTINUOUS USE)

NO PRODUCTS ANNOUNCED
FOR ABOUT 25 YEARS
WHICH WILL PRESENT
A RADICAL DEPARTURE.

NEED TO SATISFY 2
MARKETS:

A. HIGH QUALITY
   (HIGH COST)

B. LOW COST
   (LOW QUALITY)

The end-to-end position (in a network) will be maintained by the terminals, irrespective of whether the link is wire, radio, or other. Figures 9.2 and 9.3 make the point. Data terminating equipment are so called because of this simple fact. We shall speak of DTEs, however, generically—not only as terminals but also as any device occupying an end position in a network; a computer may be a DTE.

Since there may be many terminals, from one to hundreds, connected to a computer, they must be simple in design, easily maintained, rational in terms of resources, and straightforward to communicate with. The operator should have only to key in data and be able to examine the results. Since the terminals are the interface between persons and computers, they must be characterized by a working simplicity; they must appeal to the nonspecialist. This means that a terminal must reduce the description and presentation of data to an easy-to-follow form. It must communicate the information it receives to the central computer (or mini-

Figure 9.2
Components of a data communications system

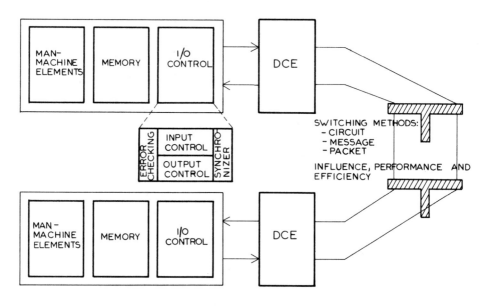

Figure 9.3
DTE to DTE data communications

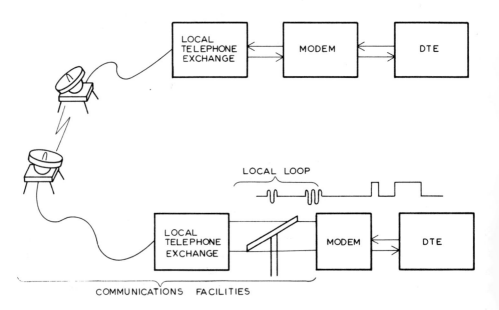

computer resource), transmitting it on-line. And it must receive data, store it temporarily, and present it to a human being.

We have spoken of interfaces, and of the terminal as an interface. Actually, as the term is used in computer technology, an interface is a set of rules covering the relationship among dissimilar functions within the same node of an information-processing system.

This bring us to the issue of codes and coding. A code is a set of signals, representing letters or numerals, used in sending messages. A person must give information to a terminal in some form, as by touching keys or using magnetic striped cards, but once the data enter the terminals, they will be coded, so to speak, in a form intelligible to the computer, as, for instance, a string of bits.

This is one of the basic functions a terminal will perform. It is not the only one.

Building Blocks

The typical DTE consists of a microprocessing unit (MPU), which is something like the central processing unit of a bigger computer, a read-only memory (ROM), which is a storage device that a user can only read, not write on, a random access memory (RAM), which is a storage device on which a user can both read and write on, and a peripheral interface adapter (PIA), which handles the devices attached to the mainframe, such as the input-output units. These parts combined with an appropriate power supply, and bus drivers,* make up the DTE; see Figure 9.4. The function of the control bus is to carry control signals to all the electronic components of the system. Such signals originate at the control unit ("decode and control" in the diagram) and more particularly in the timer section. Control means, simply, ensuring that the right thing happens at the right time. The data bus transfers the information between the different components of the DTE or, to be precise, from the peripheral interface adapter to the memory, from the memory to the microprocessor, and then back, etc. The control bus and the data bus are, for all practical purposes, two distinct subsystems, each with its own functions.

An integral part of the DTE, and a very important one, is the real-time clock. It serves as an interval timer. Let us look at its functions.

It gives the right timing and control impulses to all units of the machine.

It makes it possible to measure a given time interval.

It ensures that the different units of the computer begin actions at fixed times.

It helps check that the duration of a certain program does not exceed given limits.

It also provides the time of day in operations for which this is necessary.

---

*A conductor or group of conductors in the form of a bar, serving as a common connection for circuits; also called a busbar.

Figure 9.4

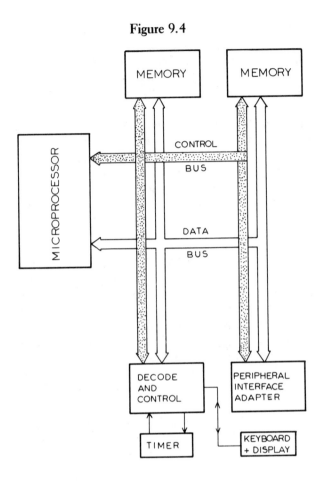

The peripheral interface adapter (PIA) allows the attachment of such terminals as the keyboard, the printer, the video, and, eventually, the line controller for teleprocessing; see Figure 9.5. The minimum the user will need is a unit for input and output. Through this unit he will enter a control program in memory, which will tell the DTE what it should be doing. The user will enter data for storage and for treatment. He will receive the answers. Input and output units are designed to help the user communicate with the machine, and vice versa.

Some of the vital peripherals are the storage devices. A storage device contains data and programs, as does a memory device, but it differs from memory in several respects. For one thing, whereas a memory device in a typical terminal holds 64, 128 or 512 kilobytes (thousand bytes), a floppy disk will hold 256 K to 1 megabyte. For another, the cost per byte will be much lower on a floppy disc than on a hard disc or a central memory device. The access time will be much higher in the floppy disc than in the central memory. The memory devices are directly at-

Figure 9.5

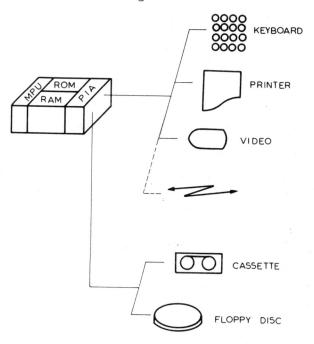

tached to the system through an interface controlled by a microprocessor; the storage devices are coordinated through the peripheral interface adapter, also known as a peripheral control unit.

To recapitulate: *Memory* and *storage* mean different things with DTEs. We usually speak of "memory," "central memory," or "high-speed memory" when referring to random-access memory. We say "storage" when referring to external devices able to hold information, such as floppy discs, cassettes, magnetic tapes, or high-capacity discs.

A floppy disc—so named because of its resemblance to the discs in a juke-box—is a handy extension of the storage capabilities of an intelligent terminal or a minicomputer. The addition of a cassette recorder to a system which had only floppy discs is an example of the increase in the number of component units. Whether a floppy disc or a cassette is used in connection with a terminal, and for transmission purposes, data will be retrieved from storage, sent to the central memory, and forwarded to the device asking for it.

The characteristics of storage are capacity (expressed in characters or in bits), access time (expressed in milliseconds), rotation time (expressed in milliseconds for drums and discs), and transfer time (expressed in bits per second). They should be kept in mind when choosing a device to add to a DTE. If the work is mainly batch, a cassette device may be best; that would be so even in the case of data transmission, provided that the transmitted data may be forwarded serially. If, on the other hand, messages are received with random reference to information in storage, as a file, a floppy disc is better, because, as we shall see, it allows direct access. *Direct access*, also known as *random access*, is a prime matter in information technology.

Transmission Speed and Interfacing

An important characteristic of a DTE is its transmission speed. The most widespread standard speeds of data transmission vary from 50 to 300 to 2,400 bits per second, but 9,600 bits per second and higher are possible; the ratio of 50 to 9,600 is 1:192. Though the moving gear behind the transmission speed is the modem, the terminal also plays a key role, applied to a network.

Given the abilities, and limitations, of the human operator, and other factors, the speed of transmission is in direct relation to the possession of buffer memory, which is a transit memory that helps distinguish the high speeds of the electronic equipment and transmission line from the far lower speeds of the electromechanical devices of a terminal.

Although most of the terminals installed today operate in less than 600 bits per second, the trend is definitely for terminals to work faster and faster, especially in business, industrial, and financial applications. Higher transmission speeds are advisable in case of heavy data loads and also for a better exploitation of the central computer resources and of the available line capabilities.

From a projection of the interfacing work it should be doing, a terminal is designed for a certain speed of transmission. To satisfy the requirements, not one but a whole lot of component units must be properly projected, in particular the input devices, the memory, the physical interface, and the modem; see Figure 9.6.

If all data processing equipment and transmission facilities were designed and built by one vendor, the relationships might have been, by design, sufficiently interrelated to preclude the need of hardware and software interfaces. As matters stand, however, data are handled by equipment from several vendors and are sent over telephone lines that were never intended for their use. The operations executed during the transmission phase include the following:

Storing the messages to be transmitted

Queueing them

Converting them from computer code into various transmission codes

Introducing the needed characters for transmission

Transforming the messages into characters

Breaking up the characters into bits

Initiating the message proper

Figure 9.6

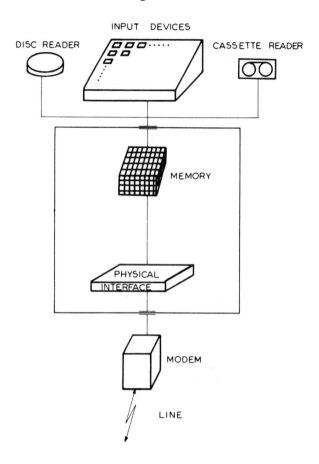

Forwarding the bits on-line in a timely manner

Supervising the transmission process, with the possibility of repeating messages in case of error

Giving a warning of the end of text, end of transmission, and the like

The Line Controller

The on-line connection of a computer to a terminal, and vice versa, required a line controller. A line controller is an interface between the lines and the terminal. Its structure may range from a very simple one to a sophisticated one that is equipped with a large memory and has special line control programs (Figure 9.7). Sophisticated line controllers are capable of running the transmission network autonomously and also managing the flow of messages.

Some line controllers only effect a physical connection between the line and the computer, providing an interface; others carry out network management functions autonomously by supplying corrected input messages to the central computer and by receiving output messages to be relayed to the computers or terminals. In any case, the line controller is a necessary interface when computer devices talk to one another over short- or long-distance telephone lines. Its basic tasks are to initialize, signal for errors, add and delete, and start and stop, and signal the end of the transmission.

The simple line controllers can transfer data between the central memory and the terminals, transform characters, serializing them by bit, do the opposite, i.e., give a character (parallel) structure to serially transmitted bits, and synchronize with the computer for incoming messages and for those to be transmitted.

We must bear in mind that to take advantage of the central processor's or microprocessor's high speed, it is necessary to have at least a small buffer (for example, one character size) present in the line controller. The exchange of characters between the central unit and the line controller takes place through this buffer. Other tasks include checking the received data for freedom from error, eliminating the start–stop bits during the phase of receiving, transforming the code received into the character structure desired by the computer and, during receiving and transmission, signaling "end of text" or "end of transmission."

In the literature the line control procedures are also known as data link control (DLC). The easiest way to remember about them is to know that they are hardware and software conventions, used for transferring data and controlling information devices. To provide a link between separate and often diverse information-handling units a connection must be established, synchronization of the parties to the exchange obtained, messages passed, and the inevitable errors detected and corrected.

Eight technical characteristics help differentiate one line controller from another:

1. The number of connecting lines: line control units may be designed to handle just one line or a hundred lines; generally, for a given line control, the number of lines is variable, from a minimum to a maximum. This choice, once made, brings the other seven technical criteria into perspective.

2. Speed of transmission: the speed of the various lines can either be the same or not.

3. Permitted transmission techniques (telegraph, modem).

4. Codes of transmission: the line controllers may be divided into three main groups: those that accept all codes, those that accept only some codes, and those that accept only one code.

5. Connecting line: public (message-switching) or private (point-to-point, multidrop).

6. Number of wires making up the single lines (2 or 4, or 2 and 4 wires).

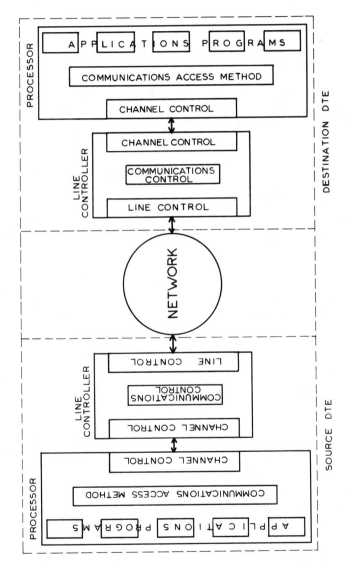

Figure 9.7

7. Direction of transmission: simplex, half-duplex, full duplex.
8. Type of transmission: asynchronous, synchronous, or packet.

The type of transmission is defined by the number of connecting lines. This is a fundamental aspect, which helps distinguish the various line controllers.

Computers, Minicomputers, Microprocessors, and Terminals

Terminals are made of semiconductors, as are microcomputers, minicomputers, and computers. All are composed of five basic units: input, output, memory and storage, arithmetic and logic, and control (and so, incidentally, is the finest information machine to date, made by nature: the human nervous system). What then is the difference between them?

To start with, to some people the term *microcomputer* means "microprocessor." To others the two words do not mean the same thing. We shall say that a microcomputer is a full system with input–output, memory, arithmetic logic unit, and so on. A microprocessor is a central processing unit on a chip, and does not have self-standing capabilities; it is a machine within another machine (a computer, an auto, a refrigerator).

Fundamentally, the word microprocessor refers to a single, integrated circuit "chip," which contains (according to some reckonings) the power of a very small computer. A microprocessor usually cannot do anything without the aid of support chips and memory. By contrast, a microcomputer is a fully operational computer system based upon a microprocessor chip.

A computer is any device, usually electronic, that is able to accept information, compare, add, subtract, multiply, divide, and integrate, and then supply the results in some form of human-to-machine communication. The operations are indeed performed just as well by a minicomputer, a microcomputer, and a person who computes.

But a computer, as we habitually think of one, is a complex piece of equipment; it may have many input–output units, billions of bits of high-speed memory, different storage devices, and, lately, many processor units. Furthermore, over the last fifteen years computers have been supplied with sophisticated software whose development usually costs more than that of the hardware.

Computers are designed to solve a large range of problems both technical and scientific and are adaptable to a variety of operations. Microcomputers are computers at microprices; indeed, by today's standards Univac I, the world's first commercially available computer, is a microcomputer. (This fact alone dramatizes the sharp drop in production costs due to technological developments.) But while a modern large-scale computer (at a cost of, say, fifty times that of the minicomputer) will be characterized by multi-access, multiprocessing, and multiprogramming, the user of the minicomputer will be well advised to keep his machine on monoprogramming. The more limited software support (offered by the minicomputer manufacturer) of the maintenance service and of assistance in system skill are variables that partially (not wholly) justify the price difference between minicomputers and their larger brethren.

We come to the conclusion, therefore, that the main difference between computers, minicomputers, and, eventually, microcomputers (not microprocessors) is one of end use. End use includes the software libraries, which are available, the system's support, and the "multi" properties mentioned above. Whether one needs all these or simply wishes them, a price must be paid to have them.

Terminals, we said, are installed to collect, maintain, and extract data from memory. In extracting data they operate upon a data pool kept at the central computer resource. The memory at the local terminal may be no more than a buffer, but some terminals possess substantial memory capabilities, the intelligent terminals. Intelligent terminals are programmable. Although the terminal is the peripheral device of a computer, a minicomputer, and even a microcomputer, an intelligent terminal may incorporate in itself a whole microprocessor.

The early terminals were mostly of the teleprinter type: a typewriter with a line controller. Today the mechanical parts—the keyboard and the printer—remain the most expensive and the least reliable of the components. Figures 9.8 and 9.9 illustrate this difference. Figure 9.8 presents the functional blocks of the now famous terminal, the IBM 2780, which has been the most copied in the history of computing. The input–output buffer, the line buffer, and the encode–decode unit are the heart of this equipment. But an intelligent terminal, while preserving this structure, is a much more sophisticated device, as Figure 9.9 shows. Microprocessors are built into the terminal so they can perform and control the various operations of the units. Microverification, for instance, helps check the operational integrity of the arithmetic and logical unit (ALU), channels, buffers, and storage units, which operate automatically when the system's power is on. They validate the integrity of the data flow, write in and read back a specified bit pattern in memory, control the integrity of the DTE by running through a set of instructions, compare an accumulated checksum to a preprogrammed checksum, and validate the overall integrity of the device. Thus, if an error is detected in the processor or channel or a problem in an input–output attachment, a condition of error will be presented to the user.

Intelligent terminals evolved as a function of demand and also of the sharp drop in the prices of storage devices; see Table 9.1. The abilities of the DTE are a powerful extension of computers and minicomputers. With the increasing use of telephone lines for processing purposes, new perspectives are opening up. No wonder that microcomputer based terminals and the communications gear are getting the lion's share of the market (Figure 9.10).

Figure 9.8
Functional block diagram of the IBM 2780

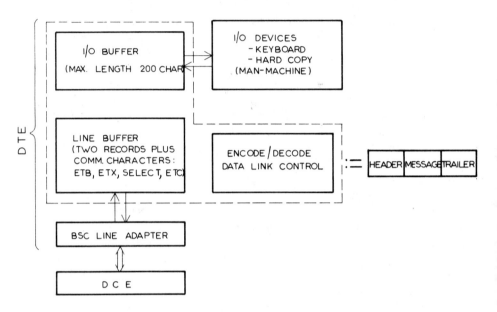

Figure 9.9
Functional block diagram of intelligent terminals

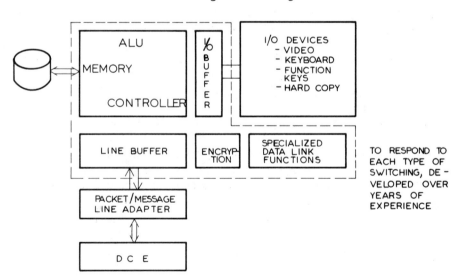

Table 9.1
Storage Devices for the 1980s

Type	Possible Capacity (megabytes)	Access Speed (seconds)	Cost Goals ($/megabyte)
VLSI	0.25 to 5	nanosecond	2.000 to 5.000
Bubble memory	1 to 20	k microseconds < 1 millisecond	400 to 1.400
Moving head disc	50 to k × 1,000	millisecond	15 to 25
Mass storage	Trillions	second	0.3 to 1.0

For any type of storage, the basic selection criteria are: cost, access speed, capacity limits, reliability, other performance criteria, and availability. VLSI, very large-scale integration.

Figure 9.10

(*The American average is 10%; however, organizations well-launched in real time have about 20% and this chart concerns this population.) (PTT is Poste, Telegraph and Telephone, in Europe)

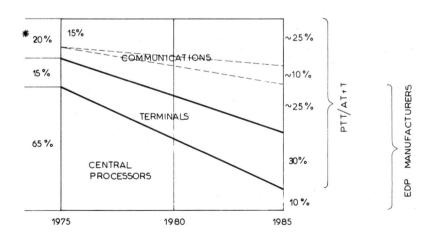

10
Modems

The goal of a modem is to permit terminal-to-computer and computer-to-computer communication over a telephone line. The primary function is the modulation/demodulation of carrier signals so that digital information may be transmitted over an analog communications link, usually a conventional voice-grade line.

To communicate over a telephone line, the computer or terminal at either end must be equipped with a modem. The modem converts binary data coming from the terminal (or computer) to analog signals suitable for transmission over a voice line (and vice versa).

There are various types and speeds of modems which operate differently from asynchronous modems. However, asynchronous (nonsynchronous, start/stop) modems are the most frequently used. They are growing in popularity as the number of systems equipped with such units increases.

Most specialists feel that modems will be in great demand through the 1990s, given the continued lag in strictly digital datacomm offerings. Sometime in the next decade, once local digital loops become commonplace, we will see a drop-off in modem use. A datacomm user should therefore seek help in making a selection among the various features offerred by modems. He should distinguish between vendors that serve end users and those that sell to original equipment manufacturers. He should also determine whether the application is high speed (2.4 KBPS and above) or low speed.

Different manufacturers serve each speed category. Most often, low-speed modems are asynchronous and high-speed modems are synchronous. Short haul modems (line drivers) handle high-speed (for instance, 9.6 KBPS) data transmissions over short distances (less than 35 km). Higher speed, special purpose modems operating at 56 or 64 KBPS handle computer-to-computer data transfers or transfers between special purpose terminals and CPUs. However, 64 KBPS is not the high end of modem function. Data transfers in some instances may occur at rates as high as 1.5 MBPS.

A vital factor to consider in modem selection is performance. If higher performance is required, modems with special circuitry to monitor line and signal characteristics may be employed at perhaps a 30 percent higher cost. In lower-speed modems, adaptive equalization may be employed. Devices using these circuits are about 20 percent more costly than modems offering fixed equalization.

For users who do not have demanding requirements, a medium-performance, low-cost modem will be technically adequate and cost/effective. The potential modem user should also investigate the range and quality of service offered by vendors.

In a sense, modems and multiplexers (or muxes) are the glue that hold a data communications system together. They will be around for years. Innovations in datacomm technology will enable modems to perform new functions in network control and diagnostics, and multiplexers (described in the following chapter) will work closely with local area networks and as X.25 gateways, to cite two examples of future applications.

The Use of Modems

If we look conceptually at a terminal-to-computer connections, end-to-end, we will see at the extremities the DTE equipment linked through channels and switching points. The object of the links is transmission which takes place on physical media (twisted wire, coaxial cable, and optical fiber) and on microwaves (radio links and satellites).

Transmission can be effected at different speeds and capacity levels. A clear distinction must be made between:

low capacity (say, 2, 3...24 voice-grade channels);

medium capacity (up to 300 voice telephone lines);

high capacity (from 300 to 10,000 and up).

The speed may vary, and here the range is very great:

sub-voice-grade lines operate at 50, 70, 100, 300, and 600 BPS;

voice-grade lines operate at 1,200 and 2,400 BPS;

wide bandwidth lines reach 56 and 64 KBPS and up to 100 and 200 MBPS.

We will return to this issue in more detail.

Finally, the lines may operate in an analog or digital transmission basis. The former is the older, voice-grade solution—and, as stated, brings into evidence the need for modems.

A different way of looking at this subject is to say that computers and terminals are user-level devices. Space, frequency and time affect line efficiency, and interfaced between the line and the terminal is the modem (data set, DCE).

Digital data, as it is manipulated by a computer (or a terminal), is represented by pulses, or square waves. Such waveforms cannot be applied directly to the tele-

Figure 10.1.

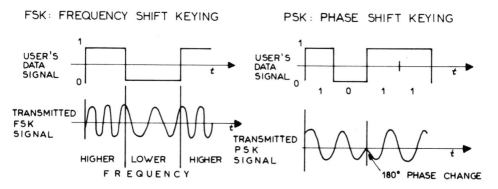

phone network because their frequency spectrum would not be faithfully preserved. The pulse signal must first be converted to a modulated-wave format which has no DC (direct current) component and fits well into the voice transmission band. The new format must also be rugged enough to survive transmission impairments, such as frequency, while still permitting accurate recovery of the original baseband signal.

Digital data has been represented on telephone lines by waves that are amplitude modulated, frequency modulated, or phase modulated (Figure 10.1). Correspondingly, three basic types help characterize the design of modems based on:

1. Amplitude shift keying (ASK)
2. Frequency shift keying (FSK)
3. Phase shift keying (PSK).

Combinations are possible as, for instance, ASK and PSK, which is used for high bit rates.

In a general sense, ASK modems tend to be the least efficient in terms of bandwidth and signal processing. Single sideband solutions help augment the efficiency but also involve a greater sensitivity to noise and higher costs. Therefore, the largest number of ASK modems are to be found in less than 300 baud applications and synchronous environments.

Amplitude modulation was favored in early data channels. At the present time, AM is mainly of interest in transmitting multilevel symbols (particularly where one sideband is eliminated).

FSK modems work in the range of 300 baud to 2.4 KBPS, and may be synchronous or asynchronous. CCITT has brought foward Recommendation V.21 for FSK modems at 300 baud working on public switching networks.

Original offerings of PSK modems have been in the range of 600 baud to 2.4 KBPS and are basically synchronous: clock pulses are recovered from the received signal. The CCITT recommendation for 600 baud PSK modems is V.22. (Many modern data sets use phase modulation because it is relatively insensitive to transmission impairments.)

As the speed of transmission increases the modems tend to become more sophisticated, but their cost and sensitivity to noise increases as well. CCITT Recommendation V.27 describes the standard for a modem at 8 phases, while Recommendation V.29 sets norms for ASK/PSK high bit rate offerings.

The type of modulation chosen should be a function of the application. Binary frequency modulation in the form of FSK (frequency shift key) is preferred for reasons of simplicity and economy, but does not support bandwidth efficiency. The differential phase-shift key (DPSK) is a good choice for medium bandwidths. With DPSK, the phase of the cycles in a particular time period is compared with the phase of the cycles in the previous time period.

The majority of modems are designed to accept and deliver a serial stream of binary data to the terminal interface. Some types handle a character at a time by accepting and delivering binary signals on several parallel interfaces while others use acoustic coupling to telephone handsets.

A class of modems worth mentioning is that designed for microcomputers. Low cost, economic modems are complete data communications system for PCs and can expand the capabilities of the PC, providing data communications for business, home or school. Such micromodems typically consist of three parts:

1. A printed circuit board holding the modem, ROM firmware and the serial interface.

The board plugs directly into the PC, eliminating the need for a serial interface card. The on-board ROM firmware enables the modem to operate in three modes to perform different tasks: terminal, remote console, and program control.

In terminal mode, the PC can be used to call and communicate any other microcomputer timesharing system or videotex service that has a compatible modem. In remote console mode, the PC can be accessed like a timesharing computer, one user at a time.

2. A microcoupling devices connecting the PC directly to the telephone line, eliminating the losses and distortions associated with acoustic couplers.

This device waits for a dial tone, dials numbers, answers the phone and hangs up when a transmission is over.

3. The possibility to add an external memory device containing programs with varied applications.

Software or firmware allows modems (and micromodems) to autodial, autoanswer and hang up the telephone. Using simple programs, they transmit and receive data.

With autodial, a modem recreates a phone number, dialing automatically. In an intelligent unit, multiple tone signals are generated and stored in memory. To dial, the machine recalls the signal. The CO or PBX receives such signals and acts to complete the connection just as with any other connection. This convenience feature allows computers to call one another and communicate through telephone lines without requiring an attendant to dial the phone number of the receiving station (or computer system). Basically, automatic dialing is an audio processing technology made possible through the conversion of sound to electrical signals and back to sound again.

Autodial makes cost optimization possible as the modem can dial-up destination telephone numbers unattended, such as at night when transmission rates are lowest. One of the devices offered on the market stores up to six telephone numbers, has a redial capability, and is controlled through the operator's keyboard-interactive approach.

Autodial modems work with both pulse and Touch-Tone dialing, and can be configured for use with PBXs where pauses are inserted in the dialing sequence. Modems can be designed for specific machines or series of machines.

Correspondingly, *autoanswer* is the capability of a device to answer a ringing telephone. A variety of units from facsimile asynchronous exchange (FAX) machines to computers and automatic answering services use this facility. The function is provided by a device outside the telephone set that detects a ringing signal and seizes the line which, in turn, sends an off-hook message to the PBX or CO.

An automatic answering function can be accomplished by devices as simple as the answering machine. Communicating word processors, FAX and other office systems use this function, thus eliminating the need for telephone attendants and without impeding communications.

Noise and Line Losses

Even if it is possible to establish a type of modulation/demodulation which assures protection from a specific type of disturbance, this will only be relative as the telephone line is subjected to different types of disturbances with varying levels of intensity present at every moment. Noise and line losses are the result.

Though generalizations can be dangerous, other things being equal, the more a modem works at high speed, the more it is subject to analog-type disturbances. Just the same, the more important are the losses, noise, ratio of signal-to-noise, burst noise, and shifts of frequency.

Noise arises for different reasons: thermal noise comes from the amplifiers, noise is generated by the induction of power cables, we have to live with the effects of echoes, and there may be noise due to the use of a PCM system. In short, noise is present in all telephone lines.

There is also a special type of disturbance. *Burst noise* is due to peaks which present a similar level to the data signals, and a greater amplitude at the baseline. The most common reason for burst noise are electromechanical switches of a central telephone office.

When relays and other switches operate in adjoining channels they create electrical transients which reflect themselves in transmission lines. Other causes are lightning and impulses from equipment-like radar.

Important, of course, is the fact that noise in transmission lines and terminating devices leads to errors. Among the predominant reasons for data errors are:

the incorrect level of or absence of a signal (about 45 percent of all errors);

noise due to multiple causes (about 35 percent of all errors);

burst noise (about 10 percent of all errors);

other reasons (about 10 percent of all errors).

Attention should also be paid to line losses. Some analog parameters are relatively easy to count end-to-end provided we have the right instruments. The measure of losses is defined as the amplitude of the reference signal which is sent minus the amplitude of the reference signal received. The unit of measurement is the decibel.

Test signals vary from country to country but tend to stay in the range of 800 to 1,020 Hz. Even if the loss may fluctuate in function of the length of the telephone line, the equalization of the amplitude at the extremity of the reception is regulated by a loss around 16 dB.

CCITT Recommendation H.12 indicates that the total maximum loss must be below 28 dB. This is an upper limit as, in practice, the loss in reference is much less. It is, however, important that the measurement is done end-to-end and not through a loopback.

Technical Issues with Modem Selection

A number of technical distinctions must be made when considering or choosing a data set. One of the most basic is that of synchronous and asynchronous communications. For asynchronous transmission, two signal states are used, and the lengths of the intervals are prescribed by the transitions of the binary data wave. For synchronous transmission, the intervals are uniform in duration. The choice of signal states is usually made an integer power of two to simplify the relationship to the binary data being handled.

A third major technical reference is the availability or nonavailability of diagnostics. Users encounter at least four categories of modems today, as far as diagnostics are concerned.

First are modems that carry out full-scale network analysis, where features such as analog line characteristics and the RS-232C are measured and monitored. Tests are conducted during normal data transmission using out-of-band signaling. The diagnostic information is carried within a second carrier frequency, separate from the data channel.

Second are units that carry out diagnostics for modem functioning instead of complete network diagnostics. With these devices, we can look at local and remote modems and the communications lines linking them. Such checks give only a spot control of the line, and slowly degrading lines may be detected. Data transmission must cease while tests are performed.

Third are modems that give a status indication on their front panel, such as request to send or clear to send. Such short messages can be useful but do not constitute comprehensive diagnostics.

Fourth are facilities that show only whether the modem is on-line. This is the lowest cost (and simplest) feature and is in great demand from personal computer users who do not need extensive diagnostics. Just the same, users who have a small number of modems in a point-to-point or polling configuration do not necessarily need modem diagnostics.

Modem diagnostics is particularly advisable for larger users with networks of computers and terminals who need to identify problems as they occur. There is, in fact, a trend in modem diagnostics that affects a network's ability to be compatible with larger X.25 packet-switching systems. Modems that use in-band signaling for diagnostic information are compatible with X.25 networks, but the user has to halt data transmission while sending diagnostic information. The alternative is out-band signaling. It permits continuous send/receive (since a separate band is used for the diagnostic information), but the user cannot access X.25 networks. He is restricted to conventional analog networks due to modem design.

AT&T's Dataphone II provides three levels of control for users with operations of differing complexity, and users can easily upgrade from one level to the next. The first level employs a control modem with one or more tributary modems. Each modem in the network monitors its own condition as well as the status of the received line signal. Observations are automatically transmitted to a central control site. The second level permits centralized control of small and medium-sized networks from a console. The operator at this console can continuously monitor each modem in the network and the lines connecting them. Faults are displayed on the front panel in realtime. The third level gives the user a complete communications-management center, including a network controller, video display, keyboard and an optional printer.

Design trends are pointing toward faster speeds of many common modem applications. Until recently, the fastest modems for asynchronous full-duplex transmission over the public switched dial network had 1.2 KBPS capacities. Now the trend is to doubling and quadrupling modem speeds at reasonable costs. One offering at 4.8 KBPS also presents computer-controlled fallback to 2.4 KBPS.

Users see many full-duplex, asynchronous/synchronous modems for two-wire transmissions over the DDD network. The increase in operating speeds does not stop at 2.4 KBPS.

This is not the first example of a *bilingual* modem. AT&T's Data Set 212A permits data to be transmitted in two different formats at two different speeds. At the low speed, it operates with a frequency shift keyed (FSK) carrier signal. The frequency of the carrier signal transmitted over the telephone channel is controlled by the data signal from the customer's equipment.

Data can also pass from the equipment to the 212A in a different format:

1. In the high-speed mode, the data set can furnish timing signals to the terminal, and the data bits must be phase-locked to the timing signals. This is a "synchronous" operation.
2. Again in the high-speed mode, without the timing signals the operation of the set is called "character asynchronous."

With character asynchronous operation the data bits are fed to the data sets as "characters" which are groups of 9 or 10 bits, depending on the type of data terminals.

These are Bell System equipment. Since the Carter phone decision of FCC, many independent (interconnect) companies offer their modems to the market. Table 10.1 presents the CCITT and Bell standards for Data Sets.

Bilingual modems today cost up to $5,000 but can be useful in dial backup for 4.8 KBPS leased lines. For instance, only two units are required instead of the four now needed in half-duplex dial backup arrangements. Another application is to replace leased line arrangements currently carrying a medium traffic load (2 to 4 MB of data a day) as in a remote job entry solution. By using a full-duplex modem, it may be possible to achieve 40 percent to 50 percent increases in throughput.

Many data sets are designed to be operated over two-wire or four-wire circuits. When half-duplex operation is acceptable, the two-wire circuit may be used, saving the cost of one line, but this operation is more complicated because equipment must switch between the transmit and receive modes. (A complication with synchronous data sets is that a pattern must be transmitted after each line turnaround to lock the receiver clock to the transmitter clock. The resultant lost time may be important in some applications. Therefore, some data sets require four-wire circuits, as do most line drivers/receivers, for either type of bidirectional transmission.)

A further distinction should be made between units designed for short and long haul transmission. Short haul—referred to a modem—usually means a device operating at distances of 3 to 5 miles. Many data communications requirements call for long haul design characteristics.

Finally, it is part of the technical function of a modem to provide for good quality services. Three topics are specifically related to this reference: conditioning, equalization, and scrambling.

Conditioning involves tolerances. A voice-quality line has electrical characteristics conditioned by tolerances. Hence, the "purchase of conditioning" is essentially the price paid for high quality.

Equalization involves how the modem compensates for the characteristics of a particular telephone line, since a tremendous variety of transmission characteristics can exist on any given line. Equalization is effected through microprocessors and

Table 10.1
CCITT and the Bell Standards for Data Sets

Bell Type	CCITT recommendation*	Speed (bit/sec)	Line, no. of wires	Line usage	Modulation**	Mode†
103/113	V.21	0–300	2	Dial or leased	FSK	Asyn.
202	V.23	0–1,200	2, 4	Dial or leased	FSK	Asyn.
201B	V.26	2,400	4	Leased	PSK	Syn.
201C	V.26bis	2,400	2, 4	Dial or leased	PSK	Syn.
208A	V.27, V.27bis	4,800	4	Leased	DPSK	Syn.
208B	V.27ter	4,800	2	Dial	DPSK	Syn.
209	V.29	9,600	4	Leased	QAM	Syn.

*CCITT is the International Telegraph and Telephone Consultative Committee. These standards are generally implemented in Europe.
**FSK, frequency-shift key; PSK, phase-shift key; DPSK, differential phase-shift key; QAM, queued access method.
†Synchronous or asynchronous.

algorithms, which allow automatic reactions to changing conditions. This minimizes errors due to line distortions.

The digital loop mode of operation is a way of testing the data set. Test equipment is connected to the near-end set and both the transmitter and receiver are tested by having the receiver output connected directly to the input of the transmitter at the far end of the connection.

Scrambling—via a scrambler—changes the data so that it appears to be a random pattern. This eliminates long strings of "1"s that can cause modem problems, usually of the clocking circuitry.

We can now see that the new family of data sets with diagnostic features must be designed to keep pace with changing market factors: (a) small size, (b) efficient handling of short messages, (c) fast start-up, and (d) compact touch-tone receivers.

Agile Modems

Switched data or voice channels can best be served by a feature characterizing the growing population of intelligent data sets. *Frequency agile modems* are high performance communications systems. The 55 to 75 MHz band is made up of 128 switched channels. This band closely resembles a PBX system.

The switching of frequency channels within this band is accomplished by variable frequency (frequency agile) modems and their internal control mechanism. Through manual or automatic direction, this mechanism can be set to any of a number of frequencies.

In the case of manual control, a user can call the computer room to see what ports are available on a particular computer and request that a port be reserved for the user's node. The user then switches the variable-frequency modem to that channel to achieve a connection.

With automatic switching, an intelligent switching device keeps track of whatever channels are available at all times. A node can make requests to transmit, or the switching device can actually poll all the devices on that band to determine if there are requests to transmit.

In either case, the switch assigns the frequency agile modems of the sending and receiving devices to the frequency of the open channel over which they can communicate. The respective modems tune to the assigned frequency and exchange information. If there are no available channels, the device requesting to transmit is notified. It must try again at another time. Also, if all ports of the destination device are in use, the sending device will get a busy signal.

Smart modem solutions also offer high performance data communications for personal computers. Typically, they feature 300 baud originate/answer capabilities and are RS-232 compatible. Agile modems are programmable and commands can be entered directly from the keyboard, including special *set* commands. (Set commands allow the user to select or change various operational parameters such as dialing speed, escape code character and length of wait for a dial tone. The data set system analyzes and executes commands and, in response, sends result codes.)

Another modem feature is the packaging of the modem with another network element, such as a multiplexer. These *integral modems* offer a number of special features. It is also possible to set modem speed or other configurations at the central site. Such parameters will be automatically downloaded to the remote site.

Still another offering is the *modem eliminator*. Used between a terminal and a computer, the modem eliminator functions like a line driver. It can carry data in half-duplex or full-duplex mode, synchronous or asynchronous, at 1.2 to 19.2 KBPS.

The User Site

At user sites, data sets can be both a much needed device and a continually nagging problem. Modem manufacturers install the unit but do not recommend to the user what options should be strapped in. This is entirely up to the hardware and software requirements in the computer system. Computer manufacturers should make those recommendations in their communications manuals.

The following examples describe the technical side of a data set family—each type having a different price tag.

Modem A provides synchronous 4.8 KBPS operation over voice-grade four-wire lines or the public switched network. A fast turnaround time of 50 milliseconds is standard and insures maximum data throughput rates. A comprehensive LED (light emitting diodes) package monitors overall unit operation. Options include an asynchronous-to-synchronous converter and a remote diagnostic test system that permits checking the entire data communications system from a single master site.

Modem B is low-power, solid-state for transmission and reception of synchronous 2.4 KBPS serial binary data. Front-panel test switches permit fast selection of test modes, and front-panel indicator lamps display control and data functions to simplify fault diagnosis.

Modems C provides automatic answering of incoming calls and will automatically switch to the original mode of operation when calls are dialed.

Modem D will transmit data at 1.2 KBPS over private lines with conditioning at rates up to 1.8 KBPS. The operation is half-duplex on two-wire private lines, or full-duplex on four-wire lines.

Modem E is designed for low-speed data transmission. In the acoustic mode, the unit is portable and can be utilized with any one of a number of data terminals. A carrier indicator light is provided to monitor the operation of the unit.

Unfortunately, as user requirements change, the best selection made under today's criteria might turn out tomorrow to be a poor choice. Both present and projected usage needs must therefore be considered, and due attention placed on technological advances.

Standard Interfaces: RS 232, RS 422, and RS 449

On repeated occasions reference has been made to Recommended Standards (RS) 232, 422, and 449 for physical interconnections. Let's look at what they represent in terms of normalization.

The interfaces between modems, computers, and terminals for long-haul transmission over wire, as well as direct local wire connections between computers and terminals, are defined by the standards of the Electronics Industry Association (EIA) and are widely accepted in the United States (for example, EIA RS 232C) and the recommendations of the International Telegraph and Telephone Consultative Committee (such as CCITT V.25). Examples of existing standards that are widely accepted and implemented in the lower layers of network architecture are EIA RS 232C and CCITT V.24, and more recently EIA RS 422. These standards define conventional connections of data equipment and modems.

By definition, physical standards provide an efficient, compatible interface between two different hardware devices. An interface is a point, device, or logical connection (protocol) at which a transition is made between media. Such media may be power levels, modes of operation, line disciplines and so on.

In the strictly physical sense, such as regarding RS 232 and RS 449, the interface standard regards contact surfaces on each side of mating connectors (special pins) that face each other when mated. Such standards define the electrical, physical, and functional characteristics of interfaces for the direct connection of data terminating equipment in point-to-point configuration for data transfer, using balanced voltage digital circuits. Different standards apply to asynchronous and synchronous data transmission.

Pin connectors are the simplest type of interfaces. Other physical (hardware) units used as interface devices are converters. They may allow a range of connections, such as parallel units to serial units or the interconnection of various types of serial devices to each other, including connector changes. In this way, balanced circuits can be mixed with unbalanced circuits, current loop circuits can be attached to noncurrent loop circuits, and proprietary interface configurations can be interfaced to more standard configurations.

Data rates, coding, handshaking, buffering, flow control, and electrical or mechanical differences are made compatible for total integration of desired system components even though there may be interface incompatibilities. Since standardization is not the predominant characteristic of hardware manufacturers, a wide range of interface converters are available to allow different units to talk to one another.

Figure 10.2.

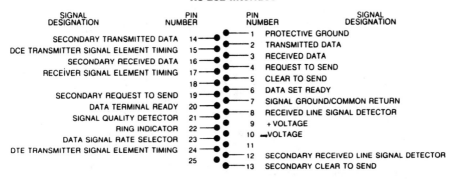

RS-232 Interface

SIGNAL DESIGNATION	PIN NUMBER		PIN NUMBER	SIGNAL DESIGNATION
			1	PROTECTIVE GROUND
SECONDARY TRANSMITTED DATA	14		2	TRANSMITTED DATA
DCE TRANSMITTER SIGNAL ELEMENT TIMING	15		3	RECEIVED DATA
SECONDARY RECEIVED DATA	16		4	REQUEST TO SEND
RECEIVER SIGNAL ELEMENT TIMING	17		5	CLEAR TO SEND
	18		6	DATA SET READY
SECONDARY REQUEST TO SEND	19		7	SIGNAL GROUND/COMMON RETURN
DATA TERMINAL READY	20		8	RECEIVED LINE SIGNAL DETECTOR
SIGNAL QUALITY DETECTOR	21		9	+ VOLTAGE
RING INDICATOR	22		10	−VOLTAGE
DATA SIGNAL RATE SELECTOR	23		11	
DTE TRANSMITTER SIGNAL ELEMENT TIMING	24		12	SECONDARY RECEIVED LINE SIGNAL DETECTOR
	25		13	SECONDARY CLEAR TO SEND

Let's take a closer look at the RS 232C communications interface. The *transmission type* is asynchronous (start/stop) with serial-bit data. The *data character* format is 1 start bit, 7 data bits, 1 parity bit, and 1 stop bit (a total of 10 bits). The connector is the standard 25-pin cannon or equivalent type (female contacts and male shell) in accordance with ISO-IS 2120 mechanical characteristics (Figure 10.2).

The *bit transmission* order ensures that the least significant bit is sent first; the parity bit follows the data bits. Start and stop bits are character framing bits. The parity bit is always checked on EVEN parity. ODD parity characters are printed as a diamond when parity error reporting is disabled by the proper dip switch.

The transmitting gross start/stop distortion is less than or equal to 2 percent of the bit time. For instance, the printer sends the stop bit with edges that can be shifted at a maximum of ± 2 percent with respect to their nominal position. With RS 232C, the *receive margin* is better than 40 percent. The printer samples the last bit of a 10-bit character in the range of ± 10 percent around the nominal bit center of the received character.

The *data bit rate* is between 1.2 and 9.6 KBPS when the local connection is selected. It is 300 baud to 1.2 KBPS when the remote connection is selected. In accordance with RS 232C std. and CCITT Recommendation V.28, the minimum assured distance is 50 feet (15 meters) for all supported data rates.

The communications standard RS 422A is full-duplex. Local connection is supported by this interface and no control signals are provided. Both RS 422A and the Recommendation V.11 are designed for point-to-point configurations.

RS 422A specifies the conditions under which cable terminations and fail-safe circuits must be used. Although it does not specify the wire size to be used in the cable, distance figures are based upon the use of overall shielded No. 24 (0.5 mm) multiple twisted pair cables. (RS 422A and V.11 documents provide guidance for the use of other wire sizes.)

In the specific case of a printer-to-host connection, with the ISO circuit identi-

Figure 10.3a.

RS-449 Interface

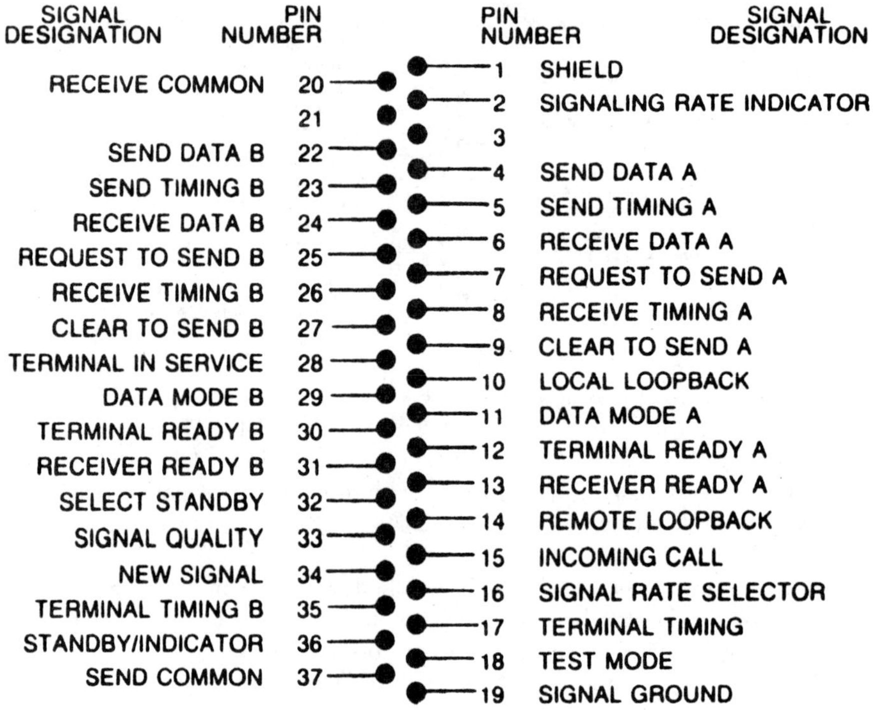

SIGNAL DESIGNATION	PIN NUMBER	PIN NUMBER	SIGNAL DESIGNATION
		1	SHIELD
RECEIVE COMMON	20	2	SIGNALING RATE INDICATOR
	21	3	
SEND DATA B	22		
SEND TIMING B	23	4	SEND DATA A
RECEIVE DATA B	24	5	SEND TIMING A
REQUEST TO SEND B	25	6	RECEIVE DATA A
RECEIVE TIMING B	26	7	REQUEST TO SEND A
CLEAR TO SEND B	27	8	RECEIVE TIMING A
TERMINAL IN SERVICE	28	9	CLEAR TO SEND A
DATA MODE B	29	10	LOCAL LOOPBACK
TERMINAL READY B	30	11	DATA MODE A
RECEIVER READY B	31	12	TERMINAL READY A
SELECT STANDBY	32	13	RECEIVER READY A
SIGNAL QUALITY	33	14	REMOTE LOOPBACK
NEW SIGNAL	34	15	INCOMING CALL
TERMINAL TIMING B	35	16	SIGNAL RATE SELECTOR
STANDBY/INDICATOR	36	17	TERMINAL TIMING
SEND COMMON	37	18	TEST MODE
		19	SIGNAL GROUND

fication *transmit* (T), an indeterminate level is output when the printer is powered off. A mark signal is present when the printer is not sending data. With *receive* (R), mark state fail-safe circuitry is present to prevent spurious receptions when the cable is disconnected or the driver is powered off at the host side. A mark level is expected when the sender is idle.

The *signal ground* (G) is always connected to the O Volt of the power supply. The *cable shield* is optionally connected to the frame ground of the printer via a suitable jumper. Table 10.2 identifies the communications signals and associated characteristics for RS 422A.

Pin assignment for the 37-pin connector supported by RS 449 is shown in Figure 10.3a. Figure 10.3b identifies the CCITT V.35 interface. Table 10.3 compares pin assignment functions in RS 232 to those of RS 449.

CCITT V.11 concerns the electrical characteristics of balanced voltage interface circuits, and V.24 presents a list of interchange circuits between DTE and DCE. (In regard to connector standards, refer to the ISO DIS-7477 draft or requirements for DTE to DTE physical connections, and the ISO DIS-7480 draft for start-stop signal quality at DTE/DCE interfaces.)

With reference to asynchronous interfaces, EIA RS 404 and ISO DIS-7480

Table 10.2.
Communications Signals and Associated Characteristics for RS 422A

ISO Circuit ID	Signal Source	ISO 2110 PIN No.	Signal	State	Electrical Level	Logical Level
T (A)	Printer	13	Transmit	Mark (stop)	$T_{(A)}$ more negative than $T_{(B)}$	"1"
T (B)		14				
R (A)	Host	16				
R (B)		19		Space	$T_{(A)}$ more than $T_{(B)}$	"0"
G		7				
SHIELD		1	Receive	Mark (stop)	$R_{(A)}$ more negative than $R_{(B)}$	"1"
				Space	$R_{(A)}$ more positive than $R_{(B)}$	"0"

145

Figure 10.3b.

V.35 Interface

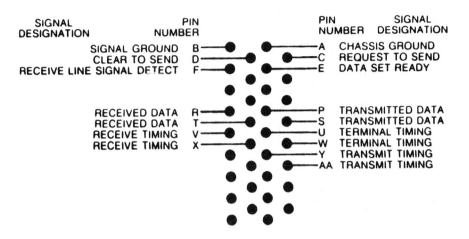

SIGNAL DESIGNATION	PIN NUMBER		PIN NUMBER	SIGNAL DESIGNATION
SIGNAL GROUND	B		A	CHASSIS GROUND
CLEAR TO SEND	D		C	REQUEST TO SEND
RECEIVE LINE SIGNAL DETECT	F		E	DATA SET READY
RECEIVED DATA	R		P	TRANSMITTED DATA
RECEIVED DATA	T		S	TRANSMITTED DATA
RECEIVE TIMING	V		U	TERMINAL TIMING
RECEIVE TIMING	X		W	TERMINAL TIMING
			Y	TRANSMIT TIMING
			AA	TRANSMIT TIMING

provide on-signal quality. For an asynchronous interface observing fail-safe requirements, the maximum cable distances as a function of speed are:

Bit Rate	*Distance*
up to 20 KBPS	1.25 km
250 KBPS	100 m
1.0 MBPS	25 m
1.7 MBPS	10 m

From 20 KBPS to 1.0 MBPS the applicable maximum distance may be derived by
interpolation following the algorithm:

$$\text{distance } (m) \times \text{bit rate (KBPS)} = 25,000 \text{ (m.KBPS)}$$

In no case may the distance exceed 1.25 km.

A synchronous interface using the optional fail-safe circuit respects the
throughput and distance described for asynchronous operation. Since a fail-safe
function is not required in synchronous transmission, the following applies when
connection is not fail-safed:

Bit Rate	*Distance*
up to 80 KBPS	1.25 km
1.0 MBPS	100 m
10.0 MBPS	10 m

Table 10.3.

Pin Assignment Functions RS 232 and RS 449

RS 232		RS 449			
		37-PIN		9-PIN	RS 449
25-PIN	Description	A	B	Auxiliary	Description
1	Protective Ground	1		1	Shield
7	Signal Ground/Common Return	19		5	Signal Ground
	DTE Common	37		9	Send Common
	DCE Common	20		6	Receive Common
2	Transmitted Data	4	22		Send Data
3	Received Data	6	24		Receive Data
4	Request to Send	7	25		Request to Send
5	Clear to Send	9	27		Clear to Send
6	Data Set Ready	11	29		Data Mode
20	Data Terminal Ready	12	30		Terminal Ready
22	Ring Indicator	15			Incoming Call
8	Received Line Signal Detector	13	31		Receiver Ready
21	Signal Quality Detector	33			Signal Quality
23	Data Signal Rate Selector (DTE)	16			Signaling Rate Selector
23	Data Signal Rate Selector (DCE)	2			Signaling Rate Indictor

147

Table 10.3 (*continued*)

RS 232		RS 449			
25-PIN	Description	37-PIN A	B	9-PIN Auxiliary	RS 449 Description
24	Transmitter Signal Element Timing (DTE)	17	35		Terminal Timing
15	Transmitter Signal Element Timing (DCE)	5	23		Send Timing
17	Receiver Signal Element Timing (DCE)	8	26		Receive Timing
14	Secondary Transmitted Data			3	Secondary Send Data
16	Secondary Received Data			4	Secondary Receive Data
19	Secondary Request to Send			7	Secondary Request to Send
13	Secondary Clear to Send			8	Secondary Clear to Send
12	Secondary Received Line Signal Detector			2	Secondary Receiver Ready
	Local Loopback	10			Local Loopback
	Remote Loopback	14			Remote Loopback
	Test Indicator	18			Test Mode
	Select Standby	32			Select Standby
	Standby Indicator	36			Standby Indicator
	Select Transmit Frequency	16			Select Frequency
		28			Terminal in Service
		34			New Signal

Intermediate values may be derived by interpolation. Here again, in no case may the distance exceed 1.25 km.

Different versions of the DTE-to-DTE interface can be defined. Typically, one will apply to an asynchronous format data transfer, the other to a synchronous format. They differ in that the asynchronous interface does not provide timing signals between the DTE.

Four general classes of interchange circuits are involved: ground circuits, data circuits, timing circuits (synchronous interface), and control circuits (optional).

In DTE, protective ground is electrically bonded to the equipment frame. It may also be connected to external grounds (through the third wire of the power cord). Protective ground is not an interchange circuit in the RS 449 and X.24 standards. However, national and local codes with respect to earthing must be observed. Such regulations may preclude the interconnection, without DC isolation, of equipment which is not connected to the same safety ground.

To facilitate the use of shielded interconnecting cable, an interface connector contact should be provided for the shield. This permits the cable connecting the DTE to be linked to tandem connectorized sections, with shield continuity accomplished by connection through this contact in the connectors. If connection through a capacitor is used, it may be applied at one end only and the shield connection at the other end must be direct to the frame ground.

11

Multiplexers, Concentrators and Front-ends

The preceding chapters described a good deal of the gear necessary for data communications. Lines, switches, control programs, modems, computers, and terminals are part and parcel of this gear. The subject has not been exhausted, however; we must talk of multiplexers, concentrators, and front-ending.

Multiplexing is a regrouping of signals into a one-way transmission. This can be done at the line; physical media, such as coaxial cable and optical fibers, permit a high level of regrouping, and so does satellite broadcasting. The practical limit is set by interferences. The best examples of multiplexing technology are those we discussed in chapter 6, frequency-division multiplexing and time-division multiplexing.

Rules and standards for frequency-division multiplexing have been specified by the international committee CCITT:

> 12 channels: 60 to 108 kilohertz
>
> 60 channels: 312 to 552 kilohertz
>
> 960 channels: 60 to 4,028 kilohertz
>
> 2,700 channels: 3,122 to 12,388 kilohertz
>
> 10,800 channels: 4 to 61 megahertz

Computers and communications networks, though they use extensively frequency division and time division, still require a higher level of intelligence.

Multiplexing, concentration and front-ending interface between the source and the destination of the data, and by so doing they bring forward the need for conventions, or protocols.

Protocols are formal sets of conventions governing the format and the control of data. They constitute logical levels of connection to the physical line (carrier). The simple, early ones were of the Stop–Start variety; the modern ones contain advanced concepts. Primarily, they standardize known, not new, functions, of which there are two. The first is contact which is identification, synchronization, and creation of a virtual channel; these facilities concern source and destination. The second is transfer, which includes error detection and correction (EDC) and delivering of the message. Given the importance of the subject, we will devote several chapters to the basic notions and the variety and use of protocols.

The Process of Multiplexing

In a data communications process the line may act as a multiplexer of messages from different DTEs connected to that line. This is especially true of an intelligent line.

An intelligent line, which is a line equipped with a microprocessor and memory, can act in one or more of the following ways:

Polling, addressing

Polling, unpacking; compacting

As high-speed accelerator

As asynchronous or synchronous gateway

Buffering

Error controlling, including ACK, NAK, repeat, time-out

As a multiplexer

Lines are only now becoming intelligent, and they are controlled by the telephone company; for this reason there is an interest in developing and implementing separate media: the concentrators and multiplexers.

Multiplexers are physical devices and are selected on the basis of supported channels, line interface modules, automatic testing capabilities, and display facilities. See Figure 11.1.

The most intelligent device currently available is the statistical multiplexer, or stat mux. It works in a form of TDM that dynamically allocates communications line time and capacity to each of the various attached terminals. This allocation takes place whether a terminal is active or not. Buffering and queueing functions are also included.

A stat mux is an atypical intelligent multiplexer of its class. (Usually, one way to divide multiplexers and concentrators is to look at the former as nonintelligent and at the latter as intelligent.) Are nonintelligent muxes a vanishing species? Specialists say *no*. When local digital loops are finally marketed, the low cost of multiplexers may make them a favored choice—but digital loops won't be available until the 1990s.

Keep in mind that the FDM (frequency division multiplexing) can only handle a few channels, and consequently is not often the correct alternative for large data-

Figure 11.1
Multiplexer

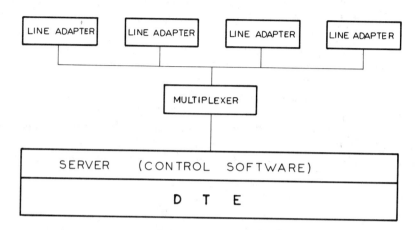

comm networks. However, FDM provides the advantage of a multidrop function in which a number of terminals share a single line. (The latest stat muxes also offer this capability, using special data protocols to label sequences of data for the different drop points.)

Choosing the right stat mux can be a problem. Desirable features of stat muxes are: data compression, full-duplex protocols (for data transmission on high-speed link), error-control methods, and diagnostic and networking capabilities. Such devices provide operational and statistical management reports, offering data on such parameters as delays, errors, and buffer utilization besides transmission volume and billing information. These are useful management reports enabling the datacomm expert to detect line deterioration and to plan ahead to make the best use of the system.

In terms of complexity and capability, some multiplexers have become sophisticated and handle a range of network functions. For instance, they can compensate for time delays introduced in satellite data transmission. (If not compensated for, such delays interfere with acknowledgments in synchronous data transmission). Also, through packet assembly/disassembly, data can be converted from asynchronous to X.25 format, enabling users to link-up with larger packet-switching networks.

The capability to provide access to X.25 networks is an important stat mux feature. Instead of having simple point-to-point or multipoint access, the user can access X.25 networks via a virtual circuit. (Be cautious of vendors' claims that they have an X.25 capability; they may only mean that they have an HDLC (high-level data-link control) feature.)

Another feature to consider is wideband trunking which is significant for bisynchronous composite transmissions over 9.6 KBPS aggregates.

Port contention and switching can enable larger numbers of terminals to access a limited number of ports on a host mainframe or mini. By employing port contention and switching for multiple "dumb" asynchronous terminals, the user can have a large number of terminals accessing ports on a host computer. Some users are employing twice as many terminals as computer ports. With this feature, a network supervisor can go on to any remote terminal and sign on to the system. This expedites network diagnostics and control.

Dynamic allocation of mux bandwidth is still another way to increase systems throughput. With some units, through a touch-sensitive front panel, users can reconfigure the mux without going inside its box to physically change switches. Parameters that can be changed include input and output data rates and data formats.

Betting on Concentrators

A *concentrator* can be quite similar to a multiplexer; some vendors advertise their product as "concentrator/multiplexer." By definition, a concentrator (or remote data concentrator) is a single-sided communications processor that concentrates data from many lines onto a smaller number of lines.

Technically, concentrators differ from multiplexers in several respects:

They are only needed at one end of the line, unlike muxes which are needed at both.

The upline or composite line consists of a number of lines, unlike with muxes where the composite line is usually a single line.

They may have much more capacity than multiplexers, handling up to 3,000 or 4,000 lines.

They generally deal in a single protocol, usually the native protocol of the host.

Data concentration is a logical function that combines a series of communication links into one physical line; see Figure 11.2. This may be done with hardware (multiplexers) or with software and hardware (processors).

Concentrators also are physical devices; they are selected according to efficiency, traffic load, reconfiguration capabilities, configurations of line interfaces, and diagnostics (centralized and local loopbacks).

Both multiplexers and concentrators regroup low-speed lines into a high-speed trunk, but there are differences; see Figure 11.3. With the multiplexer *n* lines, corresponding to an equal number of terminals, are multiplexed into *n* channels. Normally, all lines coming from the terminals to the multiplexer are of the same speed. At the output side the line uses frequency division or time division. The messages are of fixed format. The *n* lines feed into the concentrator, but the

Figure 11.2
Concentrator

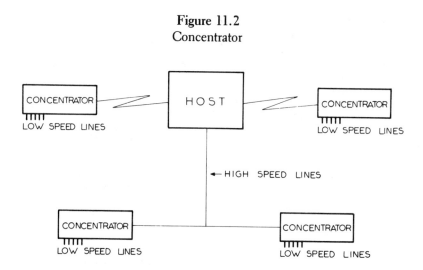

output is one channel. The lines connecting the *n* terminals to the concentrator may have various (mixed) speeds. The high-speed line at the output side will carry formatted messages and blocks of messages.

The concentrator has to be an intelligent machine. It requires software. Multiplexers have long been unintelligent equipment, but this is changing.

Line adapters, if programmable, provide maximum flexibility and throughput. Their capabilities may include character of frame synchronization, special-character detection, filler-character transmission, control-code generation, programmable data set control displays, and diagnostics. In general, the functions of line-management interfaces are to:

Serialize and deserialize the bits

Control transmission

Establish control procedures (points 2 and 3 via software)

Bring traffic into equilibrium, to manage different lines

Control the code of the transmission with the help of tables in memory

Supervise the speed of transmission

Interface on the channel, as a function of the type of lines used

These functions may be realized through hardware or software. Hence the line-management device has a dual interface: with the operator and with the mainframe.

The input-output possibilities are enhanced through data communications capabilities, and they involve direct memory access with start and end of block detection; the interrupt-per-character systems are less efficient and less costly.

Microcomputers may be used as interfaces to existing network structures, central processing units, and terminal and software modules.

Figure 11.3
Multiplexer and concentrator compared

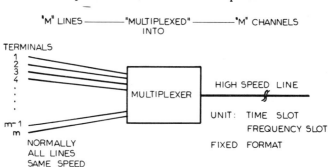

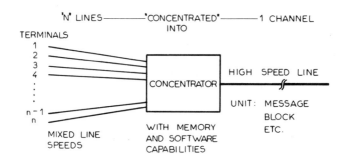

Miniprocessors and microprocessors are fairly inexpensive tools that maximize throughput, provide gateways, build concentrators, extend the life of available hardware and software, and, in general, create the structure for flexible and expandable communications systems.

There is, of course, an overlap between intelligent muxes and multidrop concentrators. An important feature, for instance, is the use of stat muxes as multidrop concentrators, using multidrop lines instead of point-to-point lines. Such solutions have special units to serve both as master node concentrator at the central site and as slave concentrator at each node. Some companies—rather than using a front-end on an IBM host (such as the 3705) to do the multidropping—use a centrators. An important feature, for instance, is the use of stat muxes as multidrop concentrators, using multidrop lines instead of point-to-point lines. Such solutions have special units to serve both as master node concentrator at the central site and as slave concentrator at each node. Some companies—rather than using a front-end on an IBM host (such as the 3705) to do the multidropping—use a concentrator, and there is no minicomputer front-end or cluster controller that can perform this task.

This last reference brings attention to the characteristics of central resources.

The CPU *architecture* must insure that the instruction set is adequate for the protocol to be utilized, provide byte operation for the bisynchronous mode and bit and byte operations for bit-oriented protocols, and guarantee Boolean and shift operations for error check codes.

Within this context, networks and *subnetworks,* literally parts of a network, are characterized by dynamic bandwidth allocation, alternate routing, subnet partitioning into distinct subnets (each dedicated to a user), resource selection, "hunt groups" (groups in which to make automatic searches for available facilities), and "camp on" (automatically stacking requests for facilities until they become available). Subnetworks will be discussed later in this book.

In essence, the distinction between multiplexers and concentrators has been a source of confusion. The two solutions are closely related, and some vendors use the terms interchangeably. This is regrettable, particularly as purchasing or leasing data communications hardware can be risky and costly, the more so if we make errors in product selection. While higher speeds, greater sophistication and enhanced reliability are available with modems, muxes and concentrators, efficiency is assured only if we know what we are looking for.

Front-ending is the means of moving data to and from the lines and the data communications software. Front ends must offer aggregate throughput support, subject to numbers and combinations of line adapter, special features (switching, queueing, first-in and first-out (FIFO), and contention), standalone test capability (automatic and manual), reliability, and price comparison of per-port costs.

Historically, the development of front-end facilities started with the Time-sharing experiments at Dartmouth College (the General Electric solution). Two alternative approaches have been followed ever since; the use of the mainframe to front-end for communications purposes through software support, and the employment of a separate processor (the front-end) to handle datacomm tasks.

The idea of a separate processor (Figure 11.4) carried the day. Consciously or unconsciously, datacomm users have been employing ends and message switches for years, but technology suggests that soon these devices may become obsolete.

A new piece of datacomm hardware, the satellite/gateway processor, is on its way to replace front-ends and message switches, along with PBXs, concentrators, and protocol converters. The capabilities of these units are consolidated into the *gateway.*

The gateway consists of a small computer attached to two or more networks. A message destined for some other network will go to the gateway, which will look at the address and decide how to reroute it. In a system comprising only two networks, the gateway's job is very simple—the addresses will be for one network or the other.

With a multinetwork situation, the job is more difficult. The message may not be directly addressed to a network but to another gateway closer to the final destination.

Let's, however, start with the fundamentals. A conventional *front-end processor* (FEP) is a device logically situated in front of a host to implement a heavy volume

Figure 11.4
Maxicomputer, projected for the 1980s

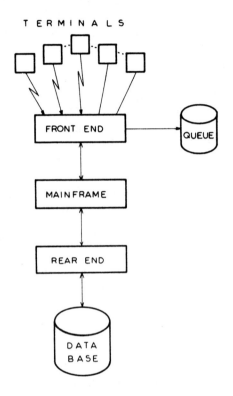

Figure 11.5

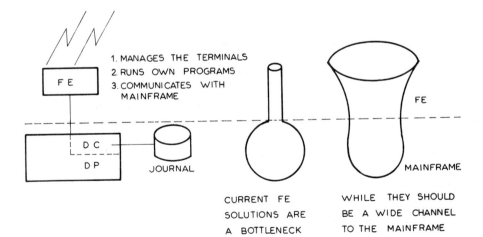

of network communications through specialized handling. This device is different than the message switch. The latter can be defined as a processing unit able to accept traffic from many low-speed communications lines, routing the data streams to a central point. At that point, the messages are concentrated for processing.

Front-end processors tend to handle larger word sizes and have faster cycle times and larger memories than message switches. They are also able to interface more communications devices.

The functionality assigned to a FEP ensures that in a realtime network a front-end failure can be catastrophic. To protect against this eventuality, a spare front-end is usually maintained.

Reconnecting the communications lines from the failed front-end to the spare front-end is done with a switching matrix. Situations involving multiple front-ends call for a switching matrix able to automatically map any of the different groups of lines into the connection capabilities of the spare.

To manually reconnect the lines to a spare front-end may, optimistically, take 6 to 7 seconds per line. With a network control center (NCC) and an automatic switching matrix, the outage can be reduced to a few seconds. (We will return to this issue.)

The size, features, and costs of automatic switching matrices vary, as they range from manually activated relay arrays to computer-based systems. Computer-driven solutions can do full line-group switching as well as individual line switching.

Such approaches typically feature statistical line-management reporting (through software), multilevel password security, monitoring and testing, recording capabilities, and local/remote site operations. Though the primary purpose is to maintain fail-safe operations for larger systems, they also provide numerous features that ease day-to-day work.

Such references are evidently more important with centralized computer resources (Figure 11.5) than in a distributed environment, but the concept of front-ending finds its way into local area networks. The bus interface unit (BIU) is a micro-processor-suppoted front-end processor.

Assisting the Central Resources

To reduce the mainframe load, line polling, line management, terminal management, and both physical and logical terminal mapping should be done by front-ending. To further reduce this load, communications programs, line tables, terminal tables, queue management, and journaling should be done by the FEP.

A message queue may require a long buffer. Taking it off the central resource relieves the mainframe, but also brings up two problems.

First, the software for the front-end tends to be complex. To ease requirements, manufacturers often use the transaction-oriented software of the mainframe to, for instance, do the journaling and intermediate data storage functions, thus burdening the memory.

Second, with complex communications environments, the front-end tends to de-

Figure 11.6
Data communications time/KK

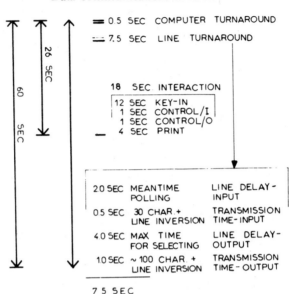

velop heavy housekeeping requirements. It must simultaneously communicate with the mainframe, manage its own operations, and handle the lines, terminals, and concentrators attached to it.

The turnaround time is thus increased, and as the number of terminals grows, it develops into a bottleneck. (See Figure 11.5.) Figure 6 shows acceptable time values. (Figure 11.6.)

Let's repeat front-end functions. Depending on available software support, these include:

interaction with the CPU (sometimes even used to connect two CPUs, as a hot switch)

message switching

communications

line concentration

data conversion

editing and networking responsibilities.

Editing and validation by FEP help reduce costs and, to a reasonable extent, increase the flexibility and portability of the data. For instance, we can store data into the front-end in a format compatible to subsequent handling by the mainframe (which is not necessarily the format used at the terminal's level).

Front-ending can enhance data security, an example being the entry and preparation of messages by the SWIFT network. This involves authentication, use of multiple terminals, formats, and security checks.

To a certain degree, specifically for environments which are not too complex, front-ending helps cope with functional heterogeneity. Here we return to the reference of off-loading the host processors by moving as much communications processing as possible into the FE unit.

By the same token, FE processors affect the availability and reliability of the communications path(s) from each terminal to the host—a statement which is the more correct if they produce acceptable data throughput and guarantee minimal delay characteristics. However, the job may become too complex for one front-end machine and may disturb the response time requirements. Recall that computer-based equipment (and its handling) is influenced by:

human factors,

contention, queues, connects

the nature of data (interactive or inquiry-response)

control requirements, interfaces and protocols.

Typically, software organization at the front-end level will appear as in Figure 11.7. Such software will be most effective if parametric approaches are taken to reflect environmental considerations; topology: hosts, terminal trunks; technical characteristics of the transmission system: carrier trunks, subsystems, switches, concentrators; and, if possible, the adequacy of procedures such as fallback configuration requirements which must be continuously maintained.

Diagnostics should include routing error detection, a testing capability, malfunction isolation, fail-soft requirements, and reporting and backup.

Software should also provide for a number of architectural prerequisites, including points for expansion, throughput increases, modular design, and the necessary interfaces. In the last analysis, software quality will have a great impact on response time, network delays, and general interface capacities.

Breaking Down the Front-End Tasks

Whether hierarchical (star) or nodal (horizontal) solutions are adopted, it is advisable to review and evaluate critically the concept of front-ending and to break down the earlier approaches into a layered solution, making use of specialization. We have said that the original front-ending was intended to relieve the central processor of most or all of the overhead responsibilities related to communications, but that the communications requirements kept on growing, so that the work load, overwhelming the capabilities of the front end, was turned back to the host. It became evident with practice that this was not efficient, and something had to be done about it. Channel control programs, for example, were created to

Figure 11.7
Needed software organization at front-end level

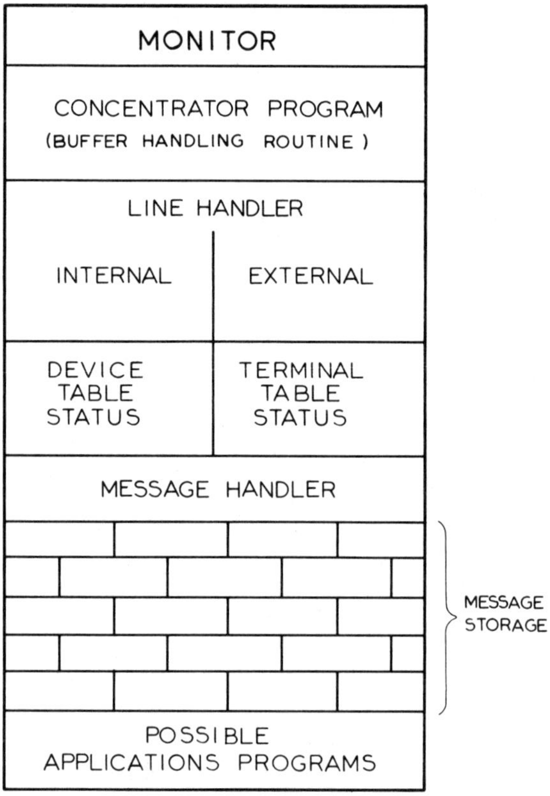

be self-standing and microprocessor-implemented. They were given functions, such as the transfer of communications characters from data blocks in main memory programs, message delimiting, some editing, and control character deletion.

This separation of functions at the communications end followed a broader view of the system. The tendency has been to divide the computer architecture, not into a host and a front end, but into the data base machine, the main processor (host), and the front-end machine. Each was subsequently subdivided into component parts, and those into smaller elements. Figures 11.8 and 11.9 outline the component functions of the data base machine, of the main processor, and of the front-end machine. Specialization is the modern approach to system design, whether we talk of the front-end equipment or of the system as a whole: The data base machine is specialized in rear-end operations consisting of four groups of three elements each. The host also has four groups of operations to

Figure 11.8

Data base machine

A. Information elements (items)
   Files
   Data descriptions

B. Codes
   Data formats
   Edits

C. Access requests
   Integrity
   Security

D. Add
   Delete
   Upkeep

Host

A. AP and utilities library management

B. Character transforming, encrypting, decrypting, compacting, expanding

C. Session supervision

     Get messages

     Process them

     Return them

D. Process handling

     Queue requests for resources

     Interpret AP

     Execute AP

Don't deal with the terminal, but with the function of the system and the way the AP work together.

Division depends on AP, environment and optimization.

perform. But, as will be appreciated, the front-end machine is the most functionally intense in terms of assessments. As the requirements increase, so do its duties.

The division is far from conclusive. It depends on the applications programming (AP), the operating environment, and the optimization we wish to accomplish, and this is true of the more detailed levels of breakdown, in particular the division between the line functions and the main supervisory activities of the network. There is a real division between overall communications control, line control, and character control. Each level is answerable to a specific group of

Figure 11.9

Front-end machine
(works on block/message level)

A. Addressing work stations (polling decisions)
   Queueing for distribution (downstream)
   Editing and sending data

B. Receiving requests (polling decisions)
   Addressing host
   Delimiting data enclosures (segmenting
   and blocking)

C. Handling sessions
   Establishment
   Maintenance
   Validation

D. Assuring network status
   Turning DTE and lines
   on/off
   Changing assignments

E. Protecting data
   Buffering FE level
   Quarantining

F. Journaling
   Statistics (traffic, failures)
   Checkpoint and
   recovery (Generally, data
   traffic regulation)

Front-end machine executes top-level functions

Typically handles only 10% of the data communications work load, particularly if journaling is moved to DC machine and upper level.

Its operations are customer oriented (here lie the differences between banks, airlines, and commercial and industrial companies).

Tables at the front-end level are on a total network basis. Functional tables are moving downstream and become specialized and more primitive.

---

functions driven by specialized tables for communications control. Together with the control programs these tables must be transferred to the appropriate control device, usually through a downline-loading procedure.

Specialization and functionalization have both preceded and followed this process. In a specialized channel controller, for example, space exists (for each channel) for a list of consecutive control words. Each is used to store main-memory address information. It indicates the area to which data are to be delivered in a "receive" process or from which data are to be obtained in a "transmit" process.

A channel control program directs the movements of each character. It can cause the character to be processed in a simple manner within a minimum of time or to conduct extensive checking and editing functions. This has been done at the original front-end level in most cases, but character handling beyond the basic operations of message delimiting and block checking developed at the expense of throughput speed. More powerful algorithms, such as cyclic redundancy checks

(CRC), though they improve data integrity, aggravate the throughput situation. Therefore, the separation of functions and dedication of a microprocessor to a homogeneous functional group is technically valid and operationally efficient.

The Data Communications Machine

Figure 11.9 demonstrates how the principles we have outlined are put into practice. Notice that the low-level functions, now assigned to the data communications (DC) machine, represent some 90 percent of the total communications load, which is not only an elegant design but also a necessary one, now that terminals do not number 50, 100, or 200, but 2,000, 10,000, and 20,000.

Notice also that in this structure care has been taken to divide the functions unevenly, the greater part being brought toward the lower levels. The 5, 20, and 75 percent distribution of load is not a superficially arrived at division of labor but a carefully thought out approach. While the upper level is unified, the middle level can be divided into a discrete number of components. Further, the lower level is divided into a larger number of homogeneous processors each implemented by a microprocessor. This lower (character) level of the data communications machine is in essence a "microline controller." The design depends on individual protocols, and that fact underlines its flexibility.

As we have said, the statistically uneven division of assigned labor is intentional. For an example of handling at the lower level we have considered the character-oriented tasks. At the lower levels the functions are simpler, and a multiplicity of more primitive devices can be dedicated to them. This tends to create a hierarchical structure within the data communications machine.

Let us now briefly look at the line control tables, which belong to the higher level. The line control table is logically divided into two halves. The first 32 bytes, say, are dedicated to the receiving channel of the line and the next 32 to the transmitting channel. Both input data and programming work space are critical elements. A change in configuration is implemented through a change in table, which in turn changes the procedures to be followed. Microprocessors handle several of the table's functions, and parts of the table are moving down stream. Code, line speed, and numbers of lines handled are critical factors in the design.

Typically, the microprocessor has random-access memory and is downline-loaded by the front end. Reliability is easily assured at that level. One idea is to have one backup microprocessor for each four in action, with hot-standby capability.

The microline controller depends on the individual protocols. Program-supplied input data provide information required for character configuration, interruption control, status, error conditions, and the like. The programming work space may be used in any manner needed by the communications-handling program.

The following is an outline of the upper, middle and lower levels of the datacomm engine.

DB MACHINE

A1. Information elements (items)
A2. Files
A3. Data descriptions

B1. Codes
B2. Data formats
B3. Edits

C1. Access Requests
C2. Integrity
C3. Security

D1. Add
D2. Delete
D3. Upkeep

TO

HOST

HOST

A. AP and utilities library management

B. Character transforming, encrytpion/decryption, compacting/expanding

C. Session Supevision
   * Get messages
   * Process them
   * Return them

D. Process handling
   * Queue requests for resources
   * Interpret AP
   * Execute AP

Don't deal with the terminal, but with the functions of: (a) THE SYSTEM; (b) THE WAY THE AP WORK TOGETHER.

Division depends on AP environment optimization.

FRONT-END MACHINE (works on block/message level)

A1. Addressing workstations (polling decisions)
A2. Queueing for distribution (downstream)
A3. Editing and sending data

B1. Receiving requests (polling decisions)
B2. Addressing host
B3. Delimiting data enclosures (segmenting and blocking)

C. Handling sessions
    * Establishment
    * Maintenance
    * Validation

D1. Assuring network status
D2. Turning DTE and lines on/off
D3. Changing assignments

E1. Protecting data
E2. Buffering FE level
E3. Quarantining

F1. Journaling
F2. Statistics (traffic, failures)
F3. Checkpoint and recovery

Generally, data traffic regulation

FRONT-END MACHINE (executes top-level functions)

* Typically handles only 10 percent of the data communications workload—particularly if journaling is moved to the DC machine/upper level.

* Operations are customer-oriented (here lie the differences between banks, airlines, commercial, industrial, etc.)

* Tables at the FE level are on a total network basis.
  Functional tables move downstream and become
    * Specialized
    * More primitive

FRONT-END MACHINE (works on block/message level)

TO

DC MACHINE (handles 5 percent of DC workload)

Upper level can be handled by the FE machine; matter of choice, environment, software.

1. Queueing
2. Communicating with FE (e.g., inform terminal it has failed)
3. Acknowledgements
4. Status (line; DTE) decision, restoration
5. Routing decisions

6. Load splitting
7. Message editing

DC MACHINE (handles 20 percent of DC workload)

Middle level—standardized product specific per line discipline; not AP

1. Execution level routing
    * Poll
    * Call/send
2. Send blocks to low level; receive same
3. Error recovery
4. Error detection on protocol basis (e.g., missing header)

Software or microprocessor at middle level is data link control oriented.
DC MACHINE (handles 65 percent of DC workload)

Low level—also a standardized product

1. Character handling
    * Input
    * Conversion
    * Output

The issue here is specialization by protocols: BSC HDLC TTY.

2. Status (character basis)
3. Error detection (character basis)

The loads are usually distributed as follows:

10%FRONT-END MACHINE (works on block/message level)

TO

90%DC MACHINE/UPPER LEVEL

* Management by software
* Set of tables able to maintain line management
* ACK, NAK, EOT, ERP

DC MACHINE/MIDDLE (LINE) LEVEL

* To be implemented by microprocessor
* Will encompass a group of lines and involve—

    1. Procedure/line discipline (BSC XDLC SS)
    2. ID
    3. Line speed; number of lines
    4. Work space (data storage on temporary basis)
    5. Microprocessor-implemented tables

DC MACHINE/LOWER (CHARACTER) LEVEL

* All character-oriented tasks
* Code (6 or 8-bit ID a factor)
* Code conversion (if needed)
* Basic level of ACK

To be implemented by microprocessor for a single line or small group of lines.

TO

ELECTRICAL INTERFACE TO THE LINE (DCE)

Communications line(s)

* * *

In conclusion, let's look at the way a data communications engine works with and without front-ending.

Without front-ending

1. Much of the CPU time is devoted to servicing the teleprocessing network.

2. The access method has logical control of all lines, and processes data from the station.

3. The access method communicates directly with each station. Each line has a different subchannel address.

4. Concentrators, if used, will have only physical control of the lines.

5. The number of lines in the teleprocessing network can be no longer than the maximum number of subchannel interfaces.

With front-ending

1. The CPU spends less time servicing the teleprocessing network. CPU resources are available for more application processing.

2. The access method has few line handling responsibilities. It can devote more time to message processing.

3. The access method communicates with all stations through a single interface.

4. The FE has both logical and physical control over the teleprocessing network. It can also process data.

PART THREE

Protocols

12

What Is a Protocol?

A protocol, also called a line procedure or a line discipline, is a set of conventions governing the format and the control of data (the control covering input, transmission, and output). A protocol is a well-defined procedure that is clearly understood by all parties. It constitutes the logical connection to the physical line of the carrier. It is an orderly exchange of data between computers, terminals, and other communications equipment, a logical setup supplementing and complementing the computer-to-computer or terminal-to-terminal connection. The procedure constitutes a predetermined dialogue scrupulously maintained by both ends of a communications link. At the particular level of the link it consists of an interchange of characters or character sequences that guarantees the control and integrity of the message transfer.

The protocol is a new concept, but it standardizes known, not new, things. Broadly speaking, all protocols have two functions. One is contact, which includes identification and synchronization as, for example, the creation of a virtual channel; synchronization concerns both source and destination. The other is transfer, which comprises not only the transmission functions but also error detection and control and the assurance of delivery of a message the protocol has received; see Figure 12.1.

Network architectures are layered, and so are protocols. In data communications we have protocols addressing themselves to the data link, the routing, and the logical link, but we need them also for error detection and correction, access to the data, and management of the memory; see Figure 12.2. Notice that the protocol level for the management of memory is higher than those for access, and access higher than error detection and correction; still, that last is higher than the data communications protocols.

We distinguish transparent from virtual protocols. A transparent protocol sends data through the system without particular constraints due to low-level details; the

Figure 12.1
Protocols

PHYSICAL SET-UP

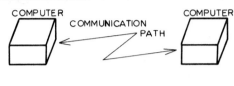

LOGICAL SET-UP

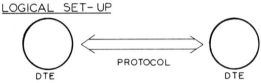

A PROTOCOL IS THE LOGICAL ABSTRACTION OF
THE PHYSICAL PROCESS OF COMMUNICATION

PROTOCOLS ARE ALSO CALLED 'LINE PROCEDURES'
OR 'LINE DISCIPLINES', BUT LAYERED PROTOCOLS
ARE MUCH MORE SOPHISTICATED THAN THIS SIMPLE
CONCEPT

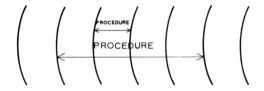

IF DIFFERENT PROCEDURES ARE USED, WE MUST
RECONSTITUTE THE ORIGINAL MESSAGE AT DELIVERY.

user cannot see it, but it is there. A virtual protocol obeys sequence and other constraints. It is, therefore, handy to have transparent protocols, but it is not easy.

The early line disciplines, using the Baudot code, had no inherent control of the link. They relied totally on sequences of data characters to implement supervisory functions. Later work led to protocols with better control. Each manufacturer, however, created protocols that reflected the needs of his particular product, usually optimized for a specific implementation. This is the story of binary synchronous communications. The protocols of the 1960s were character-oriented and generally incompatible with one another.

Protocol Reliability

A protocol is reliable only if it provides end-to-end accountability for flow control, connection management, and delivery of messages. For a message to be delivered,

Figure 12.2

WE MUST DEFINE

PROTOCOLS:

1. MEMORY MANAGEMENT
2. D B
3. A P
4. MESSAGE MANAGEMENT
5. DATA COMMUNICATIONS

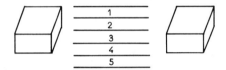

COMPUTER-TO-COMPUTER
TERMINAL-TO-COMPUTER

a number of functions must be carried out, such as packaging, headers, sequencing, acceptance, acknowledgment, and, if necessary, retransmission.

The design study must consider the topology, the network's objectives, the network's characteristics, and the connections to be provided. It must be done with the understanding that processes do not know each other and do not know how to make use of the flow control information and must be instructed.

Reliable protocols support and sustain the communication mechanism, which is structured around the concept of a conversation. Its operational commands are as follows.

Connection: The creation of a data path (the term *data path* may be used for both virtual circuit and dataform solutions).

Transmission: The sending of information over a logical link.

Reception: The information received from a logical link, synchronized with data transmission via a flow control mechanism.

Interruption: The notification of the object at the other end of the logical link, of some unusual condition or event.

.Disconnection: The destruction of a logical link, returning any resources back to the system.

Conversations are established and terminated by means of physical or virtual connection between sender and receiver. Connection is the process of dialing; transmission and reception are the processes of speaking and listening. Message routing, error control, and physical link management are transparent to the users.

Modern protocols extend the functionality of communications processes while reducing the requirements for implementation and the conditions for refusal. The option negotiations of the Telenet system, for instance, are based on four expressions:

Desire	*Command*
Receiver to begin	DO X
Receiver not to begin	DON'T X
I start	WILL X
I don't start	WON'T X

Echoing is done through the basic commands DO ECHO, WILL ECHO, DON'T ECHO, WON'T ECHO. In Telenet the remote-controlled transmission and the echoing support responsive approaches, which in turn make possible the use of remote and very inexpensive hosts.

The receiving host or other DTE, upon receipt of a message coded at the origin (by the sender), not only uncodes and prints it but also enriches the content (text actuated by codes). This process, controlled by remote hosts, can also enrich data at the source terminal (which gives an idea of the range of modern protocols). In fact, such functions account for much of the difference between the ólder and better known physical links (twisted wire, coaxial cable, or radio beam) and the new virtual, or logical, links. By the same token, the aforementioned services are some of the assets of a value-added network as opposed to the older telegraph and telephone services.

Access Methods

The "access method" is a protocol. It directly affects response times, reliability, costs, and other problems. Costs are directly related to the ability of one user to share the resources with others. A data communications network most efficiently shares those resources which are allocated only when data are actually being sent. The classical polling protocols are particularly inefficient, for example, since the messages must be sent continually, even when they contain no meaningful data.

A message-by-message protocol is a desirable alternative to polling. (The same arguments may apply to private lines and dial-up connections.)

How can the method of network access affect the response time? The two principal ways in which terminals and computers now have access to each other are through the switched telephone network and through polling over dedicated lines. In the switched network the response times are long because the time needed to make a connection is long. In polling—considering only the more common half-duplex polling for the moment—the response times again are long, because one transaction with one terminal must be completed before a transaction with another can begin.

Full-duplex polling allows for some overlapping of operations, but not enough to alleviate the problem substantially, and a radically different approach is needed. Ideally, messages and responses would be presented to the network in a fashion that would altogether overcome the disadvantages of polling; several transactions would be carried on simultaneously at a single access port. One solution is to distinguish transactions from each other by including identifiers within the messages; then the messages are identifying their sources and destinations, making polling unnecessary. For this to work, the network and its users must recognize and know how to handle the identifiers, which means that a network access protocol must be established, defining the formats of the data messages and control messages and their sequence. The components of such a protocol are the following eight:

1. Configuration: pass-system configuration information between subsystems involved in a network exchange as, for instance, the operating system and the file system
2. User identification: authentication, passwords, and accounting information
3. Attributes: details relative to the representation of the data base and the files being accessed, among others
4. Access proper, specifically:
   a. Type of access or type of operation, as opening a new file
   b. File name and file specifications, in the format required by the remote node
   c. Mode of access, whether sequential, random, or keyed, etc.
   d. User-oriented access operation, as "get," "put," etc.
   e. Optional files and record processing (user exits)
5. Control (device, file): sending of control types of information to a device or file system, which also allows the access mode to be changed from previous settings
6. Continuation of transfer: activation of alternative recovery strategies, as "try again," "skip," "abort"
7. Acknowledgment: acknowledgment of access commands
8. Completion: indentification of the termination of access for remote systems and the recovery procedures, for record transfer

Procedural Requirements

Several demands aré posed on the new services. The link control procedure must recover from failures of the computer or circuit and also allow resynchronization of various communications parameters.

A good example of the range of services that protocols and network architecture must provide is the system developed in the late 1960s and early 1970s, the Arpanet, which has been taken as a standard ever since. It is a distributed assurance mechanism, which involves the following:

> Access rights
> Retrieval capability
> Additions
> Deletions
> Modifications
> Batch terminals
> On-line systems
> Connective-action mechanism
> Layered-protocol dependencies
> Considerations of data base management systems
> File access
> Data dictionaries

These are fundamental functions within a distributed data assurance environment, since the services must not only transfer data but also add to them, delete from them, and modify them to and from the data base. This calls for overall design, audit trail and control, error detection and correction, synchronization, testing and logging, and protocol sensitivity.

Performance evaluation, balancing procedures, study, examination, and steady reporting on conditions are organizational responsibilities. They include process unit access, authorization and authentication, query validation, process limits control, and isolation by distribution point (no spreadover). Their mechanizations require a physical sensitivity (to errors created or infiltrated), proper journaling, operating statistics and, as stated, protocol responsibility.

Procedural requirements are a relatively new problem in protocols; we shall return to them in the next chapter. First we must look at the fundamentals, which afford exceptional insight into the way the system works.

Synchronous and Asynchronous Transmission

We have said that the exchange of data between two units requires a protocol. At the level of data link control (communication) protocols are established when the one DTE must speak and then the other (Figure 12.3). This exchange of information may be carried on asynchronously or synchronously.

Figure 12.3

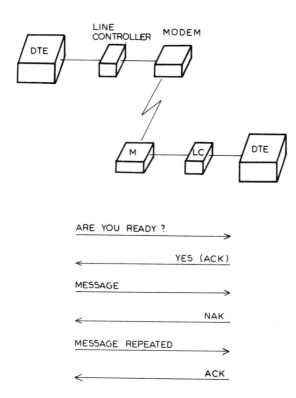

In a synchronous line discipline a clock always times the transmission, and synchronization bits are sent first, followed by data. In an asynchronous line discipline (the older of the two) there is no clock timing the transmission; instead, start and stop bits "bracket" the character, and transmission is character by character. Teletype line procedures, for example, support only asynchronous transmissions on point-to-point lines; a message of this type contains only text, no header or trailer.

The choice of a synchronous or asynchronous protocol depends on a number of things. The synchronous are the more efficient—a background factor in their development—but it is not possible to mix two disciplines on the same line. Most terminals work in an asynchronous mode. Computer-to-computer communications usually are synchronous; given the amount of data to be transferred, efficiency is quite important. But terminal-to-computer communications or multidrop lines can very well be asynchronous, which is not true of modern, horizontal networks.

Slow speeds, say 50, 200, or 300 bits per second, call for the asynchronous mode, and more than 1,200 bits per second nearly always need the synchronous.

Some terminals are designed to work only synchronously, others only asynchronously. Still others may work in either mode, changing "line management devices" when they switch from the one to the other (line control functions have been discussed in chapter 4).

As we have noted, asynchronous protocols operate largely on a character-by-character basis. Of the many kinds one of the best known and most widely used is the teletype. ITT's Model 35, for example, uses an 11-bit frame for each character: 1 start bit, 7 data bits, 1 parity bit, and 2 stop bits. Thus the start–stop is character by character. The error detection is poor; as in many of the protocols, *no* parity check is performed by the receiving terminal. If a check is made and an error detected, a standard error character is inserted for the data characters by the receiving device. Only when a computer is used will an error check be made, character by character; in case of error, all the characters starting with the word or block in error must be retransmitted.

Asynchronous protocols are important because many of today's terminals use them and because they work on both full-duplex and half-duplex lines and therefore impose no particular restraint in that respect. Networks incapable of handling asynchronous protocols refuse a wealth of new devices, because only the new terminals are compatible with them. Packet-switching protocols have made evident the need of gateways able to handle asynchronous devices, within a network utilizing more advanced disciplines.

Synchronous Protocols

Binary synchronous communications (bisync, BSC) have the best known and probably most widely used synchronous protocols. Because in this mode it sends multiple characters per block, the overhead is less than in the asynchronous mode. It operates, however, only on half-duplex lines, so that for each block transmitted at least two line turnarounds are needed; a turnaround means that after a block has been transmitted the direction of the line must be turned around for sending the acknowledgment, then turned around again for sending the next block. Each turnaround takes 100 to 300 milliseconds; this is a loss in efficiency, except when a "supervisory" wire facility—offered by many telephone companies at no extra cost—is used for indicating which way the message is going. Figure 12.4 presents a typical binary synchronous protocol. The ETX, or end of text, terminates the last block of a message and requires a reply. Preceding any SOH, or start of header, of any block of characters are the synchronization signals, usually referred to as SYN; terminals normally omit 2 to 8 SYN characters.

The procedures are not absolutely standard. For instance, IBM suggests following the SOH with a special character, possibly a dash, that will not be used after the STX. This would help prevent a line error from changing SOH to STX. Other

Figure 12.4
Typical binary synchronous protocol

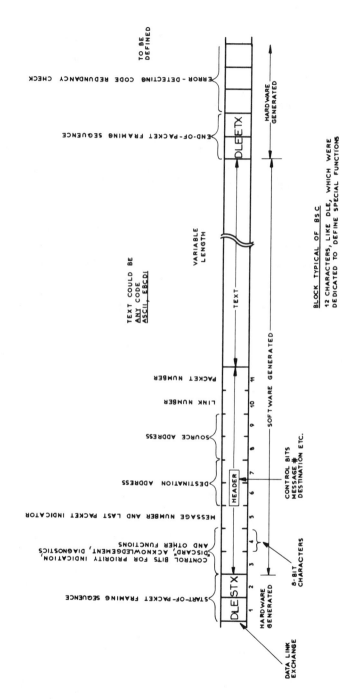

dialects do not follow this procedure. Figure 12.5 presents three binary synchronous dialects. Table 12.1 identifies the most frequently used characters in binary synchronous communications. The protocol is character oriented. Its codes may be ASCII (7 bits plus parity), EBCDIC (8 data bits), or Transcode (6 data bits), and the transparency mode. It uses block-by-block acknowledgments for correct or incorrect receipt; the ACK0 and ACK1 are two forms of positive response employed alternatively in a series of blocks, and NAK is used when a data error in transmission is detected.

Binary synchronization allows for polling and addressing on multipoint lines. As a discipline, it has a rigorous set of rules for establishing, maintaining, and terminating a communication. It has many variants, though in its origins it belongs to a previous generation of protocols and does not fit the modern model we shall be discussing in the following chapters.

One of the criticisms of BSC is that the different protocol functions, present in a layered approach, have not been separated into independent components. In some of its variants it is not a pure link control protocol but mixes device control of applications functions with communications functions. It does not separate the link-management component from the data-transfer component. Therefore, error recovery, once initiated, must be completed in a given system before other systems may be selected. Moreover, the acknowledgment message is not block checked. This is as much a failure as not block checking the data and can result in undetected duplicate or missing messages. Yet it should not be forgotten that the binary synchronous is one of the two earliest synchronous protocols (the other is

Figure 12.5
Three binary synchronous dialects

1. USER-DEFINED HEADER MESSAGE

STI	TRI	SOH	HEADER TEXT	ETB/ETX

2. MESSAGE PARTITIONED INTO BLOCKS

STI	TRI	SOH	HEADER TEXT	STX	TEXT	ETB/ETX

OPTIONAL

3. TRANSPARENT TEXT MESSAGE   NON-STANDARD CODES ACCEPTED

STI	TRI	SOH	HEADER TEXT	DLE	STX	TRANS TEXT	DLE	ETB/ETX

OPTIONAL

STI - STATION INDEX
TRI - TERMINAL INDEX, EBCDIC VALUE
      TO SELECT DEVICES FOR 2780
      SIMULATION
SOH - START OF HEADER
HEADER TEXT - CONTENT, USER-DEFINED

STX - START OF TEXT, NORMAL MODE
DLE STX - START OF TEXT, TRANSPARENT MODE
DLE ETX - END OF TRANSPARENT TEXT
ETB/ETX - END OF BLOCK/END OF TEXT FOR
          FORMAT 2 (FILE TRANSFER)

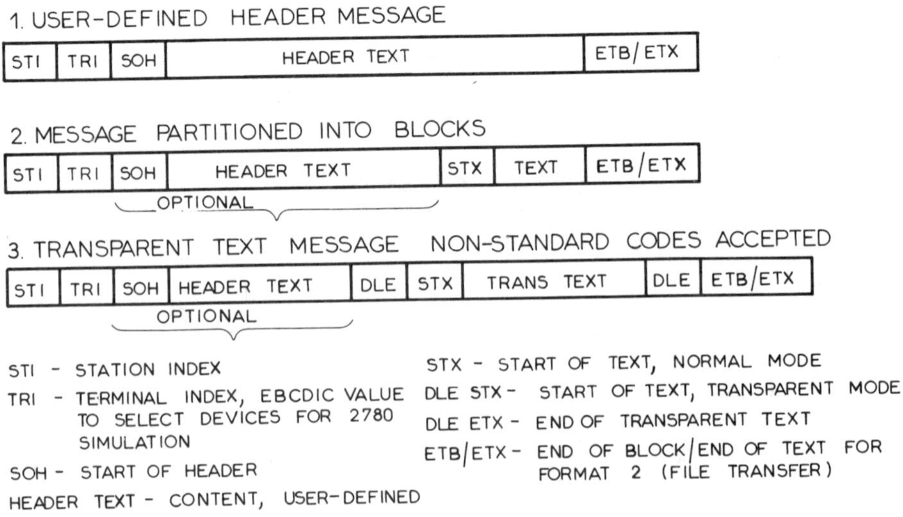

Table 12.1
Frequently Used Characters for Defining and
Assuring a Block of Data in Binary Synchronous Communications

ACK∅ ACK1	Acknowledgment
ARQ	Automatic request for transmission
DLEEOT	Data link escape and end of transmission
ENQ	Enquiry: demand for something
EOT	End of transmission: "I give you back the control," "reset"; a necessary in polling and selecting; can force the end of a transmission
ETB	End of transmission block: requires a reply indicating receiving station's status
ETX	End of text
ITB	Intermediate text block: helps divide a data block into sub-blocks; after it the line management automatically adds CRC, CRC.
RVI	Reverse interrupt: modifies a situation, as when the receiving end wants to change direction of transmission, such as transmitting instead of receiving; largely device dependent; chiefly used by IBM
SOH	Start of header: device dependent, used for some types of machine, used in some types of message
STX	Start of text
SYN	Synchronous idle: establishes and maintains synchronization
TTD	Temporary transmit delay: transmitter's ACK; if the time out is exceeded, transmitter uses it; if receiver cannot reply immediately, transmitter, to avoid an error situation, sends WACK
WACK	Wait for acknowledgment: "wait," sent by receiver

General Electric's VIP) and could not possibly contain any potentialities unrevealed by a dozen years of practice.

Terminals for Synchronous and Asynchronous Protocols

Table 12.2 presents a remarkable collection of terminals which, as of mid-1983, were being offered on the market. Some of these terminals have become standards; this is true of IBM's 2740 and 2848, among the interactive terminals, and of the 2780 among the batch-oriented terminals.

Computer and communications manufacturers typically follow IBM protocols as a de facto standard. Some vendors (Burroughs, Honeywell) also provide their own line disciplines.

Table 12.2
Terminals

Among protocols we distinguish:

Protocol	*Implementation*
TTY	For asynchronous communications
2780/3780	For point-to-point private lines, identified by some manufacturers (Olivetti, etc.) as BSC I

The 3780 provides a transparent mode and permits data compression.

2780/3780	For point-to-point public lines (sometimes referred to as BSC II)
3270	For private line multipoint implementation (BSC III)

The 3280 is available on native and SNA versions.

An aged terminal is the 2848 which substituted the 2260 terminal of the 1960s. Another aged line discipline is VIP by Honeywell.

The following are manufacturer offerings:

IBM

PC and PC XT	Synchronous and asynchronous line disciplines (1981, 1983)
	Microcomputer power: 3270, SNA, Plan 4000, Omninet, Ethernet 3Comm, LAN-1
3270	Compatible with BSC/SDLC, SNA; emulates 2740; works in clusters (1974)
3278	(idem)
	Models 002—1,920 characters to 005; 3056 characters rides presentation; matrix: 7 x 14 to 7 x 12
3279	(idem); color video; graphics
3290	Multiple Application Screen (MAS); 4 spaces of 1,920 characters each, or one space of 9,092 characters; compatible with the 3270 line
8775	Control unit
3274/3276	Control units
3268	Printer; 132 characters per line; up to 340 cps
3287	Bidirectional printer, B/W and color; 7 x 8 matrix; 80 or 120 cps
3262/3289	Printers, 132 characters per line
7436	Printer; idem
5210	Desktop printer
3736	Printer
3732	Video unit, 15" monitor, 1,092 characters
3178	Video unit, 1,092 characters, detachable keyboard
5251/5291	Video units (with System 36)
5292	idem; color
3262	Printer (with System 36)

Table 12.2 (cont.)
Terminals

5219/5224 5225/5226	Family of printers (with System 36)

NCR

1780/5080/1770	ISO Asynchronous; BSC 3270; SDLC/SNA; 3624 Emulation
7740	TTY (in communication with 5000 BAS or 9020/9040/ 9050/9300)
7900-2111	TTY
7901-0101	TTY
796-301	Polling/selecting, asynchronous
2262	ISO Asynchronous, IBM 2848, IBM 3270, NCR DLC
5000 BAS	BSC 3270, SDLC/SNA, NCR DLC, 3270 Emulation
721	Programmable front-end and concentrator; message switching/store and forward
7750-3000	IBM 2780/3780
DM V	TTY; IBM 2780/3780, IBM 3270, 3270 SNA, Omninet LAN
TOWER 1632	TTY, BSC 2780/3780, 3270 SNA, X.25, Omninet
MODUS	TTY, IBM 2780/3780, 3270 SNA, Omninet, Ethernet
9020/9040/9050	2780/3780
9300	IBM 2780/3780, IBM 3270, SDLC/SNA

Burroughs

ET 2000	Video, 14-inch monitor; 200 characters; 256 KB, MS DOS, intelligent terminal
B 20	15-inch monitor; 256 KB to 1 MB; BTOS, CP/M, MS DOS, UNIX, Burroughs P/S; IBM 2780/3780; IBM 3270; IBM SNA; X.25
ET 1100	Video 14-inch monitor, 2000 characters; polling/ selecting, nonintelligent
EF 3000	Banking terminal, 5-inch monitor; printer dot matrix, 40 characters per line
B 95	Branch concentrator: up to 512 BM main memory; up to 5 datacomm lines: BSC, SNA (RJE, IMS, CICS), X.25

Honeywell

VIP7800	Synchronous/Asynchronous (video)
TTU 1126	Asynchronous (HC)
TTU 1223	Synchronous (HC)
TTU 1710, 1730, 1732, 1738	Asynchronous, attached to 6/10
GTBH	Banking terminal

Table 12.2 (cont.)
Terminals

Olivetti

M30/M40   Asynchronous 2848; synchronous BSC, SDLC 3270
                                     emulation
                                     Assembler, Cobol, native language, WP, data entry DE
                                     700 type
M20 ST (MFU, HDU)   Synchronous/asynchronous
SP 624/644   BSC I (IBM 2780); BSC II (IBM 3270)
WS 580   Synchronous/asynchronous, substituting TC 808
TCV 280 NDL   Asynchronous (polling/selecting); synchronous
TCV 370 (cluster)   (BSC II/III)
TCV 1375/1376 (standalone)
BSC   BSC I/II/III; emulating IBM 2848
S 6000   idem

13

Circuit Switching and the Polling/Selecting Option

Protocols are necessary for shared, switched data communications services. Conceptually the services are like the dial telephone network, except that the interconnected subscriber equipment consists of computers and computer terminals instead of telephone handsets.

Communication circuits and switching centers are shared in the sense that all users have access to the same facilities on demand. A network is switched in the sense that calls can be routed via a series of switches or nodes to user points. The facilities are leased often with a fixed charge for the basic connection to the network and then monthly usage charges.

Recent services, such as the Advanced Communications Service, ACS, of AT&T, offer two basic types of transmission service: a call service and a message service. The call service gives the customer a two-way path between the originating and the terminating stations, which facilitates applications that require real-time communications, such as time-sharing and inquiry–response systems. The message service is a variety of functions for the presentation and handling of messages and for directing their movement through the network; it is needed for applications that require only one-way transmission. Data entry and remote batch are examples.

The understructure of the services reveals the differences between switching techniques. They are all based on simple principles. Switches may be intelligent or unintelligent. If intelligent, they receive data from a DTE, interpret the dispatching instructions, store the data for some period, and send them on to a destination; packet switching and message switching perform intelligent functions. If the switches are unintelligent, they are subject to circuit-switching disciplines, although, as we shall see, new developments might radically change all this.

Circuit-Switching Principles

For voice-grade traffic the telephone network is invaluable. For data communications, too, it brings computers and terminals together wherever there is a telephone line. The problem with it is the fact that it was originally designed for voice-grade traffic, not data. The question of noise will make our point clear. The human ear filters extraneous sounds, accepting only the relevant information. Terminals cannot do this, and noise is often read as meaningful data, with resulting errors. The first circuit-switching networks were analog and thus incapable of affording the accuracy inherent in digital transmission. Table 13.1 outlines the chief differences between circuit switching, message switching, and packet switching.*

The earliest service designed for data was based on point-to-point private lines. It used the analog system available, with a circuit that connected each terminal to its host. The costs of analog point-to-point private lines were, however, a major limitation, and as distances grew, they became more prohibitive. The solution, with batch-type operations (requiring the sender to have access to more than one computer or terminal), has been circuit switching. It takes place through a dedicated data switch that is in use only for the duration of the communication. The user shares the network facilities, including transmission lines and switches, with other users, buying only the transmission speed or bandwidth needed and paying accordingly.

The best example of circuit switching is the dial telephone network. A user dials the desired telephone number. The switches assign a circuit from source to destination, and, if answered, communication is established. A difficulty was that a line may be busy and delays in setup might result. So, instead of point-to-point connections, a multipoint arrangement was devised whereby a primary station authorizes a secondary station to transmit, in this way assigning a circuit. The circuit remains assigned to this particular operation until the call is terminated, during which time the circuit is dedicated to this particular operation, whether data are being transmitted or not.

The basic characteristics of circuit switching may be outlined in the following terms. First, circuit switching involves the establishment of a total path, at all initiations; this results in a serious inflexibility, given the way in which current voice-grade networks are implemented. Second, the circuit is established by a special signaling message, which threads its way through different switching centers. Third, the circuit, being a total path, is subject to the speed, and the code, limitation of the slowest link. As stated, the total path remains allocated for the transmission, regardless of utilization. When a call is terminated, the circuit is dropped, each line and switch returning to the "pool."

Three advantages of circuit switching are that the routing is simpler, the method is quite widespread today, and it is possible to attach terminals having

*Part Four, "Networks," discusses switching in greater detail within the context of *Network Architecture*. However, it is appropriate to complement this chapter with a comprehensive comparison of the three disciplines of switching. This is the object of Table 13.1.

differing characteristics. Among the disadvantages are the bit error rate, the relatively long call-setup times, the lack of automatic retransmission, an inefficient use of the circuits, and switching failures that are fatal to the communications. The greatest disadvantage is that the facilities are really built for voice-grade traffic.

Many of the problems in circuit switching are part and parcel of today's networks, the connection times, bandwidth, conditioning, and incompatibility between voice and data being examples. With the new technologies the entire way of handling the traffic will change, and circuit-switching may stage a comeback. The present-day disadvantages essentially mean that sharing common resources in a circuit switching function has its price. A protocol-based solution, designed to meet the needs of inquiry–response systems, has been the development of multipoint and multidrop networks. Multipoint networks have terminals in several locations, which communicate with a computer along a single communications line Multidrop networks have several terminals in one region, which are connected to a remote computer through one communication channel. Usually networks are exclusively neither multipoint nor multidrop, but a combination of both.

Multipoint networks use the facilities of the circuit-switching voice-grade network provided by the telephone company. The line is either "fixed" (dedicated to the user) or it is preferentially handled at the switching centers with a minimal setup time. Once the user is on a multipoint line, he must apply a protocol, a control procedure, which permits the central computer to manage a number of terminals operating on the line in question. The exact number of terminals depends on the length of the message, whether the terminal is intelligent or unintelligent, and the speed of the line. Twelve or fifteen terminals are usual. The most generally employed control procedure is the subject of the following sections.

Control Procedures: Fixed, Switched, and Multipoint

Control procedures, or protocols, should depend on the nature of the communications link, the technical characteristics of the terminal equipment, the software support, the user topology, and the applications requirements. The connections between two stations, whether terminal to terminal, terminal to computer, or computer to computer, may be one of three kinds: fixed point-to-point, multipoint, or switched point-to-point. This has been the essence of the discussion we have presented so far. We have said that the control procedures, the protocols, are most relevant to multipoint and switched point-to-point communications. In the general case we distinguish five basic phases:

Connection: A dial-up operation most relevant in switched end-to-end communications.

Establishment: Identification of sender and receiver DTEs.

Message handling: Transfer and delivery of message from sender DTE to receiver DTE.

Table 13.1
Comparison of Three Disciplines

	Circuit Switching	Message Switching	Packet Switching
1.	Uses classical electromechanical (or computerized) switching centers	A fairly intelligent message switch center is needed, with storage facilities	Switching computers are used at the nodes; they can be micromini, mini, or midi
2.	Wire circuit (or its equivalent radio link) connects the parties	No direct wire connection.	No direct wire connection
3.	Point-to-point transmission	Permits broadcast and multiaddress of messages	Can permit broadcast and multiaddress of messages
4.	Transmission is fixed bandwidth on voice-grade lines.	Usually low-speed transmission (sub-voice)	Users effectively employ small or large bandwidth according to need
5.	Network cannot perform speed or code conversion	Network can perform speed or code conversion	Network can perform speed or code conversion
6.	No delayed delivery possible	Delayed delivery is feasible if recipient is not available or lines are busy	Delayed delivery is possible as a special network facility
7.	Network and its facilities are of a generalized type	Network and its facilities are applications oriented	Network and its facilities are of a generalized type
8.	No particular optimization of speed of transmission or throughput	Optimization is made in terms of throughput	Optimization is primarily for speed of transmission
9.	No store and forward	Store and forward capability	Store and forward is possible
10.	Switched path is established for entire conversation	Route is originated for each message	Route is established dynamically for each packet

Circuit Switching	Message Switching	Packet Switching
11. Time delay in setting up the call	Call setup is reasonable	Negligible delay in setting up the call, usually the least of the three alternatives
12. Negligible transmission delay	Delay in message delivery can be substantial	Negligible delay in packet delivery
13. Busy signal if called party is occupied	No busy signal, store and forward solution	Packet returned to sender if undeliverable
14. Increased probability of blocking because of overload	Increased delivery delay because of overload	Overload results in increased delivery delay, but delivery time is short
15. No effect on transmission once connection is made	Saturation has a great impact on delay	Blocking when saturation is reached
16. Old type of real time between the parties	Too slow for conversational interaction	Old real time unnecessary, since conversational interaction is assured through modern technology
17. Messages are not filed at the nodes	Messages can be filed at the nodes	Messages are not filed except for journaling purposes
18. Protection against loss of messages is responsibility of the end user	Protection against loss of messages is responsibility of the network	Protection against loss of packets is responsibility of network with virtual circuits, of user with datagrams
19. Any length of transmission is permitted	Lengthy messages can be transmitted directly	Lengthy messages are divided into packets (1,000 to 8,000 bits each)
20. Economical with low traffic volumes, if public lines are employed, but very expensive with private lines	Economical with moderate traffic volumes	Reasonably high traffic volumes needed for economic justification, but less expensive than private lines

Termination: Return of the system to its initial state, releasing the resources from their temporary assignment.

Disconnection: Corresponding to hanging up in a voice network; particularly relevant in switched end-to-end communications.

Let us now examine the basic characteristics of each type of connection, i.e., the fixed point-to-point, the multipoint, and the switched point-to-point, along with an outline of the procedures.

In a fixed point-to-point arrangement (Figure 13.1) a DTE needing to send a message to another can initiate its action with ENQ (enquiry). The receiving DTE responds with ACK (positive acknowledgment), which indicates that the destination is ready to receive a message. The sender then sends the message, and the receiver responds with another ACK, if it accepts the message. It is up to the sender to terminate the communication; this is done with an EOT (end of transmission), which returns the system to the idle state. Either station may be the primary one. Notice that a NAK (negative acknowledgment) may indicate that the destination DTE is not ready to receive or that the received message is in error. The NAK depends on the phase in which it is emitted. The two alternatives correspond respectively to the establishment and the message handling.

In a multipoint or a multidrop connection the control is rather complex, since

Figure 13.1

Fixed point-to-point connection. (I/NR, invalid or no reply; ERP, error recovery procedure; EOT, end of transmission)

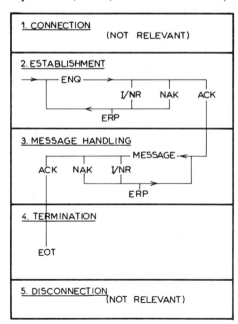

more than two stations are on the same link. For this reason a choice is made between whether one DTE masters the communications link, acting as the control station, or whether all the stations talk to one another at the same time; the latter is the case of contention.

When a master station is responsible for polling and selecting, one of two hypotheses must be made. The first is that the control station wished to send a message, and the second is that, not the control station, but one of the tributaries did.

When the master station starts a communication (Figure 13.2), it sends a SEL (selection) command. The DTE being addressed responds with an AKC, if it is ready to receive the message; a NAK brings up procedural choices that we have already discussed. When the master station is being spoken to (Figure 13.3), a tributary DTE waits for a POLL (polling) command. Then it replies with an EOT, if it has nothing to send, or with an ACK if it wishes to forward a message. The transfer procedure that follows resembles that of the preceding examples.

A basic difference between the foregoing cases and the switched end-to-end connection is that in point-to-point and multipoint the channel is a physical one, but in the switched end-to-end the channel is a logical one (Figure 13.4). In the first phase, connection, dialing is done by the DTE. After the link is established, the procedure is much like the one we have just described, except for the need to initiate and to break the connection (disconnection).

Figure 13.2

Multipoint connection, master DTE sending. (SEL, selection; I/NR, invalid or no reply; ERP, error recovery procedure; EOT, end of transmission)

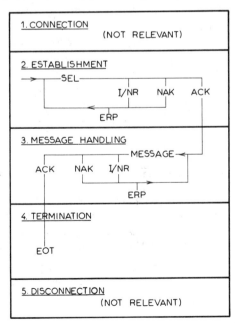

Figure 13.3

Multipoint connection, master DTE receiving. (I/NR, invalid or no reply;
EOT, end of transmission; ERP, error recovery procedure)

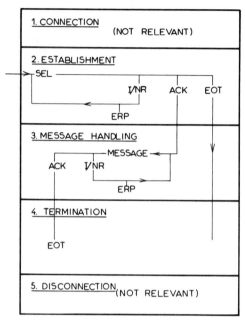

First of all, a discipline must ensure connection. This is the job of data link control (discussed in the following chapter). Quite simply, the DTE that dialed the connection sends an identification command, which includes its own identity and a request to reply. The reply includes the identifying symbols of the called station together with an ACK or a NAK. When the identification is successful (ACK), the communications process is established; a NAK, no reply, or an invalid reply, leads to a restart of the identification procedure or to an error recovery routine. A communication process will be terminated by an EOT. If either station sends a DEOT (disconnect), the channel is released, a procedure assured by the protocol we have just explained.

The Coming Possibilities

Polling and selecting is by now an old discipline, yet it is still around and will continue, probably, to characterize a large number of networks, which is why we include it in this text.

We have made frequent reference to planning for the future. Optical fibers and satellite communications are the solution for the physical media, and efficient end-to-end protocols are the solution for their logical understructure.

The lightwave communications system under downtown Chicago exemplifies the use of optical fibers. For more than a year of test service, it performed even

Figure 13.4

Switching end-to-end connection. (I/NR, invalid or no reply; ERP, error recovery procedure; EOT, end of transmission)

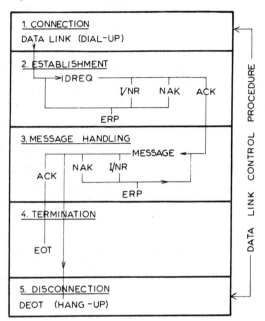

better than expected, with virtually no downtime, surpassing stringent performance objectives.*

The current domestic and international satellite systems are efficient and economically competitive. Digital data have been transmitted at rates in excess of 56 kilobits per second, and projected rates are in excess of 400 megabits. Earth stations have reached a level where sharp reductions in cost are in sight. The data systems operating by satellite are achieving bit error rates of 1×10^{-8} and better; their reliability is better than 99.99 percent.

Switching, we said, is the key component in a circuit-switching network, and efficient switching is very important because the nodes represent about 40 percent of the total cost of the large telephone networks. A good approach lies in the use of two-dimensional, time-and-space technologies that handle digital signals directly and share in the time of switching paths through nodes.

Because for many years from now no network can be envisioned that is totally based on the new technologies, the ability to transform data is a must. This can be enhanced by microprocessors attached to the switching equipment. Something similar might be said about built-in diagnostics.

---

*That there is virtually no downtime refers to the system's projected annual outage rate of 0.0001 percent, about 30 seconds per year. The accuracy of digital transmission averaged less than 1 second per day of transmission error; the 1-second intervals that were error-free stood at 99.999 percent.

In a modern, powerful, extensive data and voice network, automatic diagnostics must allow for easy trouble-shooting, not only of failures within the system itself, but also of failures in the external devices being monitored and controlled. Although field repairs may be made by replacing modules, a complete on-line maintenance is necessary for quickly locating a faulty one.

With respect to protocols a lot of work has been done for data but not much for voice—a missed opportunity, considering that technology offers a means of developing protocol chips. Voice and data protocols must complement and support, not contradict or defy, each other. The "flag" in current data protocols is not long enough for voice traffic, and there are buffering problems with voice stations and similar ones for encrypted traffic. These are vital issues in establishing, implementing, and maintaining circuit services.

Let us now look into the sort of facilities a user requires for end-to-end data communications. They must accommodate different users, different uses, and different equipment, and they could do so through the adoption of a standard format and a few well defined protocols. Although many types of terminal and computer, built by different manufacturers, can communicate with one another, virtual configurations may have to be defined, as the DTEs proliferate and too many combinations of terminal and computer make integrating dissimilar equipment too complex. In other words, the logical understructure must support the attachment of the terminals. It will be easy to branch DTEs that are "plug-compatible" with the network's specifications and to leave it to the software and the protocols to define the functional capabilities.

Packet switching is an example of a discipline able to handle computers and terminals of many vendors who observe established specifications. The switching nodes accept streams from many sources and dynamically interleave the packets of digital, high-capacity, internodal trunks. This seems a better use of transmission facilities and eventually reduces investment and lowers cost.

Already applied in a number of advanced networks, packet switching presents a significant potential. The protocols discussed in the following chapters split up a series of packets from one terminal and send them along various routes, depending on the volume of traffic, the error conditions, and other factors. At the receiving node they are reassembled in their correct sequence and delivered to the destination.

Since the switching nodes are essentially programmable minicomputers, they can be instructed for a variety of communications-processing functions that normally either are undertaken by the host computer or are not feasible at all. The intelligence inherent in a packet network provides users with several kinds of operation, from fully switched ones to closed user groups.

Such are the solutions of the 1980s. As the cost of communications continues to decline, and microcomputer technology offers features never imagined before, new concepts, functions, and services may be expected to change radically the services now offered.

14

Bit-Oriented Protocols

Bit-oriented procedures are recognized as intrinsically more efficient in utilization of resources, even though character-oriented protocols are vastly more in use today, but before microcomputer technology had matured, their computations were felt to be too demanding for widespread use. After several years of research, carried out primarily by the American National Standards Institute, ANSI, and the International Standards Organization, ISO, the new bit-oriented data link control procedures reached a reasonable level of development. The ANSI standard is the Advanced Communications Control Procedure, ADCCP. The original ISO standard was the "high-level data link control," HDLC, which in its original version, was fairly similar to IBM's "synchronous data link control," SDLC. Both ANSI and ISO started working on this subject in 1969, but IBM made one of the first announcements in 1973.

Protocols written to satisfy the second layer of the ISO/OSI model Data Link Control are also called *link access procedures* (LAP). The original SDLC, HDLC designs following asymetric structures are presently known as LAP "A". The newer versions have been link access procedures/balanced: LAP "B".

When the original X.25 recommendation was written, it reflected only LAP "A". The later LAP "B" version offered balanced structures and certain improvements. The basic difference between "A" and "B" resides in the supported functions, most particularly in establishing and terminating the connection.

The ADCCP, CDCCP, SDLC, BDLC, UDLC, HDLC, and LAP B are all "dialects" of a bit-oriented protocol. Together we shall call them XDLC. Flag sequences at the beginning and end of a frame effect synchronization (a 0 bit followed by six 1 bits and then another 0 bit). The frame includes address, user data (information) and control fields.

The Data Link

In the short twenty years of its existence the data communications industry has steadily searched for an efficient use of its resources, and the bit-oriented protocols are the latest development. Like any other line discipline, they are the content and sequencing procedures for transmission between terminal and computer, but they do so on a higher level than that of a physical medium. The communications medium concerns itself with the physical transmission of bits over a channel; the bit-oriented protocol addresses itself to the logical transmission of data. The data, in logical transmission, are grouped into physical blocks, the packets (Figure 14.1). Packets must be transmitted over a link, so some form of control is necessary. The lowest level of protocol is the "communication level," which provides the physical data link. A packet consists of a "frame" bracketed between an opening and a closing flag; we shall discuss the structures of the frame and the flag in the next sections. The frame is the vehicle for every command, every response, and all information that is transmitted by use of a protocol. It is the basic grouping. A higher grouping, called a frame sequence, is checked for missing or duplicated frames. A DTE transmitting sequenced frames counts and numbers each; the counting is referred to as N(S). A station receiving sequenced frames counts each error-free sequenced frame received; the receiver count is known as N(R). Upon receipt of an error-free frame an N(R) is incremented, indicating the next expected frame. All information frames are designated by four parameters:

I: "this is an information frame"

N(S): "send sequence count"

N(R): "receive sequence count"

P/F: "poll" or "final" bit

Supervisory frames are designated by type, such as "receive ready," "receive not ready," and "reject," followed by N(R); unnumbered frames have a command–response structure; management frames provide the data needed for activating, initializing, and controlling the response mode of the DTE in the network and also for reporting errors in transmission procedures. The time base is horizontal: left to right.

Bit orientation permits the use of positionally located control fields rather than code set combinations for link control. Framing flags and control fields divorce the link control from the pattern or code structure of the information content. This makes the bit-oriented protocols inherently transparent.

Bit orientation provides error checking of both control and text information. (It will be recalled that binary synchronous communications control only the text.) Furthermore, it is versatile in its applications and with respect to communications facilities.

Being a third-generation protocol (after the synchronous and binary synchronous protocols), the XDLC takes advantage of full-duplex lines while being able to

Figure 14.1

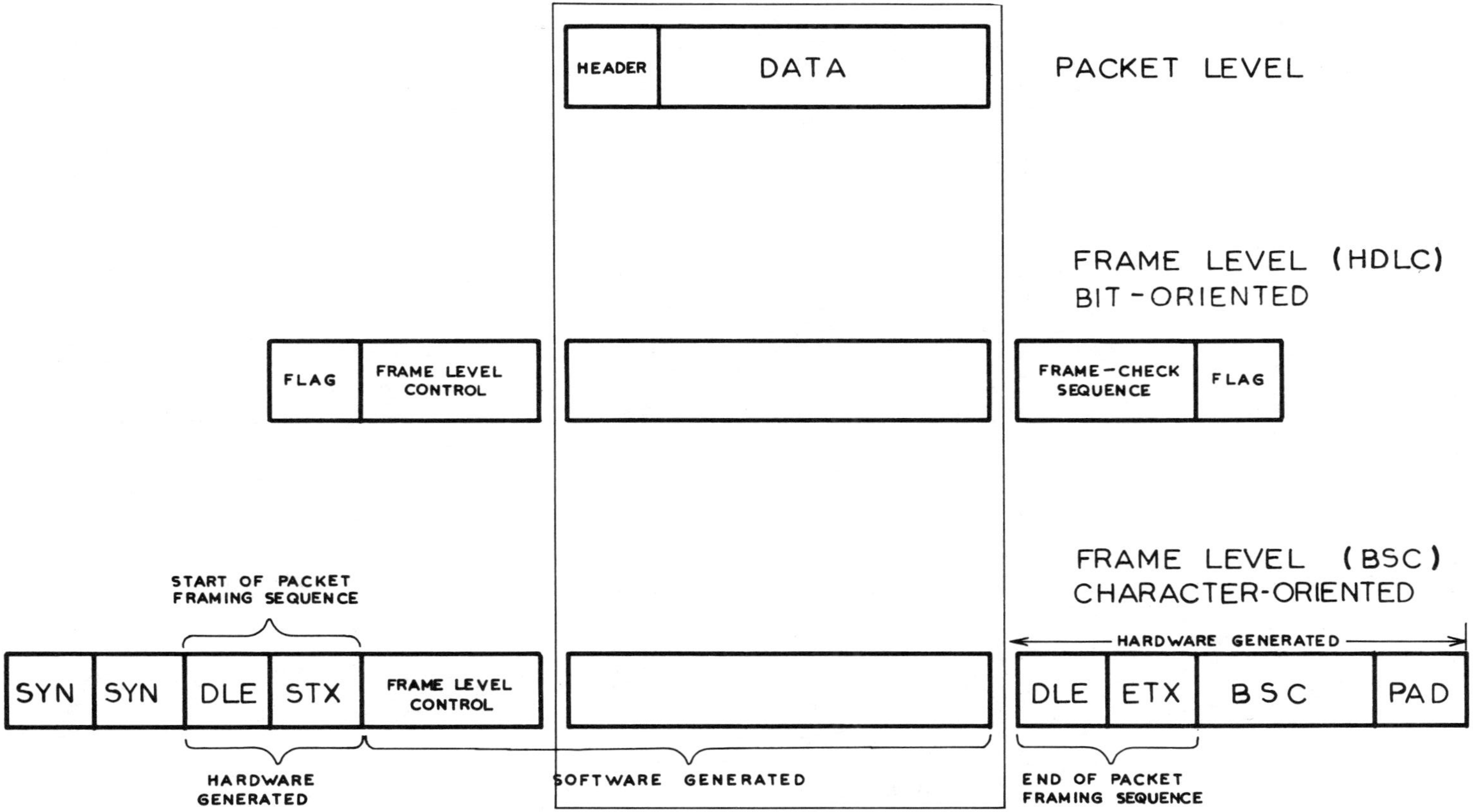

Data transparency is provided by each of the three structures. SYN, synchronous; DLE, data link escape; STX, start of text; ETX, end of text; BSC, binary synchronous communications; PAD, packet assembler-disassembler

operate efficiently on half-duplex, if need be. It also separates the lower link controls of the physical communications media from the higher controls, such as packet format control (which we shall be discussing).

The XDLC is evolutionary, and in its present form it is not the whole answer to the communications problem. It is merely a link-level mechanism, concerned solely with the transfer of data at that level. Moreover, it is, quite definitely, not a network architecture: it was not designed to control the flow of information between users in a multinodal network. It can, however, be applied between nodes or between a node and a user. The relationship of XDLC to a network architecture is straightforward if we consider their respective functions. The purpose of architecture is to transfer data between applications, or "processes"—a user program, a line printer and its software, a file system, etc.—on different systems, which systems use links between them to support the processes. The links need the assistance of a bit-oriented line access protocol.

The data being transferred should not influence, nor be influenced by, the XDLC. They may be a single character, parts of a data base, or a program to be executed. The XDLC must also be device independent, since the terminals or computers may belong to different families, and have different operating systems, different data bases, and so on. The links between systems may be temporary (dial-up) or permanent and stable. They may work at different speeds, and that, too, should be transparent to the XDLC.

The XDLC has its price. The need to distinguish between data and control characters places a burden on the implementation of software and requires a high intelligence of the hardware. Further, transparency has been achieved only in complicated ways.

Figure 14.2 shows the LAP A protocol, as an example. All the XDLC protocols have in common a number of basic characteristics:

All are synchronous protocols, though different from the binary synchronous protocols.

All are similar but not completely compatible among themselves.

All work on half-duplex and full-duplex transmission.

All may be used in loop (ring) or multidrop configurations.

All have fixed length of header, but among themselves and within their own dialects this length can vary.

All have a fixed trailer length (cyclic redundancy check).

All are bit oriented.

All in their original forms were asymmetric (new forms tend to be symmetric, like LAP B).

The difference between a symmetric and an asymmetric structure is, of course, fundamental in the development of systems with user exits and significant possibilities of growth. Table 14.1 compares some of the differences among the dialects of XDLC.

The XDLC is *not* designed for certain things, listed below. Note that the infor-

Figure 14.2
SDLC protocol (LAP "A")

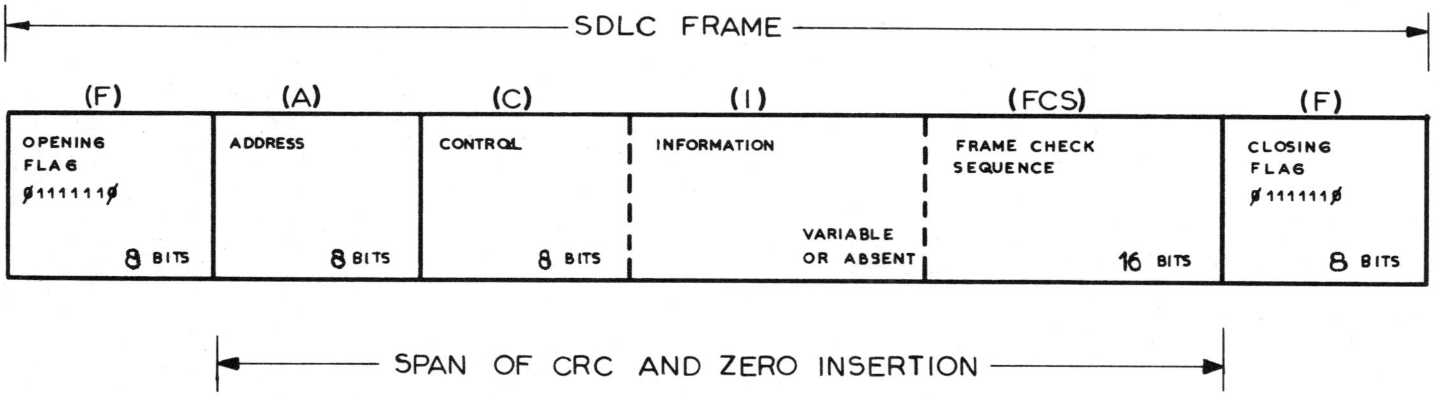

FIELD DEFINITIONS

- OPENING FLAG - FRAME BEGINNING AND FRAME SYNCHRONIZATION

- ADDRESS - SECONDARY STATION
WITH 8 BITS WE CAN ONLY ADDRESS 256 TERMINALS
BANK OF AMERICA ADOPTED A VARIATION

- CONTROL - DEFINES FRAME TYPE AND INCLUDES
SUPERVISION COMMANDS INCLUDING SHUT DOWN
OF TERMINALS; SEND/RECEIVE INFORMATION;
NO MESSAGE COUNT WITH 8 BITS.

- INFORMATION - THE DATA FIELD

- FRAME CHECK - ERROR DETECTION
CRC 16 COVERS BOTH DATA FIELD AND HEADER
PREVIOUS PROTOCOLS CHECKED ONLY THE DATA

- CLOSING FLAG - FRAME TERMINATION AND LINE FILL

Table 14.1
Comparative Table for XDLC*

Criteria	ADCCP		HDLC		SDLC (IBM)		SDLC (BOA)†	
	C	R	C	R	C	R	C	R
Frame structure								
1. Basic format	Y	Y	Y	Y	Y	Y	Y	Y
2. Extended format	Y	Y	Y	Y	N	N	Y	Y
Control field								
3. Selective reject	Y	Y	Y	Y	N	N	N	N
4. Unnumbered information	Y	Y	N	N	N	N	N	N
5. Disconnect	Y	N	Y	N	Y	N	Y	N
6. Request disconnect	—	Y	—	N	—	N	—	N
7. Check pattern in information field	N	N	N	N	Y	Y	Y	Y
8. System tailoring	Y	Y	N	N	N	N	N	N
9. Station-off disconnect line	—	Y	—	N	—	N	—	N
10. Asynchronous response	Y	Y	Y	Y	N	N	N	N
11. Balanced-mode capability	Y	Y	N	N	N	N	N	N
12. Exchange identification	Y	Y	N	N	Y	Y	Y	Y

*C, command; R, response; Y and N, yes and no.
†The version implemented by the Bank of America.

mation carried by the supervisory signals, item 8, can serve for item 7, and that the data at the bit level may be information or commands.

Asynchronous transmission

Either grouping or breaking of messages

Queries about device status

Device control

End-to-end control

Integrating of voice packets

Establishment, maintenance, and termination of a communication session

Exchange of supervisory signals

These functions are taken care of by the network architecture. That is why it is important to select an architecture—and the right one.

The Fields of XDLC

The first XDLC is the opening flag. In the SDLC and other dialects it is an 8-bit sequence generated at the transmitter. The flag indicates the beginning of a frame, is a synchronizing reference for the position of subsequent fields, and triggers a transmission-checking algorithm. All terminals monitor the network in an idle state; they become active when they detect an opening flag. The 8-bit flag is also an integral part of the trailer; by being repeated at the end of the block, it provides synchronization, part of which is indicating beginning and end.

The frame thus closes with a flag. Both the opening and the closing flags have the binary configuration 01111110, that is, a 0 bit, followed by six 1 bits, followed by a 0 bit. Senders send complete 8-bit flags; receivers search continuously, on a bit-by-bit basis, for the frame synchronization.

For transparency throughout the frame (Figure 14.3), and to avoid duplicating the flag, the transmitter inserts a 0 bit after five successive bits anywhere between the beginning and the ending flags, which bit is then detected and removed at the receiving end; see Figure 14.4. That is to say, in order to safeguard the 8-bit flag, *if* the same bit pattern appears in the information field, it is sensed by the transmitting equipment, and an extra 0 bit is inserted after the fifth 1 bit (one more bit is thus added to the information field). At the receiving end the equipment feels for a string of 1 bits and, when it finds the 5-bit string, it deletes the extra 0; in this way the message is restored. This so-called bit stuffing is one of the reasons that SDLC cannot be used for asynchronous transmission.

The address field immediately follows the opening flag. It identifies one or more secondary stations on the link. Each secondary station normally has an individual and a group address, the latter being shared with other secondary stations. The address field is useful when messages must be accepted from, or go to, several terminals. In the SDLC dialect the field is 8 bits long, a length which allows identification of as many as 128 terminals—clearly a hierarchical structure for systems that may have several thousands of terminals. In other dialects the address is a multiple of *n* octets. In this extended mode the secondary link address field is a sequence of 8 bits, which constitute a single secondary station address when the least significant bit is 0; the following octet is an extension of the address field.

Figure 14.3

Data transparency. The Problem: how to tell where a packet begins, and still be able to send any data pattern. The Solution: sender adds special bytes or bits which receiver removes, preserving original data pattern.

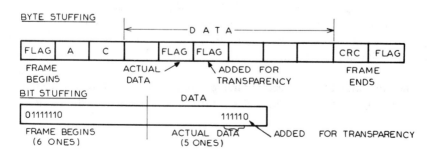

Figure 14.4

Bit stuffing. Procedural steps: (1) Transmitter examines frame content for five consecutive 1's; (2) Inserts a 0 after the fifth; (3) This breaks the *possible* sequence 01111.11110; (4) The message is then transmitted; (5) Receiver examines frame content for five consecutive 1's; (6) If the sixth bit is 1, flag is assumed; (7) If the sixth bit is 0, the bit is discarded; (8) Message takes original form again.

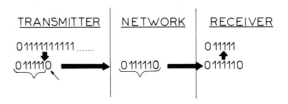

The address field is terminated by an octet having a 1 in the least-significant-bit position. Figure 14.5 compares the address fields of SDLC and two other protocols.

The XDLC control field identifies the type of frame, whether informational, supervisory, or nonsequenced; see Figure 14.6. It includes the frame acknowledgment and the poll and final fields and generally provides the signals needed to operate the data links. Its bits identify the frame type, the sequence numbers, and the command or the response mode.

If the leading bit in a frame's control field is a 0, the transmission constitutes an information frame.

One 3-bit value is a count stored at the transmitter, N(S); it designates the number of frames already sent in a sequence.

A second 3-bit value, the total stored at the receiver, N(R), gives the number of error-free frames previously accepted in the sequence.

The remaining bit in the control field acts as a send or receive indicator, such as poll (primary) and final (secondary).

If the leading bit in a frame's control field is a 1, then the protocol examines the second bit, to distinguish between a supervisory and a management frame. A supervisory frame initiates and controls subsequent message transfers. It has six additional bits: three for the receiver count, two for a command or response code, and one for a poll or final indicator. It is utilized for acknowledgment, polling, temporary interruptions, and error recovery. A management frame, on the other hand, is a means of operating communications devices; its six additional bits include 3-bit and 2-bit command and response codes and a 1-bit poll or final indicator (Figure 14.7).

The nonsequenced management frame is utilized for data link management: an opening flag, an address field, and a control field, which form the header.

Figure 14.5

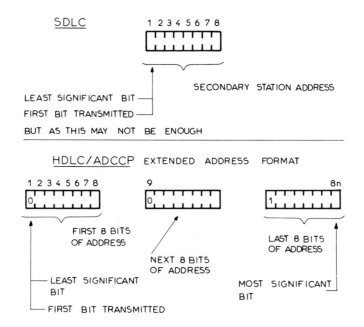

Figure 14.6

- INFORMATION FRAME (UTILIZED FOR THE TRANSFER OF DATA, ACKNOWLEDGMENT)

0	N(S)	P/F	N(R)

N(S) : SEND SEQUENCE COUNT
P/F : POLL (PRIMARY)/FINAL (SECONDARY)
N(R) : RECEIVE SEQUENCE COUNT

- SUPERVISORY FRAME (CONTAINS NO I FIELD). UTILIZED FOR ACKNOWLEDGMENT, POLLING, TEMPORARY INTERRUPTIONS, OR ERROR RECOVERY.

1 1 0	S S	P/F	N(R)

SS	SIGNAL NAME	DEFINITION
00	RR	RECEIVE READY
01	REJ	REJECT
10	RNR	RECEIVE NOT READY
11	SREJ	SELECTIVE REJECT

- NON-SEQUENCED FRAME (CONTAINS NO I FIELD EXCEPT FOR CMDR). UTILIZED FOR DATA LINK MANAGEMENT.

1 1 1	VARIABLE

MAJOR SIGNALS   D

SIGNAL	CMD/RESP	DEFINITION
SNRM	C	SET NORMAL RESPONSE MODE
SARM	C	SET ASYNCHRONOUS RESPONSE MODE
DISC	C	DISCONNECT
CMDR	R	COMMAND REJECT
NSA	R	NON-SEQUENCED ACKNOWLEDGMENT

Figure 14.7

(a) Basic mode control field, where N(S) = transmitting station send sequence number, bit 2 is low-order bit; N(R) = transmitting station receive sequence number, bit 6 is low-order bit; S = supervisory function bits; M = management bits; P/F = poll/final bit (1 = poll/final). (b) Where X bits are reserved and set to 0. Bits 2 and 10 are the low-order bits of the sequence numbers.

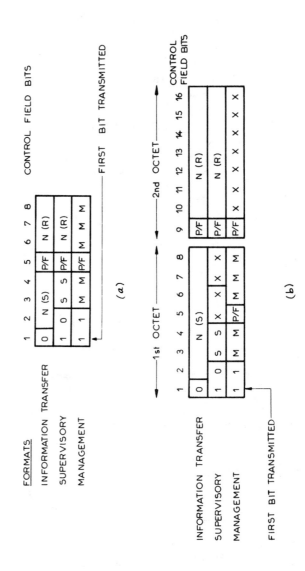

The information field, variable in length, has upper limits that depend on the implementation (factors limiting the length are channel-error characteristics, logical properties of data, and node or station buffer sizes). Under current standards, the limits are 1,000, 2,000, and 8,000 bits minus the header and trailer. The data link control is completely transparent to the contents of the information (I) field.

The header and information fields are followed by the frame-check sequence for error control. This is 16 bits long and precedes the closing flag; its object is to validate the accuracy of transmission. A 16-bit cyclic redundancy check (CRC) also controls errors. It uses a generator polynominal, $x^{16} + x^{12} + x^5 + 1$. The transmitter's 16-bit remainder value is initialized to all 1's before a frame is transmitted, and the binary value of the transmission is premultiplied by x^{16} and then divided by the generator polynomial. Integer quotient values are ignored, and the transmitter sends the complement of the resulting remainder value, high-order bit first, as the field of the frame-check sequence. The frame-check sequence, the cyclic redundancy check, and the closing flag constitute the trailer.

Frame Sequence and Acknowledgment

The following statements put in a nutshell the bit-oriented procedure we described in the preceding sections.

Information transfer is in the form of a frame.
Each frame is sequenced to allow for duplication or loss detection.
The field of the frame-check sequence provides for error control.
A transmitting station sequences and counts its frames in the N(S) field.
A receiving station counts each error-free sequenced frame it receives (the receiver count, N(R), is the count of the next expected frame).
Arriving frames whose N(S) field does not equal the receiver's N(R) field (out of sequence or duplicate) are rejected.

As many as seven frames may be transmitted before receipt of the N(R) field from the receiver. The transmitter, detecting that the receiver's N(R) has fallen behind his N(S), must retransmit consecutively, starting at the receiver's N(R) (the selective reject is optional in SDLC); this is called the "go back N" technique. Hence, when the poll frame contains the receive sequence number N(R), it permits a specific solicitation (for the station) to send I frames numbered N(S) = N(R) and following sequential I frames. This also serves as an acknowledgment to the station for all I frames by means of send sequence number N(S) = N(R) − 1. In case a terminal has no I frames to send, it responds with a supervisory frame with the F bit set to 1.

Two response modes may be distinguished: the normal response mode (NRM) and the asynchronous response mode (ARM). In the normal mode the P bit is set to 1 in command frames, to solicit response frames from the other terminal. The DTE (secondary) cannot transmit until a common frame with the P bit set to 1 is received. The originating DTE can also restrict the receiving station from transmitting I frames by sending a "receive not ready" (RNR) supervisory frame. In the asynchronous mode the frames may be transmitted by the receiving DTE on an asynchronous basis. The P bit is set to 1 when this becomes possible. If the originating DTE wants a positive acknowledgment that a particular frame has been received, it may set the P bit in the command to 1, which will force a response from the receiving DTE.

The fact that P and F bits are exchanged, one to one, and that only one P bit can be outstanding at a time, helps the N(R) count of a frame (containing a P or F bit set to 1) to detect sequence errors in the I frame. This acts as a checkpoint; it is helpful in detecting frame sequence errors and in indicating the frame sequence number for beginning retransmission.

Another important matter is the selective reject technique for frame acknowledgment.

Selective reject allows the transmitter to retransmit only the frame that has been rejected by the receiver.

After retransmission of the selectively rejected frame the transmission continues where it had left off.

This is more efficient than the "go back N" technique because all frames following the rejected one need not be retransmitted.

The selective reject technique has disadvantages in certain applications. For instance, the receiver must be able to reshuffle received frames, and efficiency may be reduced below the level of the "go back N" technique if successive frames are rejected, and the automatic handling of selective reject is fairly complex. Figures 14.8 and 14.9 compare the two techniques.

Using a Bit-Oriented Protocol in a Loop

The original protocol developed by IBM for primary and secondary stations in a loop may be seen as the predecessor of the XDLC. The IBM loop operation as applied, for instance, with the 3600 series is asymmetric. There are a primary and several secondary stations. The secondary station originates transmission only when it receives the go-ahead pattern 01111111. If the secondary DTE wishes to transmit, it must change the seventh 1 to a 0. This change produces the flag byte, which becomes the start of the message. Notice the similarity of this pattern to the opening and closing flags of XDLC.

For an example of a loop application with SDLC we shall follow an environment based on central control; see Figure 14.10.

1. Each link has an assigned primary station and one or more secondary stations.
2. A secondary station can transmit to the primary only when authorized by it.

Figure 14.8
Go back to acknowledgment. N(S) denotes the sequence number of a transmitted frame. N(A) denotes the acceptance of this and all previous frames. N(R) denotes the sequence number of the oldest rejected receive frame.

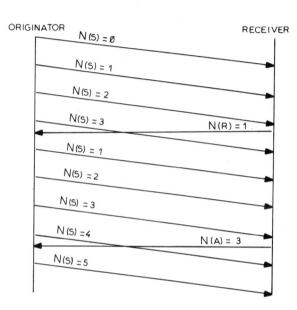

3. All secondary stations are repeaters.
4. The loop controller initiates by transmitting a specific poll to a unique secondary and an optional response poll (ORP) to a common loop address.
5. The loop controller transmits the go-ahead signal.
6. The secondary station captures the loop by converting the go-ahead to a transmit frame.
7. Eventually the secondary station releases the loop by returning to the repeater operation.

In different terms, the primary station polls the secondary for status. It sets the secondary to an initialization mode. The secondary acknowledges.

The SDLC allows transmission of up to 7 packets before an acknowledgment is required. Each block has its own header and trailer. The objective is to reduce line turnarounds in half-duplex. Furthermore, satellite transmission imposes severe earth-to-satellite and satellite-to-earth delays, which make such a procedure advisable (the 7-packet limit is indeed too low). The delay from earth to satellite and back is 0.24 second, which is the least amount of time before the receiving station gets the first packet. Acknowledgment, one per packet, would take another 0.24 second. This delay could be cut by using terrestrial circuits, which would speed the operation but complicate the system. If transmission were 50 kilobits per

Figure 14.9
Selective reject acknowledgment. N(S) denotes the sequence number of a
transmitted frame. N(RS) denotes the number of a received frame which is being
selectively rejected. N(A) denotes the acceptance of frames up to and including the
frame specified.

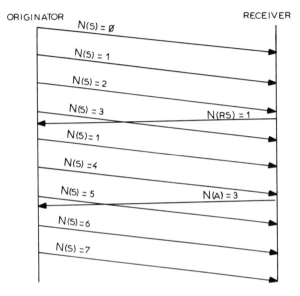

Figure 14.10
A loop application. Loop propagation time is 1 msec per 15 miles of loop length
plus the sum of secondary-DTE relay times.

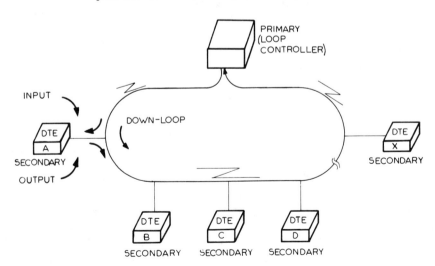

second with packets of, say, 5 kilobits in length, 10 would be transmitted before the first acknowledgment were received. Moreover, a good deal of packets would need to be kept in transit at any one time. The SDLC, however, does provide for acknowledgment in multiple packets, the acknowledgments being included in the header of a message going in the "other" direction (piggy-backing).

Detected errors do not launch a response; the receiving station does nothing. When the sending station gets no ACK within a specific time, it automatically retransmits the packet or packets in question. Packets are numbered sequentially; those that are out of sequence are detected, and the receiving station sends a NAK.

This brings us to incarnation numbers. An incarnation number, or name, is unique for an instance of the protocol module. The incarnation number, or name, is sent in each packet and is used by the receiver to filter out packets from old connections caused by a "crash" and restart. It is helpful in conjunction with sequence numbers for uniquely identifying an octet of data or control. The uniqueness of the incarnation number allows the resetting of the sequence number space to 0 at the initialization of each new path (first connection between two users).

Objectives of XDLC

The XDLC is designed to operate at the physical link, or communications, level. Its procedures should unify the standards for all distributed networks and offer new features to the user, such as file transparency, downline loading, four-wire simultaneous operations, and security. The five following functions must be performed by the data link control procedures.

The XDLC must create error-free sequential links. Practically speaking, this means two things: no bit error and observance of sequence (also provision of data necessary at the higher level of networking).

The XDLC must manage the physical link; simply, it must mask from both the user and the nested higher level the functions of the physical link. Let us recall the functions of the physical link: link turnaround, modem interface, control action, device interfaces, and others necessary for data transmission.

The XDLC must perform efficiently; essentially, this means to add as little overhead as possible, to take advantage of the performance features of the physical link, and to observe the synchronization requirements (transmitter–receiver).

The XDLC must be widely applicable. To answer this requirement, it must operate over links with different physical characteristics. It must also be available for differing applications, that is, applications independent.

The XDLC must be easy to implement. Therefore it must consist of a minimal number of states, be variable, and have processing algorithms. It must also be implementable on small systems; this is a fundamental DIS requirement.

Table 14.2 lists the chief XDLC commands and their definitions, which are helpful to keep in mind.

Table 14.2
Abbreviations and Definitions of the XDLC Commands

Abbreviation	Definition
CMDR	A DTE's indication that it received a nonvalid command
DISC	Disconnect, used for performing a logical disconnection
DM	Disconnect-mode response, used for reporting a nonoperational status
I	Sequenced information frame
NSA	Affirmative response to an SNRM, DISC or SIM
NSI	Nonsequence numbered information
NSP	Used for providing an optional response from a DTE
RD	Request-disconnect response
REJ	Reject supervisory frame, used by a station for requesting retransmission of information
RIM	Request-for-initialization mode
RNR	Receive-not-ready supervisory frame, used by a station for indicating temporary inability to accept additional incoming information
ROL	A DTE's indication that it is disconnected
RR	Receive-ready supervisory frame, used by a DTE to indicate that it is ready to receive an information frame and to acknowledge previously received ones
RSPR	Response reject, used for reporting exceptional conditions not recoverable by link-level action

Table 14.2 (cont.)
Abbreviations and Definitions of the XDLC Commands

Abbreviation	Definition
SABM	Set asynchronous-balanced mode
SARM	Set asynchronous-response mode
SARME SABME SNRME	Extended mode commands for placing the addressed DTE in the extended mode
SIM	Set initialization mode
SNRM	Set normal mode, used for placing the addressed DTE in the NRM
SREJ	Selective-reject supervisory frame
TEST	TEST frame sent to a DTE to solicit a TEST response
UA	Unnumbered acknowledge, acknowledging receipt and acceptance of the SNRM, SARM, etc.
UI	Unnumbered information, command and response, used for transferring NSI across a link
UP	Unnumbered poll command used for soliciting response frames from a single DTE
USR 0 USR 1 USR 2 USR 3	Commands and responses (user 0, 1, 2, 3) permitting the definition of special system-dependent functions not having general applicability
XID	Exchange identification, causing the addressed station to report its station identification.

15

The Nesting of Protocols

We have spoken often of the need of layering in network architectures and in the protocols supporting it. Figure 15.1 recapitulates the different levels, or layers, to which we have been making reference.

The first level, the physical interface, concerns the data circuit terminating equipment, which we have also called the modem, or data set; it has been standardized by the CCITT. The physical interface specifies a four-wire point-to-point synchronous circuit, for a transmission path between the terminals and hosts on one side and the network on the other. The CCITT standard ensures that no changes in the interface hardware of the DTE are required; the modem is on the network side of this interface.

The second level, the frame level, is oriented to communications; it is concerned with synchronous and asynchronous transmission modes and with the XDLC. We should remember that the SDLC is a type of protocol, not a specific one, and that neither it nor the other dialects of bit-oriented protocols (HDLC, ADCCP, etc.) have been standardized by the CCITT.

The third level, the packet level, has two purposes: the routing of packets from node to node and the provision of a data path (virtual circuit or Datagram service); the two functions are broadly known as networking. Performance in this area is the goal of Proposition X.25 adopted by the CCITT.

The higher levels address themselves to the user. Here the end-to-end connection is important. This may involve only communications, as identified in Figure 15.1, levels 1, 2, and 3, to be precise; but an end-to-end structure might also be carried into the user's own environment. Figure 15.2 indicates ten different end-to-end sublevels, which are defined and qualified by the user's viewpoint.

Having discussed the bit-oriented protocols and the data link control mechanism, let us see what other functions are necessary in the services of a network.

215

Figure 15.1

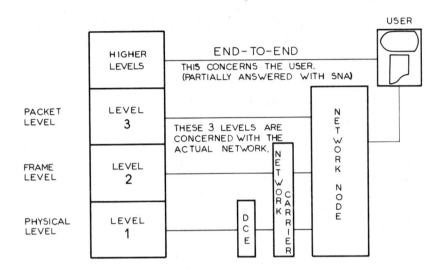

Standards for the Physical Circuit

The modem is hardware, standardized by the CCITT. Broadly, it is any communications processor, or even line, which serves as a terminal's point of entry to a network. The physical standards deal mostly with pins, signals, voltage levels and, generally, the setting up of physical connections through circuit-switching networks.

Until now the modem and DTE have had no effect on the messages; hence, there has been no incentive for the development of logical protocols for them. Electronic signals control the modem, but modems can be made intelligent. What we worry about today is what moves between the computers, namely, the message moving on the wire, which we must study and standardize, and the services offered by the host operating system. To repeat, modems can be made intelligent, and it is therefore worthwhile to review briefly the functions at the modem level and see what exactly is done.

The physical-circuit standards include both electrical characteristics and any others necessary for physically connecting to a network. At present, the American and international physical standards are adhered to by manufacturers of computers and terminals and by distributors of data communications equipment and network services. The two most important bodies setting the standards are the Electronic Industries Association, EIA, in the United States and the CCITT, already mentioned.

Typical of the standards of these organizations are the EIA's RS232, for data circuit interchange and the CCITT V.24, which is essentially equivalent. These standards define the data, the clocking, and the control leads (including the number of pins in a plug) that are used for passing data between DTEs and DECs.

Much effort has been expended in the last few years on defining new standards, which has resulted in a simpler interface. They are called the X series, and they are expected to displace, over the years, the older V series.

The principal new data interchange standard is the X.21. Agreement on it has been obtained, on the whole, between the common carriers and a number of manufacturers, but since it calls for a significant change, an interim recommendation, X.21bis, will be used first. The latter is for implementing the X.21 but retaining the V.24 physical interface. Both the X.21 and X.21bis define physical circuits for three types of service: the leased circuit (private line), direct-call switching, and address-call switching. The leased circuit is intended for continuous connection between a terminal and a network switch processor (such as a packet switcher) or between two terminals. The direct call and address call both involve circuit switching, but a direct call is one that is always switched to the same destination whenever a connection is requested, like a "hot line," and an address call is one in which the destination is designated by the terminal, like a dial-up call but without a phone dial.

Over the next several years the X.21 type of standard will be more and more prevalent. It will give the user a simpler physical interface and also more flexible and faster call-setup procedures.

Second-Level Protocols

We have described the second level of protocols, communications, through the examples of asynchronous, bisynchronous, and XDLC protocols, and we have said that it is a data link control that includes data flow initialization, control termination, and error recovery. The goal is to transfer data over the link sequentially and without error. Once the framing and link management are established, then a set of sequencing rules for exchanging messages and ensuring their correct receipt takes over.

Framing basically is executed at the receiving end of the link. It consists of locating the beginning and end of the bit stream sent over the link. Link management is the process of controlling transmission and reception over links where two or more sources and two or more destinations are active, i.e., connected to the channel in a given direction. The transfer of data is the transmission, sequentially and without error, of user data over the link. Among its features are pipelining, piggybacking, and ACK and NAK.

Data transfer mechanisms or, when they exist, the higher levels, must ensure that the data going out of a link are the same as the data entering. Assuming unintelligent lines, for this to happen at the node it is necessary to have routines for detecting missing or duplicated packets, to give identification numbers to each packet, and to maintain information on and for senders and receivers. The XDLC protocols have a mechanism for this purpose, which is that for each message correctly received a positive acknowledgment is returned, notifying the transmitter of the correct receipt of the message.

Positive-acknowledgment retransmission calls for a block check for bit errors, a unique message-identification number, an acknowledgment (based on the message number), and a timer to recover from outages and unreceived messages, for the purpose of retransmission. The message number is set up along with the initialization procedure. It is then incremented, modulo a constant value (8 for SDLC) for each new message sent. In fact, this constant value minus 1 determines the maximal number of data messages that may be transmitted before acknowledgment is required.

A timer helps the system to recover from either messages or acknowledgments received in error; in the latter case recovery can be initiated. This procedure makes for an independence of the data transfer mechanism from the link management mechanism, which permits specific response-time limits to be set.

Framing and Link Management

Framing is performed at the receiving end of the link. It calls for the synchronization of bits (and packets) in the signal being received on a link. The process of synchronization, however, is carried out by the modems (and other interface components) and, as such, is outside the logical aspects of data link control.

In bit-oriented protocols, as we have seen, the bits are grouped in meaningful patterns. This is fundamental for an understanding of control of information by the protocol and for storage into and retrieval from computer memory. These mechanisms make sure of operation over single physical channels with a short delivery time and of sequential transmission such that one message cannot "hop" over another—exactly the property of physical communication channels. They also guarantee sequential delivery from the time of protocol initialization until the failure of either system. Since failures cause a loss of synchronization, sequential delivery is not guaranteed until reinitialization.

Since the early 1960s and IBM's "byte" standard, the most used common group has been the 8-bit group which finds widespread acceptance from the 16-bit minicomputers to the 32-bit maxicomputers. The byte is a building block and, after byte synchronization has been established, the beginning and end of a message may be located. The key, then, is to achieve byte synchronization, and that is based on the characteristics of the data channel and the desired properties of the user data.

We have spoken of the search for a unique 8-bit sequence and the reason for bit-stuffing and how it operates. Identification of the starting flag marks the beginning of a message. The end of the message may be found in different ways, through the closing flag with XDLC (hence the need for bit stuffing), or a count of bytes based on a fixed message length (control messages are of fixed length).

Again, the second layer establishes the physical link, conventions handle control of the physical link, and error recovery—and that is data link control. The conventions relating to communications links usually are designed to operate with existing hardware interfaces over full-duplex and half-duplex links and with synchronous, asynchronous, and parallel circuits.

For both multiple access and error control a data link control, or frame-level, protocol must offer a means of exchanging data across the terminal–network interface (once physical connection is made), assuring effective synchronization, controlling errors on a communication link, and operating on circuits with long propagation delays (satellite circuits).

The protocol XDLC does all this and allows two different modes of operations handling, one called asymmetric and the other symmetric. In the asymmetric (unbalanced) mode one DTE acts as the primary, or control, station. Because this particular mode does not go very far in overcoming the queueing problems of polled multipoint operation, an alternative may be used: the symmetric (balanced) mode, with two DTEs. In the latter only two-point operations are considered. Each of the two stations involved acts as primary and secondary at the same time, for which reason this mode is called "symmetric."

Communications protocols are not concerned with the content or routing of messages, nor with how the messages are physically transmitted and received; the higher ones, levels 3 and up, take care of that, and they are the subject of the next section.

The Higher Levels

We have often stated that a network architecture is based on a set of network protocols, each of which is designed to fulfill specific functions. Collectively, they present a layered aspect. The left side of Figure 15.2 repeats the four-way breakdown of Figure 15.1 and is the usual depiction in the literature. It lacks, however, the needed detail. For instance, the third level performs two functions, routing and virtual link (data path), which were better depicted as two layers themselves. A ten-level picture is on the right side of Figure 15.2. Networking now becomes the third and fourth levels, network management, of which packet structure and message format are part. As we shall see in the next two chapters, such considerations deal with call setup and clearing, data transfer and interruption, flow control and reset, congestion control, and restart procedures.

At the user levels the picture becomes less definite, and work is just starting. Not even is there a commonly accepted terminology or a proper division into distinct layers. A given level may deal, for instance, with system protocol; it might

Figure 15.2
Breakdown into layers

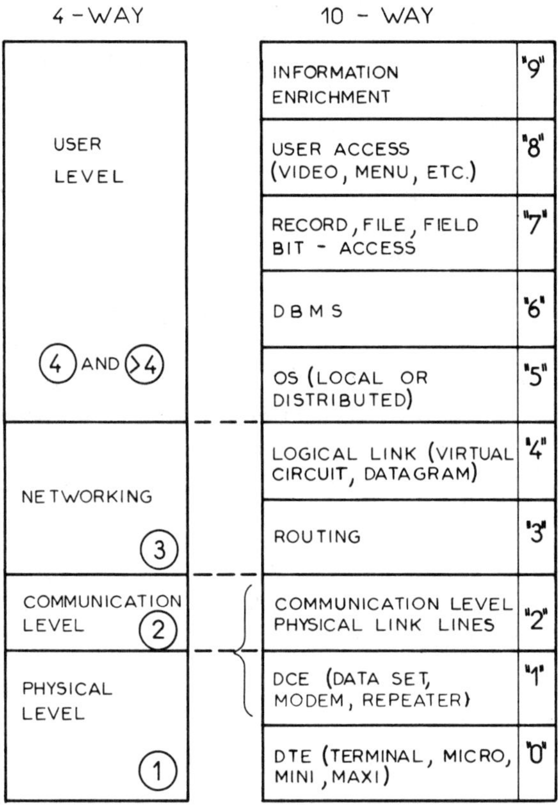

4 – WAY	10 – WAY	
USER LEVEL	INFORMATION ENRICHMENT	"9"
	USER ACCESS (VIDEO, MENU, ETC.)	"8"
	RECORD, FILE, FIELD BIT - ACCESS	"7"
	D B M S	"6"
(4) AND (>4)	OS (LOCAL OR DISTRIBUTED)	"5"
NETWORKING	LOGICAL LINK (VIRTUAL CIRCUIT, DATAGRAM)	"4"
(3)	ROUTING	"3"
COMMUNICATION LEVEL (2)	COMMUNICATION LEVEL PHYSICAL LINK LINES	"2"
PHYSICAL LEVEL	DCE (DATA SET, MODEM, REPEATER)	"1"
(1)	DTE (TERMINAL, MICRO, MINI, MAXI)	"0"

include packet or message assembly and disassembly, priorities, and code definitions and structures. Another, higher up, might deal with users' applications, such
as programs, memory access, and device independence; see Figure 15.3.

Some of the reasons that make the higher levels difficult to define are historical:
practice grew like weeds. Other reasons are functional: the transition from data
processing to data communications has not yet become clear. The functional
reasons are fundamental. The problems posed by the development and use of
distributed data bases must be taken into account.

A possible structure is shown in Figure 12.4. It separates the user's
operations—file access, process, and receiver at window—from the networking
and communications. The same user operations might be separated into data
transfer, file transfer, and remote job entry, and these might be further divided

Figure 15.3
User environment level(s)

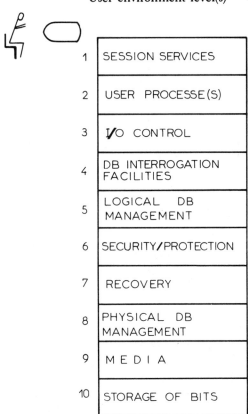

1	SESSION SERVICES
2	USER PROCESSE(S)
3	I/O CONTROL
4	DB INTERROGATION FACILITIES
5	LOGICAL DB MANAGEMENT
6	SECURITY/PROTECTION
7	RECOVERY
8	PHYSICAL DB MANAGEMENT
9	M E D I A
10	STORAGE OF BITS

into graphics and other applications. Subdivisions such as these might benefit the private networks, but they have not been considered by any formal standards organization. One reason is that the people most actively working on standards for data communications do not consider such protocols to be their province, and those working on standards for data processing have not yet recognized the need.

The question of the duplication of functions is also interesting. It may well be that, in the zeal to identify independent levels that might be standardized separately, some duplication is sneaking in. If this is so, experience with implementation should reveal the necessity for change. It is perfectly true that the progress in standards that we appreciate so well today was not achieved easily. Each standard was arrived at a step at a time, after much analysis, review, conversation, and revision. It is remarkable, in fact, how much progress has been made, considering the wide divergence of opinion when work began.

Figure 15.4
(VC, virtual circuit, R, routing—on the basis of this information ID
(identification), logical channel, control—the node will calculate, route and
establish the virtual circuit; FA, file access; W, window; CRC, cyclic redundancy
check; P, process)

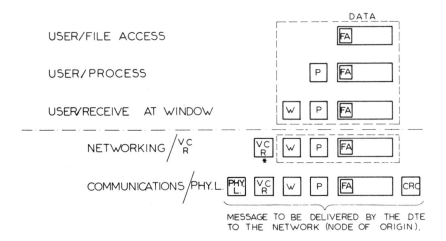

Applications Protocols

Having said that there exist no standards, but only individual solutions, for applications-level protocols, we can now take a constructive view and search to define the component parts in a typical case.

Like the communications protocols, user-level protocols may be broadly subdivided, in this case into a systems level, a data base management level, and an applications level. Each function or mechanism will consist of dialogue (the exchange of information) procedures. The objective will be to perform a specific function oriented toward data bases. The dialogues must conform to a set of rules and have definite message formats. There is nothing new in this approach; protocols have been designed for obtaining access, within the network, to input–output devices and to file services. User-level systems, however, are of many varieties, and therefore the protocols must be designed for efficiency between user systems, within different operating environments.

The routines must have general-purpose file-handling capabilities. They must allow written applications programs to create and maintain data files that may be accessed in different ways. This is difficult, because the exact structure of the information field has not been standardized. (As terminals perform more and more data processing functions, reaching agreements on standards so that different DTEs may work together becomes more urgent and, as time passes by, more complex.) One way of solving the problem of applications standards has been to introduce the concept of a "virtual terminal," which is an imaginary, logically defined terminal with all the attributes of real terminals. Within the context of a virtual terminal, character strings are defined which have a one-to-one correspondence with the features offered by specific real terminals, although the character strings may not be the same as those used by any specific terminal. There are two ways to use the virtual terminals. In one the network operator supplies a translation that transforms the applications protocol of some specific real terminals to that of the network's imaginary standard terminal. In the other the users attach real terminals that have been programmed to operate directly in network virtual-terminal protocols.

At the systems level the logical protocols necessarily deal with data exchange on a totally end-to-end basis, from operating system to applications program or from applications program to applications program. An example of a pending user-level protocol (not always recognized as such) is the so-called packet assembly function and its associated support, the packet assembler, for unintelligent, character-mode terminals. Such terminals are capable of sending only one character at a time, and they have no local processing power to implement protocols of any sort. In Arpanet this support is called a minihost. It is implemented in the terminal interface message processor (TIP), a kind of terminal concentrator, which also serves as a network switch. The network, the user, or a third party also may provide support through a separate terminal-support device such as a front end or a terminal controller that connects with the processor, which in this case is a node, acting only as a switch.

The packet assembler supports the standard networking protocol (in order to communicate through the network). In addition, a higher protocol must deal with terminal support between the packet assembler and the destination host. The host may need to be informed of, or be able to set, such terminal parameters as duplex, code, speed, and packet termination conditions.

In short, layering covers all aspects of communication between system components. Major roles are played by file access and data transfer.

Connecting a user process to a file constitutes access to the information. Depending on its internal structure and the device in which it resides, this connection takes different forms. Hence, the virtual file-access protocol was conceived to define a standard file-access method within the operating system that makes all files accessible to any processes, no matter where they might reside.

Gaining access to remote files may be described as proceeding in three phases: setup, transfer, and termination. Setup involves establishing the connection, exchanging the information necessary to authenticate the user, and addressing the file. We shall speak more about these issues.

16

Networking Functions

As a network architecture has been discussed (and documented), it must offer two levels of visibility, first to the systems expert and, second, to the user, and it includes the following:

> Overall design
>
> Protocols
>
> Message control
>
> Line control
>
> Systems management for communications
>
> Systems management for data base
>
> Systems management for operating system
>
> Applications interfaces
>
> Software standards and supports
>
> On-line maintenance

Networking is the performance of the functions assigned to the network level, level 3 of Figure 15.2. A view of these functions, including the DTE (terminal and host), the operating system, the data base, and the applications programs, is given in Figure 16.1, which identifies the characteristics of the services and also the user and network functions. Properly speaking, the networking functions are two: routing and the establishment of the logical (data) path. Yet these involve a number of faculties to be provided through network commands. We distinguish native commands, those native to the particular set, subset, etc., of an operating system, which are supported by the operating system and are nominally visible instruc-

225

Figure 16.1
Networking functions

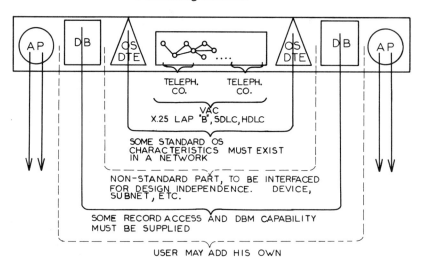

DATA ENTRY, REMOTE BATCH, WORD PROCESSING
HOST/TERMINAL COMPATIBILITY, DEVICE INDEPENDENCE
ON LINE TEST AND VERIFICATION, REMOTE MAINTENANCE, UP LINE/DOWN LINE,
VIDEO SCREEN MANAGEMENT, MENU SELECTION, APPLICATIONS LIBRARY

tions, and network primitives, which are the set of basic commands characterizing the network architecture and its subsets.

A balanced network (not to be confused with a balanced protocol) pays due attention to resources and to objectives. It gives the proper identifications (Table 16.1) and ensures software support to both node-to-node communications for basic transmission functions and end-to-end solutions including the overall transmission integrity.

The host-to-host protocol takes the applications data from the user program and adds on a protocol header. As the message is sent into a computer network, the subscriber-to-network protocol adds on its own protocol information. Then the link control procedure adds on more information, and the network itself adds on subnetwork control fields. It is in the format of the messages flowing through a computer communications network that the concept of a protocol hierarchy is most evident.

Routing

Messages are transmitted in a given form and through an established path, called the route. Routing is the process of creating the route. This is done through software at the level of the node. A fixed route involves one and only one route

Table 16.1
Identifications

User Equipment	Communications Equipment
Packet type	Priority, if any
Session number	Origination address
Send sequence number	Destination address
Receive sequence number	Incarnation number
Author	
Sender	
(Mailbox)	
Annotations	

between two stations in a network. A variable, or dynamic, route presupposes the capability of switching. The routing process should adapt to changes in the network topology and traffic, and this principle influences its functions. The routing program must be efficient enough to run in real time, as the inputs change, it must have a higher priority than data handling, and it must be adaptable to changing conditions in the environment. A network can become badly congested if obsolete routing processes are used in the face of new traffic patterns.

Variable routing coinvolves tables in the memory of the node or switch for the optimal uses of resources, congestion, flow control, delay analysis, and so on. Among the typical routing elements we distinguish the following:

Index to the routing tables

Index to the group code tables (on disc)

Static and dynamic status and parameters for lines

List of destination routing mnemonics for each assigned group code

Corresponding logical identifier for each of the codes used, for further defining the routing

Additional routing information that will yield a logical identifier

List of increments to line and station tables ordered by the logical identifiers

Routing control commands can establish alternate routing, duplicate delivery, and routing report requests, specified by the operating environment.

Point-to-point and multipoint circuits are examples of fixed routing, whereas classical circuit switching might be taken as a type of variable routing, though it does *not* involve the services offered by packet switching.

The procedures to be observed in establishing a routing discipline are deterministic (fixed) and are isolated. Each node probes the communications system but does not share information with the other nodes; this approach can be heuristic. When each node, probing, shares the information with the other nodes, it is distributed. Finally, the control must be centralized. One master node (in Tymnet, for example) calculates for the whole network the variable routing.

Routing procedures must respond to two basic questions. One is what is to be done at the node level, which brings up the two issues of traffic requirements and the "reachability" matrix (Table 16.2). The second question is the criteria of efficiency, among which we distinguish not only cost considerations but also reliability, availability, accuracy, error detection and control, and adaptability.

Adaptive routing is preferable because it offers optimization with respect to delays, shared resources at node and link levels, better throughput, and lower overall cost for about the same service.

A basic reference in terms of routing procedures is pipelining.

Networks must transmit multiple messages between source and destination, calling for high reliability and good throughput. Throughput is studied in relation to distance, source and destination, line speed, and size of packet. For optimization the last of these is balanced with, and limited by, the first two.

Figure 16.2 diagrams the functions of a routing algorithm, in which the data loads, both present and expected, the cost targets set by management, and the network services, all enter into the equation. Evaluation of performance is indivisible from function. The algorithm should be adapted as quickly as possible to the correction of unfeasible routing; it should run uniformly over all the nodes it affects, and the goals of processing should not interfere with routing. If one node starts to send incorrect routing data, the networking as a whole will be disturbed.

Routing must be carefully examined in relation to cost. The elements of cost include the following.

Nodal bandwidth: When a node is designed to perform routing besides other functions (e.g., error correction, processing), then routing must have priority.

Nodal delay: Delay at the node should be evaluated as a function of routing calculation, matrix update, store-and-forward capabilities, and error detection.

Table 16.2
Forms of the Matrix at the Node Switch

Routing Input Data	Routing Output Data
Adjacency matrix Existence of lines between nodes	Reachability matrix Existence of paths between nodes
Traffic requirements Binding of traffic to destination nodes	Traffic assignment Total path perspectives

Figure 16.2

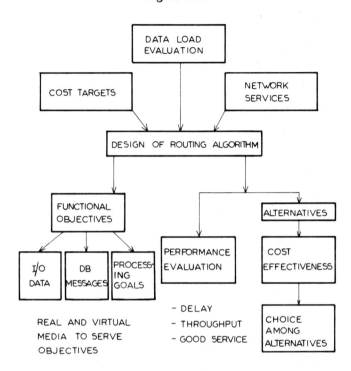

Nodal storage: The examination of storage takes into account such elements as the reachability matrix, the algorithms, data transit, and input–output buffers.

Line bandwidth: The messages to be routed, the choice of path, the length of message, and the housekeeping information, all condition the line bandwidth and are necessary for the reliable operation of the network.

Line delay: Generally, line delay increases linearly with the frequency of message routing and quadratically with the length of message, but it decreases with the line bandwidth.

The choices to be made are fundamental and are reflected in the network architecture. Figure 16.3 dramatizes this point. The Decnet protocol DDCMP is composed of a header and a trailer, primarily addressed to the communications level; between them are the networking and data sections, the latter consisting of routing and the logical link. Routing thus is included in the architecture; the logical link is discussed in the following section. Notice that other layers, a fifth or an eighth, say, have not yet found themselves in network routines.

Figure 16.3

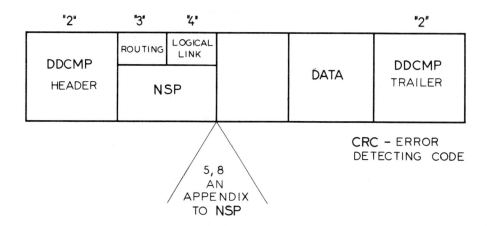

Virtual Circuits and Datagrams

The layer next up from routing imposes a choice between virtual circuits (logical circuits, virtual calls) and Datagrams, the two chief processes possible in packet switching.

With Datagrams solutions are long messages divided into sections (typically of 256 or 512 characters each) individually routed through a packet switching network. Technically, a Datagram is a packet of information sent by one DTE to another as a standalone block traveling pseudorandom routes. The disadvantages of this arrangement are that packets may arrive at destination out of sequence (Figure 16.4) or they may get into an endless loop of nodes and never be delivered; the user, not the network, must cure such troubles. The chief advantage of the concept is that the network is kept simple and the user has more flexibility, since all packets are independent and not associated with a continuous stream of data, as they are in a virtual circuit. Datagrams are also advantageous when two separate networks in the packet-switching mode are interconnected.

Among the issues to be resolved are reasonable flow control at the network interfaces, packet size, identification of Datagrams, possible need for confirmation of delivery, and notice by the network of nondelivery.

For networks operated and maintained by the company that has intelligent terminals, Datagrams are a very workable good solution.

A virtual circuit is superior to Datagrams in that it obeys the X.25 standard and the network, not the user, is responsible for reassembly of messages in the right order and the decision about what to do in case of failure. On the other hand, the

Figure 16.4
The Risk with Datagrams

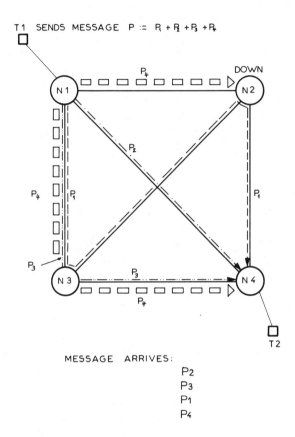

network operating system is very complex. Not only must each network ensure the basics, but it may also provide optional features. The optional facilities for all users of virtual circuits include priority or normal traffic, reverse charging, throughput selection, and closed user group.

A virtual circuit is a bidirectional association between a pair of DTEs; over it all data are transferred in packets.

A permanent virtual circuit is a permanent association between two DTEs; it is analogous to a point-to-point private line.

A switched virtual circuit is a temporary association between two DTEs and is initiated by a "call request" packet to the network.

The calling DTE will receive a response indicating whether the called DTE accepts the call. If for some reason the switched virtual circuit cannot be established, the network will transfer clearing call progress signals to the DTE indicating the reason.

A DTE may have many switched and permanent virtual circuits in operation at the same time over a single physical circuit. The number and mixture of permanent and switched virtual circuits is determined by requirements.

The virtual-circuit call method allocates a logical channel identifier, or logical channel number (LCN), to each call establishment. Packets with the same number then travel through a "virtual circuit" established for this connection, and the network guarantees the order of packet arrival. The virtual call has a better regulated message flow than Datagrams.

Technically, the virtual circuit, the bidirectional association, is characterized in recommendation X.25 as a full-duplex transmission path with integrity and accuracy of data, flow control mechanisms, supervisory and control signaling mechanisms, and sequenced data flow.

With virtual calls a specific path is set up from source to destination at the time a call is set up. If outage or noise occurs, an alternate path may be chosen. Once a path is selected and established, it is used for the transmission. When transmission is completed, it is terminated. Hence there is no risk of messages out of sequence or of endless loops, but more control than with Datagrams needs to be exercised at each node, which in turn means more software and more responsibility laid on the network.

Programs control exchanges between a DTE and another, remote DTE. An applications program prepares a logical message, which it prefixes with the symbolic name of the destination DTE. The data are then transferred to a communication access method queue, where the communication-related preparation of the message will be taken care of. While the channel controller is transferring the message over the channel to the communications control program, the latter handles the network-related functions: segmentation of message, if it does not fit into a single packet, code translation, and gathering of statistics.

Choosing Virtual Circuits or Datagram

The choice between virtual circuit and Datagram largely centers on how much is expected from the network versus how much is expected from the host computers and terminals.

To some extent the virtual circuit is a replacement for the circuit-switching or leased lines largely used at present for data communications purposes. The calling DTE goes through a call-request phase to establish a connection with the called DTE (terminal or computer); this is analogous to dialing into a circuit-switched network. A complete address must be given, just as a complete telephone number must be dialed. Once connection is established, the data phase is entered. When data transfer is complete, the terminals must clear connection before they can place other calls. Packets are delivered in the order in which they are sent. The network takes all the responsibility for the sequence as well as for error detection and recovery.

The Datagram is more like a telegram than a telephone call. Fully addressed, individual packets may be entered into the network at any time by a sending terminal. They may be delivered, however, in random order to the various recipients. The host computers are responsible for sequence and error control.

Carrier organizations worldwide are planning on virtual-circuit service because they believe it reduces disruption for their customers. They also feel that sequence and error control are their functions under the "value-added" coverage.

Supporters of the Datagram say it costs less, since less demand is placed on the network, and they also point out that host computers perform error checking in any case.

Since each approach has its advantages, it is wise to examine each carefully with a view to cost and performance. Congestion is a major factor, especially in internetworking and subnetworking. To study congestion control, for instance, we might experiment with the alternatives, virtual circuits and Datagrams, through simulation and thus establish for each of the facilities, constraints, errors, and so on (Figure 16.5). The subject of congestion is covered in the discussion of flow control.

Connection and Transmission

Beyond routing, and within the realm of procedures, the communications mechanism needs a number of basic operational commands. These are structured around the concept of "conversations" between DTEs: connection, transmission, reception, interruption, disconnection.

Figure 16.5
To study congestion control, simulate effects of different methods. Simulation should consider end-to-end and all interleaved resources, including constraints, routing algorithms, and errors.

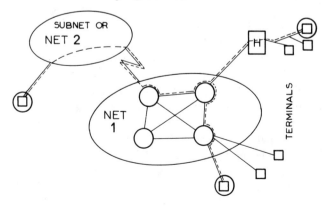

The first command is connection, the creation of a data path (virtual circuit or Datagram) between the requesting DTE and the addressed DTE. The receiving DTE is given the identity of the sender and offered some user's information, a password or identification code, for example. If the request is accepted, the data path will be created. Otherwise, the requested DTE may send back a message specifying why the connection is not possible.

Next is transmission, the actual sending of information over a data path. In packet switching the data paths are full duplex; data may be transmitted by both DTEs simultaneously.

In reception the information from a data path is synchronized with transmission via a flow control mechanism. Both DTEs on the logical link may be issuing transmitting and receiving commands simultaneously, but the flow may be heavier in one direction than in the other, depending on the communications requirements.

Interruption is a notification to the DTE on the other end of the data path of some unusual event or condition. It differs from normal transmission in that it does not require a message-receive message, it usually includes only a small amount of data, and those data must be passed on quickly. Typically, they are passed on via some such expeditious technique as an asynchronous software mechanism.

Disconnection is the destruction of a data path. The command is used on completion of the data exchange; the link is destroyed, and the resources are returned to the network. The command to disconnect may be used prior to actual completion of the connection if there is a lack of resources, or the requested object does not exist, or some other specified condition takes place.

Node-to-Node Protocols

As we have said, a protocol is a formal set of conventions, but in the literature the term is used also in another sense: the provision of the routines necessary to ensure communications between two pieces of equipment, a node-to-node protocol being an example; see Figure 16.6. It will be noted that a process-to-process or a host-to-host protocol is at a higher level than, for instance a node-to-node protocol.

Every time one protocol communicates by means of a protocol at a lower level, the lower accepts all the data and control information of the higher and then performs a number of operations upon it. Usually the lower protocol takes the data and control commands, treats them uniformly as data, and adds on its own envelope of control information.

In the following paragraphs we shall discuss the functions performed by the lower, or node-to-node, protocols and the higher protocols within Arpanet. Arpanet was developed by the Advanced Research Projects Agency of the United States Department of Defense.

Figure 16.6
Each protocol of a higher level is more critical than a protocol of a lower level. A
typical hierarchy consists of a number of protocols such as node-to-node for
typical transmission functions and end-to-end for dealing with the overall
transmission integrity. The applications, or user, level is still higher.
N = network.

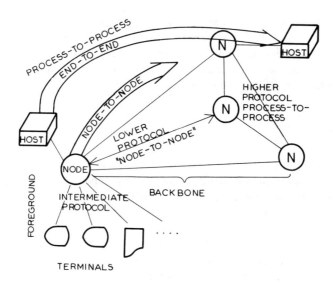

The IMP-to-IMP Protocol

The communications subnetwork of the Arpanet is composed of high-speed circuits and interface message processors (IMP). The IMPs are minicomputers that act
as store-and-forward message-switching computers and as front-end processors for
host computers.

The lowest protocol of the Arpanet is the IMP-to-IMP, which is for reliable
communication among IMPs. It handles flow control and error detection and
correction in a manner similar to the basic control procedures discussed earlier.
Another of its functions is routing. In the network are at least two paths from every
source to every destination. The routing routine in each IMP attempts to transmit a
message along that path on which the total estimated transit time is least. The
estimates appear in routing tables in the IMPs and are updated dynamically according to delays estimated internally and by neighboring IMPs. Such estimates are
based upon length of queue and recent performance of the connecting communication circuit.

The IMP-to-Host Protocol

The protocol on the next level up permits the transmission of messages between IMPs and hosts. Combined with the IMP-to-IMP protocol, it creates a virtual path between host computers. A host computer is a computer connected to the communication subnetwork of the Arpanet that provides computing services to network users.

The IMP-to-host protocol permits a host to transmit messages to other hosts on the network and to receive information on the status of those messages. Furthermore, it constrains the host computer in its network transmission such that it makes efficient use of the available communications capacity without locking out other computers from a portion of that capacity.

Host-to-Host Protocols

Higher still is the host-to-host protocol, which allows hosts to initiate and maintain communication between distributed computers. A process (e.g., a user program) running on one computer and requiring communication with a process running on a remote computer may request its local supervisor to initiate and maintain the link under the host-to-host protocol.

The protocol utilizes the lower protocols in its implementation. It maintains the responsibility for initiating links between processes, on remote computers and for controlling the flow between those processes.

Let us add that there is no absolute standard today for the host-to-host protocol. Yet we need a way to control the activities end to end and host to host. One protocol, the X.C., defines certain norms, but it is not a standard; it is applied by some users as a special-purpose layer within the host.

The protocols discussed so far were designed as a set of communications primitives for relieving users of the details of operating systems. Still higher stand the user-level protocols.

17
X.25

A standard protocol enables users with diverse terminals to access the network and to communicate with one another. The wider the use of a given protocol, the broader the movement of data over the network. The basic rule is that all parties clearly understand the sequence of actions appropriate to the data communications. The binary synchonous mode, XDLC, and so on, afford the user access to the network. The XDLC, as we have said, is designed for a network with packet-switching services. It so standardizes the format of the packets that the network has the information necessary for handling each one of them. It cannot, however, perform the tasks discussed in chapter 16, such as routing each packet, checking its path along the network, and delivering it to its destination.

Specifications must be laid out to enable recipients to obtain the degree of accuracy they want. This has been the object of Recommendation X.25 as approved by Study Group VII of the CCITT. The X.25 has gained widespread support from common carriers, manufacturers, and many expanding commercial and governmental enterprises. The standard was derived from diverse, practical experience gained from experimental networks in the United States, France, England, Canada, and Japan. It defines a packet-level protocol that allows a DTE to establish simultaneous communication with one or more DTEs on a network; it also enables the flow of these communications to be controlled.

Its functions include the routing and virtual-circuit procedures, and others, which we shall examine later. The objectives of X.25 may be phrased briefly as the following: universality in the sharing of resources, flexibility among different user systems, error detection and correction end to end in the transfer of data, and the least possible concern of the user with the mechanics of routing, monitoring, and so on. In sum, the layers to which it addresses itself are those we discussed in chapter 16.

The X.25 is the highest level in network operations and specifies the manner in which users establish, maintain, and clear calls through the network. It details the manner in which control information and user data are structured into packets. The packet header contains control and addressing information; this is most important, because a single physical circuit can thus support communication to numerous terminals and hosts at the same time. It is not necessary that the network and the DTEs (the terminals or hosts) work on the same protocol; see Figure 17.1. The network may work with X.25, but the terminals, or at least some of them, may be asynchronous or binary synchronous, in which case interfaces (gateways) are provided. The opposite may be the case, in which the DTEs are working on the X.25 but the subnetwork to which they are attached follows a different discipline.

What Is X.25?

In preceding chapters we have noted that the DTE (terminal, host) needs a hardware interface, the DCE, that this interface is standardized by the CCITT, and that it connects the DTE to the physical (communications) link. For the physical link there is a management discipline, provided in packet switching by the data link control, the XDLC, and several of its dialects, the SDLC, HDLC, ADCCP, and others. Let us remember that in their original version they were unbalanced

Figure 17.1
The internal subnetwork protocol may not be X.25, since the subnetwork tends to optimize transit time. Gateways (repacking) introduce possibilities of error.

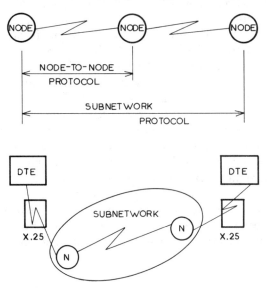

protocols and that LAP B was developed as a balanced version of data link control. Further, as we know, communications services alone, though necessary, are not enough; we need network services, routing being one of them. Thus physical link management and network services interface between the communications devices on one side and the user programs and data bases on the other; see Figure 17.2. (Once more we should note that X.25 does not meet the requirements of access to data and that higher disciplines are needed for that.)

We have already discussed the component parts of the bit-oriented frame-level protocol. The data packet format under X.25 is composed of the packet header, including packet type and logical channel number (identifier), and the user data. The logical channel number locally identifies the virtual circuit at the interface between the DTE and the network. Different channel numbers are used for a given virtual circuit to two or more DTEs. They are chosen independently. The choice of a logical (or virtual) circuit automatically means that the logical channels used at each end are occupied. This does not prevent other logical channels between the DTE and the network from being free. More precisely, the logical channels associated with permanent virtual circuits are permanently occupied; therefore the associated numbers cannot be used for any other purpose, although the bandwidth is still available for other calls. The logical channels associated with switched virtual circuits, though, are initially all free and could be used by the DTE to originate new calls or to receive incoming calls from the network. The logical channel number, then, identifies all data transfer, supervision, and flow control packets associated with that call, until the call is cleared. When all logical channels designated for use with switched virtual circuits are occupied, a new call cannot be established until a data communication is terminated and one of the channels again available.

Figure 17.2

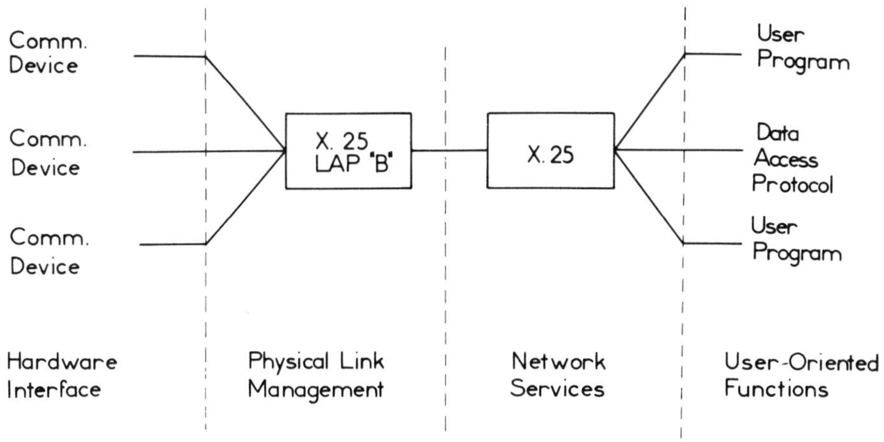

Call establishment starts with a "call request" by a DTE (Figure 17.3); this, too, is a packet. The logical channel number chosen by the DTE is 12 bits long. Another byte is dedicated to "type" the call request, say. Network address of the called DTE is composed of a string of binary coded decimal digits, the length of which is indicated and depends on whether the call is to another DTE or to a network node; if the former, the addresses are 8 decimal digits long. The facility field is present only when the DTE requires some indication in the call request packet. User data follow the facility field; they may contain any number of bits up to a given maximum length. (Datapac, for example, has a maximum of 16 bytes.)

To repeat: the first 2 bytes of information in the packet header or, more accurately, the first 4 bits and the next 12 bits, identify the destination of the packet; this is the logical channel number or logical channel identifier. The 4-bit field marked "ID" in Figure 17.3 can have only one of two values: either 0001 or 1001. The value 0001 signifies that the packet is being transmitted to an individual terminal or computer directly; the value 1001 is used for sending a transmission to a device via a cluster controller.

The two fundamental types of virtual circuit are the permanent and the switched. In the permanent one, linking terminal to computer, for instance, a

Figure 17.3

Call request packet format. The bits are transmitted starting with the low order, the bytes starting with number 1.

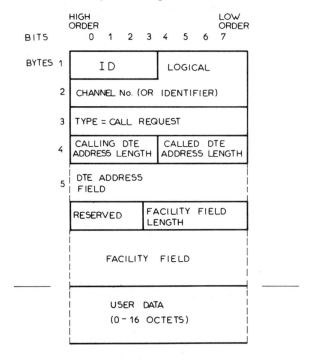

logical channel number is assigned by agreement at the time the service is initialized. In the switched, the circuit is under control of the DTE and of the network (dynamic solution); hence a mechanism is needed, and this is the call request packet, which lets the user place a call to a specific DTE. Each such attachment is assigned a number, as in the telephone network.

The call request packet assigns a currently available logical channel number, which is active for the duration of the call. It is short, compared to the generally much longer DTE attachment number; at the completion of the call, it is released for reuse.

With 12 bits available for the channel number, up to 4,096 virtual circuits may be supported simultaneously, meaning across a single physical connection to the network. (X.25 is, in a sense, the equivalent of a packet-oriented time-division multiplexer offering, in theory at least, up to 4,096 simultaneous logical connections.)

The control field within the packet header plays a role similar to that of the control field in the link header. It indicates whether the packet is a call setup request or a data transfer and whether an interruption of the device at the other end is required or the flow of data should be temporarily stopped. It also is used in error detection and control and in the handling of exceptional conditions.

The Communications Session

An X.25 data communications session is a typical transmitter–receiver dialogue: the transmitter first issues an inquiry, the receiver responds positively, the transmitter then transmits the text, the receiver continues to respond positively, and the process continues until a mutually understood end sequence occurs. If errors are found in the transmission, the packet is retransmitted.

Some networks offer further facilities to subscribers, such as a priority class of traffic, closed user group, and reverse charging. Reverse charging, for instance, may be specified in the call request packet; then the called DTE will be charged for the call *if* it accepts that call.

One outstanding advantage of the standard is built-in error-free data transmission: by means of error detection and retransmission techniques the network offers extremely low probabilities of undetected errors. The standard helps extend the network's internal protocol right up to the host computer interface by establishing, maintaining, and clearing calls and by managing the flow of data to and from the network, but it does not attempt to specify the characteristics of the virtual-circuit service.

Because a packet network can perform character set translation, totally dissimilar and hardware-incompatible terminals can communicate with each other. A basic cost advantage appears to derive from cluster configurations, when a moderate number of terminals are simultaneously connected through the network to various processes.

When a calling terminal or host wishes to establish a virtual circuit, the called DTE will receive an incoming call packet on a logical channel. This includes the logical channel number chosen by the network and used for the duration of the call, the network address of the calling DTE, and any facilities requested by the caller. A DTE actuates acceptance by transmitting a "call accepted" packet specifying the same logical channel number as in the incoming call packet. If it refuses the call, it transmits a clear request packet with the appropriate channel number. After the virtual circuit is established, data transfer takes place in both directions in accordance with data transfer procedures. When the transfer is completed, either DTE may issue a clear request packet. The logical channel reverts to the free condition on receipt of a "clear confirmation" packet from the node.

Notice the following: Data packets can be transferred on a virtual circuit only after that circuit has been established. Data packets transmitted before a call is accepted will be treated as an error condition by the network. Data packets transmitted after clearing procedures have been initiated by the remote DTE will be discarded by the network.

Data packet transfer is guaranteed (in terms of "send sequence") through a sequential numbering module 8. The first data packet to be transmitted is numbered 0. This numbering makes both the network node and the DTE able to detect the loss of data packets and to control flow across the modem. The send sequence is the P(S). Each data packet also carries a packet receive sequence number, P(R), which authorizes the transmission of additional data packets.

Figure 17.4 integrates what has been discussed so far by comparing the SDLC line access protocols with the X.25 discipline. It will be appreciated that the packet header (simplified in this diagram to its fundamentals) adds very little in terms of overhead, so the overall efficiency of packet-switching protocols is well argued.

Comparing Protocol Facilities

Digital control protocols are becoming standardized, and the packet protocol is favored by advanced users and for good reasons. The standard interface discipline it imposes more than offsets any inefficiencies or extra costs. The packet level, as discussed in the preceding section, is very efficient. The frame level (XDLC) adds some extra bytes but compares very favorably with the now aging binary synchronous protocol.

It is exactly because of these advantages that many users are attracted to XDLC, but bisync will be with us for some time to come. The real reason is investments: it is not conceivably possible to change all at once all the DTEs that are installed and operating now. Other reasons are functional: efficiency is usually a matter of volume (economies of scale play a major role), and since the more advanced protocols (packet switching for example) require sophisticated equipment, volume production and consumption are the best way to reduce unit costs. Economies of scale and economies of function are not uniform or self-evident. The Bank of

Figure 17.4

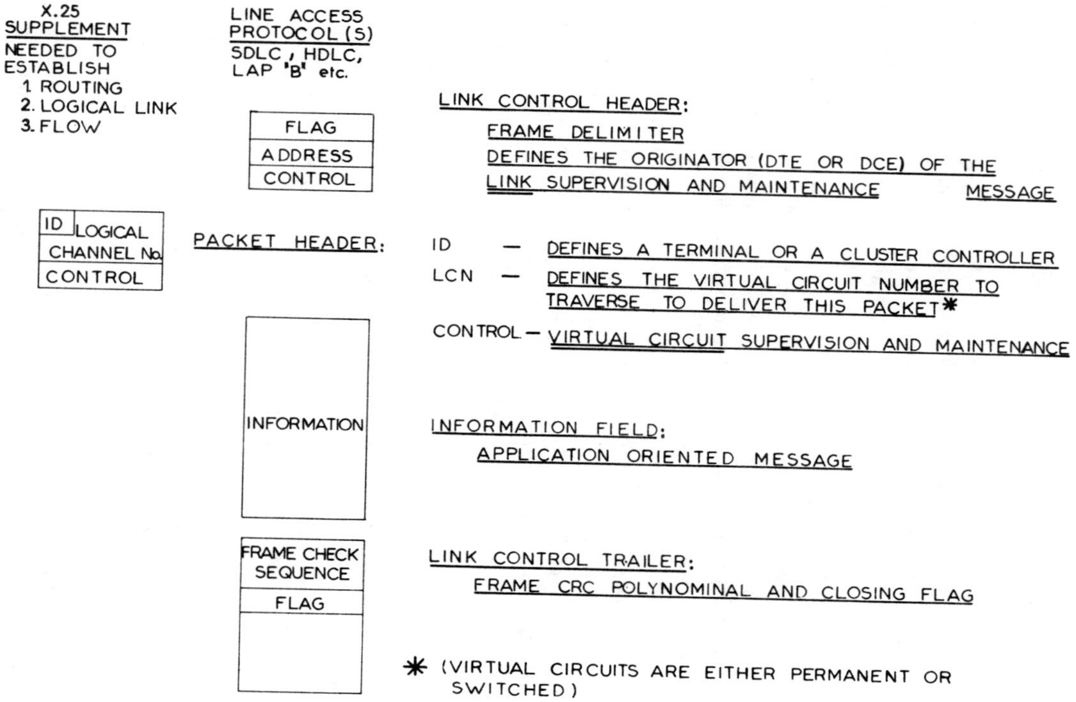

X.25
SUPPLEMENT
NEEDED TO
ESTABLISH
1 ROUTING
2. LOGICAL LINK
3. FLOW

LINE ACCESS
PROTOCOL(S)
SDLC, HDLC,
LAP 'B' etc.

| FLAG |
| ADDRESS |
| CONTROL |

ID	LOGICAL CHANNEL No
CONTROL	

PACKET HEADER:

| INFORMATION |

| FRAME CHECK SEQUENCE |
| FLAG |

LINK CONTROL HEADER:
FRAME DELIMITER
DEFINES THE ORIGINATOR (DTE OR DCE) OF THE
LINK SUPERVISION AND MAINTENANCE   MESSAGE

ID — DEFINES A TERMINAL OR A CLUSTER CONTROLLER

LCN — DEFINES THE VIRTUAL CIRCUIT NUMBER TO
        TRAVERSE TO DELIVER THIS PACKET *

CONTROL — VIRTUAL CIRCUIT SUPERVISION AND MAINTENANCE

INFORMATION FIELD:
APPLICATION ORIENTED MESSAGE

LINK CONTROL TRAILER:
FRAME CRC POLYNOMINAL AND CLOSING FLAG

* (VIRTUAL CIRCUITS ARE EITHER PERMANENT OR
   SWITCHED)

America uses three distinct disciplines for its distributed information system network:

Packet switching, among modules and among the four computers in the same module

Binary synchronous communications for the TRW banking terminals

Asynchronous communications for the money dispensers

Exactly because we foresee that packet and binary synchronous protocol structures (and also asynchronous ones) will intermix in networks, we foresee the need of gateways. The same is true of segmenting and grouping packets, between packet-switching networks operating at different packet sizes. In other words, networks of links and processes will need to interface various protocols. Most large organizations, for example, will have a line that has a binary synchronous terminal on it and will want to plug it into a larger network that is basically a packetized ring network. Asynchronous requirements, on the other hand, are not only survivals of older, starlike networks but also newer ones. Most cash dispensers are asynchronous, and that goes for point-of-sale terminals too. What is more, the numbers of both those terminals and automatic teller machines will substantially increase as time passes.

Since applications environments vary widely, for the necessary flexibility, protocols must have two basic modes of operation: the normal response mode, projected for centralized systems in which a primary station polls the secondary station, and the asynchronous response mode, for situations in which either station may transmit at any time.

Protocols are continuously undergoing revision, the balanced mode of operation being an example. We defined balanced or symmetric operations as those in which neither station is designated as primary or secondary. Let us recapitulate:

The XDLC is a type of protocol, not a specific one; it is designed to serve the communications layer.

X.25 is a superstructure, compatible with and higher than the XDLC: it is designed to serve the networking layer.

The link access protocol LAP A was unbalanced: it had primary and secondary stations.

The LAP B was balanced: it had only primary stations.

Because various protocols are used in a network, gateways must be implemented.

The X.25 standard describes several levels of interfacing. At the physical level the electrical connection between the modem and the DTE is defined. Hence X.25 takes advantage of the standard X.21 for full-duplex synchronous transmission. At the communications level the X.25 interface describes the link access protocol that is responsible for the management of the link between the DTE and the modem.

At this layer X.25 uses a subset of XDLC for framing, transparency, error detection, flow control, and so on.

At the next level X.25 describes a packet level procedure for control of virtual calls through a public data network. It may even describe a packet assembler and disassembler function. The latter involves a procedure within the node. Its goal is the handling of virtual terminals.

Rules can and have been established for the use of mixed protocols; it is not necessary to have a uniform protocol throughout. We can use locally those protocols which are the most efficient, given the application.

Flow Control

We have seen how both routing and virtual circuits are assured by the X.25 protocol and how this is done, but we must now see that routing and the establishment of a virtual circuit, though necessary, are not enough; flow must be controlled.

A basic difficulty in logical link control is how to match the sender's transmission rate with the receiver's ability to accept traffic. A good solution is an explicit allocation of resources. The receiver clearly notifies the sender of its ability to accept traffic. Flow control aims to prevent the sender from overflowing the receiver's buffers by not transmitting data too fast for the receiver. Sequence and flow control procedures can, in fact, be combined, the latter using the sequence numbers for received ready (RR) and received not ready (RNR) administered by the virtual circuit.

Flow control leads to the subject of what are called windows. A window is a logical path to be opened between two processes before data is passed (as used in flow control management). Determining window size is important. The size should indicate the willingness of the receiving process to provide buffer space (Figure 17.5); in different terms, the window size might represent exactly the available buffer space that the user has offered for receiving (this is the conservative strategy), or it could reflect a buffer space expected on the basis of previous allocations (the optimistic strategy).

A window operation is presented in Figure 17.6. The window size K permits a maximum of 6 packets to be outstanding at a given time. The lower window edge, or last P(R) received, is 3. With the transmission and acknowledgment of packets, the lower and upper window edges rotate. A receive ready packet indicates the willingness to receive K data packets. A receive not ready packet indicates a temporary inability to accept additional data packets.

A reset procedure reinitializes the flow control on a virtual circuit to the state it was in when the virtual circuit was established. All data and interrupt packets in transit at the time of resetting are, then, discarded. The reset procedure may be initialized by a DTE by transmitting a reset request packet. When the node com-

Figure 17.5
An early computer data ring for optimal flow. Similar solutions may be used today in networks, for windows.

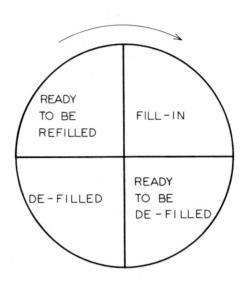

Figure 17.6
Window size $K = 6$

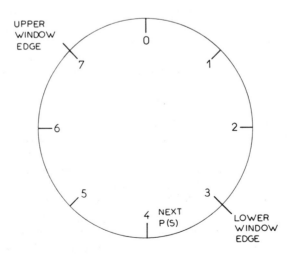

municates that the virtual circuit is being reset, it is done through a reset, or restart, indication packet.

The terminal or host uses a restart procedure as a mechanism for recovery from failures. A restart request packet is equivalent to a clear request on switched virtual circuits. A node issues a restart indication packet when the user has failed to follow the correct restart procedure or when the network has experienced a catastrophic failure.

Goals in Flow Control

A good flow control scheme must handle a long spectrum of problems that result from preventing buffer overflow in the receiver. As we have seen, the flow control strategy should consider the buffer space offered by a receiver (user). The goals and methods of flow control are as follows.

End-to-end: Flow control for a particular level of protocol should be exerted at the point closest to the final destination.

Congestion prevention: The flow control strategy should prevent queueing of messages in the protocol module so that module resources may handle messages that have a high probability of being delivered immediately.

Deadlock prevention: When congestion does occur, resources must be available to handle traffic-clearing messages.

Interplay with subnetwork: The interface between modules representing levels of protocol often causes flow control problems.

Such mechanisms may exist at each level of protocol as well as between levels of protocols. To work properly, they assume that "flow control information" is passed from the receiver to the sender. The information ordinarily reflects the receiver's ability to buffer data. It often also represents a count of some resources: a unit of buffering of a message queue element. But, as usual, reduced to its fundamentals, the mechanism reflects the interplay between available resources and the demands for their use.

Congestion Control

Congestion is a prominent concern in the design of message- and packet-switching networks. It occurs when the rate of arriving traffic exceeds the service rate provided by the network. Control procedures are of two types. End-to-end control places restrictions directly at the message source by monitoring the number of messages on the logical connection "source to destination." Local control places restrictions on the number of messages at each node of the logical connection between a source and a destination node. It has been shown that neither end-to-end control nor local control alone is sufficient to manage congestion but the two combined can potentially solve the congestion problem. Experiments have demonstrated what alternative solutions might offer. For instance, probabilistic routing is more successful than deterministic routing for congestion in locally controlled networks. The inclusion of random routing may enhance its usefulness by furnishing an analysis of alternative routing, but the most critical consideration is the steady collection of factual and documented traffic statistics.

Internetworking

The emerging network architectures, such as IBM's Systems Network Architecture, SNA, and Digital Equipment Corporation's Decnet, can ultimately coexist with public packet networks and private user's systems, given the required interfaces (gateways, internetworking nodes). An example is the recent implementation of an SNA interface by IBM World Trade for the Datapac network in Canada and the Transpac in France. IBM's network interface adapter (NIA) generates a polling routine that makes a 3270 cathode ray tube think it is being interfaced with the network. The adapter takes information from the terminal and translates it into the protocol for data link control, for transmission over the packet network. A protocol thus must be defined for signaling and data exchange.

It is advisable, however, to use operational features compatible with X.25. The following would be desirable for internetworking connections as well as for the host interface.

Extended numbering at the link level would permit more unacknowledged packets to be outstanding on the circuit; this is particularly important for long-delay channels such as satellite links.

Extended numbering at the packet level, or variable packet size per call, also would address the long-delay problem.

Accounting information on call setup and clearing packets would allow a schedule of international tariffs to be established.

It is proper to add that, where network interconnection is concerned, many problems remain. The international standardization effort is still lagging. A new common base of reference, X7X, addresses itself only to the signal level; it is a superstructure of X.25. Any new recommendation, however, that is to become an end-to-end standard must tackle the user-level protocols.

Datagrams as a choice over virtual circuits must also be settled. From certain viewpoints it is simpler to interconnect nets through them than through virtual calls; they have the lesser requirements for support services, logical complexity, and buffering. If virtual calls are adopted, the gateway has to keep status reports for, say, 4,096 of such calls, and this can be a heavy duty. Datagrams do not pose such requirements, though each one may need a fair amount of header and trailer data to support itself. This leads some to believe that virtual calls have the greater conceptual simplicity.

Acknowledgment, too, needs to be redefined for internetworking (Figure 17.7). As it now stands, an ACK will carry to DTE A a message that is valid only within the borders of Network I, to which it belongs. Documentation is another difficulty. Poorly documented networks may send an ACK, but we don't really know to what extent that ACK is valid.

Other problems arise from technical questions. For instance:

How to exchange more data than a given network can carry (under, say, X.25).

How to charge for internetworking calls.

How to effect conversion from one packet length to another (X7X specifies 128 octets as a maximum, but some networks, e.g., Datapac, allow 256).

How to "split up" the long messages (it should be done within the X7X framework).

How to assign the window sizes between internetworking points.

Figure 17.7
Here ACK means to DTE A that it is all right only to the border of Network I to which it belongs.

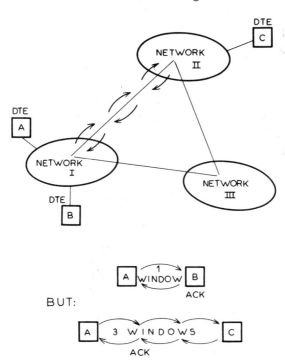

We might also point out that the experimental networks are more interested in the development of X7X than the commercial value-added carriers, and this somewhat dampens user interest.

Several of the solutions being considered today are based more on the circumstances of business transactions than on economics, service to the user, technology, and good sense.

18

Session and
Presentation Control

References have been made in preceding chapters to the advantages of layering. Each layer achieves its functionality both by itself and by making use of the services of the layer just below it. Further, the modularity offered through layering helps ensure that a layer's services are independent from the protocols or implementations actual at that level. A level's particular protocols and their implementation are transparent to the user of that level, which makes it possible to replace them, when appropriate, with other protocols.

Reference also has been made to the fact that, at least so far, there has been no standardization for layers beyond networking, and that standardization is needed to make every process addressable to every other, so that they may exchange information independently of their location, the logical or physical characteristics, and the specific goals at the time of the needed exchange. These are the background reasons. The possible solutions outlined in the preceding chapter aim to ease the dialogue at the user's site, but it is also good to look at the work the standards institutes and associations put forward.

An effort in the right direction was undertaken by ANSI (with the participation of IBM, AT&T, Honeywell, Digital Equipment Corporation, Burroughs, Univac, CDC, and Xerox, among the manufacturers, and the United States government and Boeing among the users). ANSI divided the functions beyond networking into three major blocks, which are session control, presentation control, and process control, the last embracing the actual handling of applications programs, data base management, and file access.

Figure 18.1 goes a step beyond the ANSI definition: session and presentation control are kept intact, but process has been broken down into three layers, in anticipation of future needs.

Notice that networking is, as always in this book, divided into two layers. The definition of data transport has been enlarged, too.

Figure 18.1
Interfaces

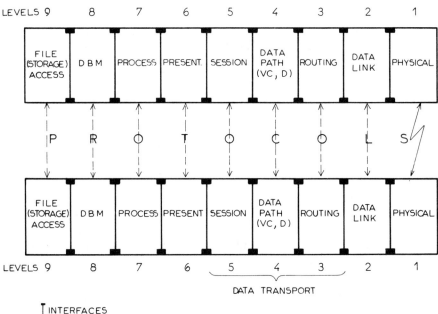

Some of the definitions advanced by ANSI and applicable at all levels of reference are the following:

DTE: an addressable endpoint at a location, i.e. a place where things happen

Connection: a logical association capable of transferring data between DTEs or processes

Data unit: a quantity of data and control information transferred as a unit over a connection

Data assurance unit: a quantity of data whose successful transfer over a connection is acknowledged

Data flow unit: a quantity of data whose transfer over a connection has been authorized

Data mapping unit: an entity used to map a data unit of the next level up onto a data unit of the current level

The Purpose of Session Control

Session control takes care of the logical aspects of transmission from one process to another, whether local or remote. Let us say that process A wishes to communicate with process B. This may be done through a terminal addressing the central memory of a mainframe or take place within the host. Whichever the case may be, it will, most likely, involve routines in the applications program library, routines in the utilities library, and data base elements. The operator of a DTE (and the program running in the central memory) will need assistance at the session level or else should be clearly knowledgeable about these three things. The session establishment and control commands are oriented to applications programming, but the data entered or removed and their form of presentation follow the specifications of file design and data base management.

Functionally, rules and supports are necessary to control and interpret the operation of devices at the work station, to execute commands on behalf of the process or processes, to receive commands from the corresponding process or processes associated with the session, and to pass them on to the process of the work station in question.

Typically, in a communications environment each work station has a mailbox name. Process A says to the session control, "I give you the mailbox number, but you must do the rest." Session control must establish whether this is to be a one-way or two-way operation and the degree of priority. The set of rules by which a session is established, maintained, and terminated covers the logical aspects of the transmission: process to process, local, or remote. Control information must assure log on and log off and a number of programmatic interfaces. The latter regard the rules by which a person–information dialogue is interpreted, so as to make available to the user the data asked for. To send, receive, establish, maintain, and terminate are activities largely falling within the scheme of Figure 18.2. Session control complements the networking operations (data path, routing) and provides the section of transport control nearest the user.

This brings us to the subject of functionality and of interfaces. Transport control aims, overall, at a reliable transfer of data between endpoints, across a communications network. The virtual circuit of Datagram provides the interconnection services with a packet-switched network. Session routines see to it that control is exercised over a person–information dialogue session.

It follows logically that the information given to session control must be enough for a decision whether this is a local or a remote request, to call the right programs into play. If it is not a local request, then session control must establish a conversation with the fourth level, data path (refer again to Figure 15.1), actuating the proper interface, and since next to the data path lies the routing, the third level, it must also look into that, for information about routing patterns and for specifications. Then it must face the other way and look at the sixth level, presentation. At this interface, session control causes the reliable transfer of data between the presentation control modules supporting processes in a network of work stations or

Figure 18.2

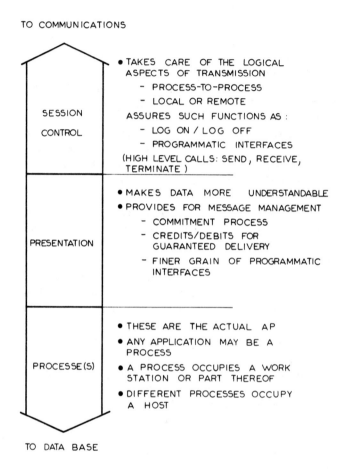

TO COMMUNICATIONS

SESSION CONTROL
- • TAKES CARE OF THE LOGICAL ASPECTS OF TRANSMISSION
  - - PROCESS-TO-PROCESS
  - - LOCAL OR REMOTE
- ASSURES SUCH FUNCTIONS AS :
  - - LOG ON / LOG OFF
  - - PROGRAMMATIC INTERFACES
- (HIGH LEVEL CALLS: SEND, RECEIVE, TERMINATE)

PRESENTATION
- • MAKES DATA MORE UNDERSTANDABLE
- • PROVIDES FOR MESSAGE MANAGEMENT
  - - COMMITMENT PROCESS
  - - CREDITS/DEBITS FOR GUARANTEED DELIVERY
  - - FINER GRAIN OF PROGRAMMATIC INTERFACES

PROCESSE(S)
- • THESE ARE THE ACTUAL AP
- • ANY APPLICATION MAY BE A PROCESS
- • A PROCESS OCCUPIES A WORK STATION OR PART THEREOF
- • DIFFERENT PROCESSES OCCUPY A HOST

TO DATA BASE

inside the host's main storage. This includes integrity and security control facilities.

Functionally, session control gives system-level support from log on to log off. Such commands as to edit, put in, test, and so forth should be covered.

In an interactive environment session control gives the video user, say, the same facilities given by intelligent devices. Some examples are simple ones, maybe an unlocked keyboard, and others complex, such as a full-width output review of an entire session. Session control should be designed to coexist with full-screen programs.

Among the basic functions we distinguish three: user support, tailoring to individual needs, and software for session "streams," as follows.

User support dynamically redefines part or all of a user's display environment; it should be possible to accomplish this function at any time during the session.

The ability to tailor the operation of the terminal to the user's individual needs demands considerable flexibility, since the user's needs may change from day to day and even during one session.

Software receives input from, and places its output in, session streams.

A stream may be thought of as a sheet of paper that one may both write on and read from; it is called a virtual sheet of paper (VSP), and, like paper, may be stacked. The same is true of data within the stream; each line of data that enters a stream is placed next to the preceding one, top to bottom, like lines of copy on paper. Just as lines of copy fill a page, data fill up streams of fixed capacity. When this happens, we say that a stream "wraps around." Not only lines in a stream but also streams in a DTE may reach a limit. Theoretically there is no limit to the number of streams a user may have, but practically a limit is set by the size of the memory.

ANSI and Session Control

We have said that the functions of session control are not yet standardized and that they are fairly complex. The software support and the interfacing with adjoining layers define whether a session is possible or not possible and allowed or not allowed. If all prerequisites are met, session control can inform the process that an exchange of data is in order. Then it will proceed to initiate the session, activate its side of transport control, and (when at the receiving end) put in action the quarantine. Procedures for quarantine are those which ensure that no access to a message or file is possible before the successful completion of the intended communication.

ANSI has proposed certain other terms, which it defines as follows.

A *session-quarantine unit* is a quantity of text that cannot be released to the receiving process until the sending process signals its completion.

A *session-commitment unit* is a quantity of data transferred during a session. It ensures the accomplishment of an element of work that is indivisible, from the point of view of consistency; for instance, it may concern itself with the consistency of data base updating across a distributed system.

A *session-interaction unit* is a subdivision of a session commitment delimited by the passing of control of a session from one work-station process to its corresponding process. Whoever is in control of the session may request termination or some other type of interaction.

A *session-recovery unit* is a quantity of data transferred during a session-commitment unit. Typically, it synchronizes the data transferred with respect to the checkpoints of the cooperating work-station processes.

A *session data unit* is a unit of data transferred between a pair of processes using a session. It is of a size that is defined independently of the size of the transport network data unit just above.

A *session data mapping unit* is an entity mapping the data unit of the next level above onto a session data unit.

This leads our discussion to the subject of presentation control.

Presentation Control

Different computer and communication equipment manufacturers have different notions of what presentation control is. Sometimes they interchange "session" and "presentation." Furthermore, in spite of the efforts extended by ANSI (in the X3 SPARC Study Group) there is no general agreement yet on the standardization of this level. The area of presentation control is, therefore, still in need of a proper definition, but by and large its activity is to adapt the information-handling characteristics of a given process to the requirements of session control and of the corresponding processes.

A process, as defined hereby, supports application and system activities, definitely including exchanges of information by which cooperation is achieved end to end with other processes. We must point out, however, that presentation control as defined by ANSI is one layer, but it really should be defined as two: a "basics" layer that includes what is projected by the current standardization effort (as discussed in this section) and an "add-on" layer that is distinctly oriented to industry and other segments of society. In that way each major segment— banking, merchandizing, manufacturing, law enforcement, and so on—may develop functional, user-oriented solutions, thereby enhancing communication between persons and data, or information.

For a better understanding of the currently projected functions of presentation control, we outline below the mission of the interface with the lower-level session control procedures, already defined.

Follow-up on establishing, maintaining, and terminating sessions, including requesting creation of a process when specified

Delimiting of data enclosures

Preparing the necessary delimiters for addressing work stations via mailboxes, a function of session control

Notifying processes upon receipt of data and data enclosure delimiters

Making data more understandable through segmenting, blocking, etc.

Providing for message management beyond the level of buffering data and controlling flow (proper to session control)

Actuating the commitment process

Providing credits and debits for guaranteed delivery

Supporting data operations beyond checkpoint, recovery, and commitment (proper to session control)

Providing the finer grains of programmatic interfaces

The protocol followed in presentation control is a set of rules by which support is given to a session for establishing, maintaining, and terminating a data transfer. The interface with session control contains the format by which control information is passed on and the rules by which it is interpreted for the transfer of data.

Specifically, presentation control adapts the existing specialized information-handling characteristics of a process to the session control interface. This calls for transforming commands, and data, to accommodate differences in sending and receiving formats, data types, data codes, and data representations; these may exist not only between different DTEs but also between different processes in the same host.

To accomplish these functions in an able manner, presentation control needs to make data more understandable, assure a reasonable homogeneity of language between processes and DTEs, adapt requests, if virtual terminals are used, to the specific machinery existing in that location, and translate local names, if programs use them, into a common reference. It must further make sure of the necessary compacting and decompacting, the enrichment of information, and the encrypting and decrypting as required.

This is, in brief, a commitment process to which could be added other functions as necessary, within a specific operating environment. For each one of them debits and credits must be given for guaranteed delivery—one of what we have called the finer grains of the programmatic interfaces.

Notice that session control and presentation control are necessary whether or not the networking and communications layers are used. Figure 18.3 exemplifies the case of the local terminal. Logical procedures for a data link probably will not be necessary, in which case the physical media should connect directly with session control.

Figure 18.3

The case of local terminal. (FA, file access; DBM, data base management; PRO, process; PRE, presentation control; SE, session control; DPA, data path; ROU, routing; DL, data link; PH, physical medium)

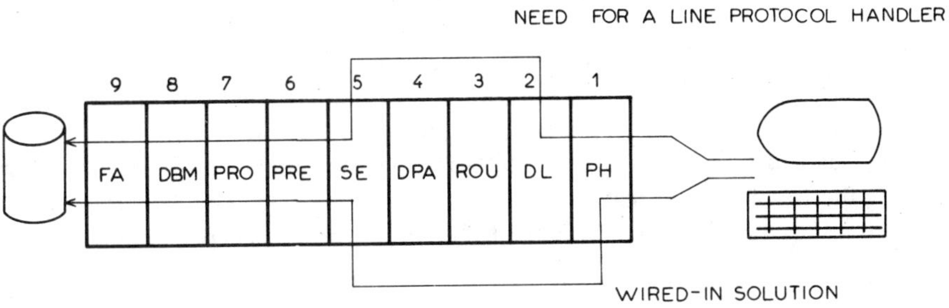

A Process-Level Protocol

A protocol for the process level, the seventh in Figure 18.1, supports applications and system activities, including the exchange of information between processes residing in the DTE or in the same host. The processes are actual applications programs and any such program may be a process. Processes occupy a work station or part thereof, and a protocol must guarantee that different applications programs cooperate in the achievement of the objectives and requirements. From presentation control to data link, all lower levels are designed to facilitate this; indeed, that is the purpose of data processing and data communications systems.

As ANSI aptly delineates, the objects of interest at the process level will be specific to each broad applications field. For a bank's current-accounts protocol, they will be customers, balances, accounts, deposits, withdrawals. For a manufacturer's order-entry protocol, they will be customers, sales orders, products, inventories, in-process orders, bills, receivables. For a distributed data base access protocol, they will be files, records, sets, items, access requests, processes, data descriptions. For a programming language, they will be procedures, statements, labels, items references. Regardless, the end point is file access, the ninth layer in Figure 18.1.

The multiplicity of tasks and interests sees to it that a process-level protocol is defined in terms of the data formats and their interpretation, the presentation control services, and the session control services. Each and all of these levels must take into consideration the control procedures for integrity and security—their object, extent, design, and impact.

Notice that the eighth level, the data base management system, determines whether it can have direct access to the data asked for by a process or whether it requires help from a surrogate data base process at some other session node (Figure 18.4). Activities relating to data base management and file access (ninth layer) will bring into play routines that may be typed according to processing: transaction processing, program development, file transfer protocol, integrity control protocol, and terminal interaction protocol. These call for fairly different data-handling methods.

Such protocols thus specify the rules by which the information passing between processes of two DTEs, or between processes within a host is put into format and interpreted.

Many different interprocess protocols exist, but they fall into two major classes: basic information systems and applications systems. As of now, neither particularly conforms to any standards, though both badly need to.

Establishment of a session, high-level language interfaces (possibly converting the language statements into packets, observing chosen protocols), data base inquiries, data audits, and software transparency (whether remote or local) are among the functions in great need of standardization. They largely pertain to the fifth to ninth layers, where much of the attention in network studies is now focusing.

Figure 18.4

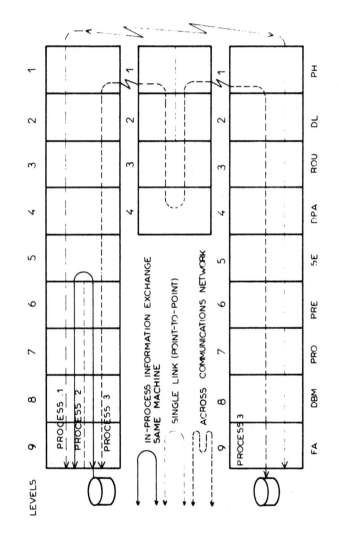

19

Standards for Presentation Level Protocol

A graphic presentation is informative, stimulating, animated, and able to keep the user's attention. For this reason, both PLP, the American standard, and CEPT, the new European standard, pay particular attention to presentation features.

Like any other standard, those made for graphic presentation cannot be short-lived. But unlike several other standards, those applicable to computers and communications should pay special attention to technological evolution.

Science and technology improve the means and processes at our disposition. The new generation of satellites expand the available bandwidths; optical fibers enter long haul chores; and LAN bring communications capabilities to the PC under every desk. These facilities widen our horizons and our implementation ideas.

Standards should properly reflect development, both current and projected. By so doing, they promote a mutual compatibility of information systems, helping to encode text, data, graphics, and display control information. This is the basic objective of the presentation level protocol which should conform to the architecture defined in the layered reference model of ISO/OSI—something both PLP and CEPT try to do, each in its own way.

Within each standard, specific rules have to be observed throughout the logical layers: from data link and networking to transport and session control. While the session layer is responsible for binding and unbinding the presentation entities, transport addresses itself to congestion and flow control—the assurance that transmission takes place.

The Observance of Protocols

The formats, procedures, and rules followed for encoding text, data, graphics, and control type messages are common to the host and workstations at the end user

261

level—whether intelligent or nonintelligent. A complete Videotex implementation obeying the ISO/OSI multilayer standard requires seven protocols, one for each level.

As stated on repeated occasions, a protocol is a set of rules, procedures and formats governing the exchange of information between peer processors. The description, verification and implementation of protocols is an important subject in any network. Protocols must be unambiguous and formal methods should be available for their verification.

Protocols must be observed by every participating entity and their implementation must be carried out automatically. As a set of rules to control interactions between two or more entities, a protocol is subject to a formal description. As any finely tuned mechanism, it should feature a finite set of:

1. internal states
2. input signals from the network management and the execution environment
3. input signals from both the higher and the lower layer of the architecture
4. output signals to those same entities (network management, executable environment, higher and lower layers).

The formal description and representation of protocols is a prerequisite to their utilization. For manipulation purposes, a protocol compiler acts as a sort of translator which generates the object from the source program.

To support interprocess communications, a protocol must reflect strategies which allow the functions proper to the layer to be executed in a proper manner. For instance, a transport control protocol will ensure that the input flow of messages is limited in accordance with the reception possibilities of the destination entity.

This is the goal of flow control, whose object is to make the throughput closely related to the receiving capability of an entity. Though a mechanism similar to that used to detect message loss or duplication may be employed for flow control, specifics proper to that layer must be observed. A throughput depends on:

bandwidth

the nature of the attached devices

the processes running on them

their communications requirements

message size

retransmission timeout

buffer

allocation strategies

roundtrip delay.

Several of these factors are interrelated. If the number of lost or damaged messages is not negligible and the transmission medium is not congested, retransmission timeout can be chosen to be short to perceptibly reduce the average transmission delay of messages. However, since the sending process keeps a copy of each message transmitting but not yet acknowledged, the size of the buffer used by the sender limits the number of outstanding messages.

The architecture may impose its own prerequisites. If the delivery of messages must be made in the same order as submitted, the receiver should keep the arriving messages in a buffer as long as a message is missing. This, however, reduces the reception capability of the destination entity.

Definition of the acknowledgement discipline is very important for flow control. A roundtrip delay is the amount of time between the sending of a message and the return of the corresponding acknowledgement. Acknowledgements may be forwarded to the sender systematically after each successfully received message, or following several received messages. The latter is used when systematic return of acknowledgements results in significant loading of the transmission medium.

When acknowledgement is returned only after receiving several messages in succession, the result is an increase in roundtrip delay associated with a successfully received message. Roundtrip delays may involve retransmission by the sender of messages which have already successfully arrived at their destination.

Acknowledgement after every received message also has its drawbacks. Increase in traffic due to housekeeping operations is one example. A similar case can be made about the usage of resources at the destination entity.

Message size can have a direct effect on both the sending and receiving buffer area. In this sense it affects flow control, and thus flow control performance. Large messages require a larger buffer space, call for a greater amount of bandwidth, and cause more transfer errors—and therefore more retransmissions.

Short messages produce propagation and roundtrip delays and require a smaller buffer area, but the overhead is increased as a header and control information are of fixed length. With short messages, acknowledgements and other housekeeping chores are more numerous as the message size is short, while switching time is fixed independently of message size.

Presentation Control

CEPT and PLP are addressed to the sixth layer of ISO/OSI: presentation control. In the hierarchical structure, from lower to higher protocols, the presentation layer stands above session control whose function is to coordinate the distributed functions through the initiation and termination of processes; start/stop of process steps; transaction commitments; updates; journaling; backup; recovery; and resolution of concurrency conflicts. In this sense, session control specifications define the format of messages requesting initiation and termination of a process.

The object of presentation control is to follow-up on session establishment, maintainance and termination—including the function of requesting process creation. The presentation layer delimits data enclosure and prepares the necessary delimiters for addressing workstations via mailboxes, a function to be accomplished by session control.

It is the responsibility of presentation control to notify processes upon receipt of data and data enclosure delimiters, to make data more understandable through segmenting, blocking, and so on, and to provide for message management beyond the level of buffering and controlling data which is proper to session control. Presentation involves actuating the commitment process, provides credits/debits for guaranteed delivery, and supports data operations beyond checkpoint, recovery and commitment (which is the function of session control). In brief, it assures finer programmatic interfaces.

The protocol followed in presentation control is a set of rules by which support is given to a session for establishing, maintaining and terminating a data transfer. The interface to the session layer includes the format by which control information is passed and the rules by which it is interpreted in order to transfer data. The purpose is to

make data more understandable

assure a reasonable homogeneity of languages between processes and devices

if virtual terminals are used, adapt requests to the specific machinery existing in that location

if programs use local names, translate these names to a common reference.

Presentation control must also assure necessary compacting/decompacting, provide for information enrichment, and guarantee encrypting/decrypting as required. In short, the presentation control layer provides the network functions for the user layer.

The presentation and communications requirements of processes must also be examined. A valid strategy for myriaprocessor (PC and LAN) or long haul datacomm implementation is to keep text and data handling at the WS level, thus reducing communication of matters such as the updating of a common (local or central) database, the necessary interprocess communications, and the necessary, user-oriented presentation procedures.

In terms of data transport, mainframes and minicomputers pose different load characteristics than communicating WS, calling for broadband rather than baseband connections. Hundreds or thousands of workstations on a network amount to a significantly greater load than the two-digit number the typical installation featured in the past.

The bandwidth places constraints on the number of in-transit messages. If the carrier is loaded with in-transit messages because of a large window, any message retransmission will be made by reducing new data transmissions so that useful throughput will be retransmission-limited. If the bandwidth is not entirely loaded with new incoming messages, any message retransmission resulting from loss or failure will be made without modifying the throughput.

In either case, control procedures must be implemented. For instance, detection of lost or damaged messages can be achieved by using sequential ordering of messages when submitted by the sender. The size of the sequence number space attached to each message will typically be finite. The receiving throughput, transmission bandwidth, and sequence number space affect the protocol to be chosen.

Similar references can be made at the presentation level of reference, regarding the design of the protocol responsible for the encoding of text, data, graphics, and display control. Here, rather than being preoccupied by bandwidth and available windows, emphasis is placed on

color maps and color values

cursors and cursor manipulation

drawing points

escape sequences and final characters

G-sets and their repertory

geometric graphic primitives

logical picture elements (PEL): the geometric construct associated with the drawing point whose size determines the stroke width of graphics primitives

macros and opcodes

mosaics and pictorial information

picture description instructions (PDI)

physical picture elements (pixel), the smallest displayable unit on a display device

relative coordinates

unit screens.

Notice that though "pel" and "pixel" have often been used interchangeably in daily communications (even among specialists), they are quite distinct from one another. *Pixel* identifies the physical, and *pel* the logical picture elements.

The syntax for the presentation level protocol rests on currently existing national and international standards and recommendations. Independence of display hardware is achieved through the usage of simple geometric picture description instructions. The latter constitute the basis of the coding scheme.

The CEPT Standard

The standards established by PLP and CEPT efficiently answer the prerequisites which we have outlined. In so doing, they presuppose full support by lower-level protocols: session, transport, etc, through transparent, error-free communications channels. This is in conformity with the functions described in ISO's reference model.

In its graphic inventory, CEPT includes seven sets with new mosaic signs. This compares favorably to the so-far prevailing "alphamosaics" of Viewdata. The CEPT presentation level standard is designed to manipulate illustrations, to support text and data, and to be informative on its own right. Since colors animate the picture, the new standard offers 8 basic colors, each at two levels of intensity: full and reduced brightness. Black is used in reduced intensity to make part of the picture transparent, whether background or foreground. Besides the basic colors, 16 other color values are available from a range of freely defined and useable combinations.

The character size can be of four values, ranging from relatively large to small signs. Underlining is available for alphanumeric characters without changing their shape or color characteristics.

Inverting causes the exchange of foreground and background for a given sign. Flashing is another presentation element which can be used to attract attention by itself or in combination with inverting.

The facility of covered-up signs can be activated by the user or by the system for security reasons. This is an important characteristic with on-line access for home banking, POS (point of sales), electronic messaging and other services.

Windows can be used as rectangular frame sections defined through sign positioning. A window interrupts the videotex picture and can be manipulated as a separate function from the rest of the frame. Windows may also permit bringing in video pictures to an otherwise text, data, and graphics-oriented frame—and conversely, video pictures can have windows making feasible the presentation of videotex information.

Dynamically redefinable character sets (DRCS) allow the user to take advantage of the resolution capacity of the TV screen. The system supports 94 signs (at a 12x10 point raster) or 188 signs (at 6x10). This is considered sufficient for most applications. (A DRCS contains definable characters whose patterns can be downloaded from the host.)

The combination of high picture resolution with attribute changes per sign and the usage even of a limited amount of redefinable signs can lead to impressive results. The alphamosaic mode of presentation, followed by CEPT, employs control signs and sign sequences. These are coordinated in the basic control sign inventory (C0) and the additional control sign list (C1).

The object of a C-set is control functions. The C0 and C1 comprise 32 character positions, each arranged in 2 columns by 16 rows (We will return to this concept.)

The C0 signs are combined in functional groups according to their operating characteristics—format control, cursor and other machine controls, protocol functions (acknowledgement, confirmation), and code extension (such as shifting to change the meaning of a coming sign). Control and presentation signs are grouped in the transmission code. Character sets can be recalled through control sign sequences introduced from a library.

The control characters of C1 modify the presentation attributes of definable signs and change the picture content. In the standard set, different codes and modification possibilities are available. The model allows alternative usage through a loading procedure for each of the available sets.

The PLP Standard

PLP (presentation level protocol) is the American standard advanced by ANSI and propelled by AT&T. It is alphageometric, though it handles mosaics as well. It features 8 G-sets (graphic sets) vs. the 7 G-sets of CEPT.

The G-set refers to one of four sets: G0, G1, G2 or G3, each of which comprises 94 or 96 character positions arranged in 6 columns by 16 rows. A G-set repertory is the collection of available code sets that are subject to designation as one of the G-sets.

In the general sense, the graphic character repertory consists of the list of graphic characters, including accented letters and signs obtained by the composition of two or more graphic symbols. A *geometric graphic primitive* is a locally stored picture-drawing algorithm that can be called through a specific opcode and associated operands.

With PLP:

operation in both 7-bit and 8-bit environments can be accommodated

ASCII alphanumerics, a set of supplementary graphics characters, and the DRCS are provided for the encoding text (Figure 19.1)

both alphamosaic and alphageometric primitives can be used to create graphic displays.

Mosaics are compatible with Prestel and Antiope coding. Geometric primitives are compatible with the PDI (picture description instruction) of Telidon.

A DRCS contains a maximum of 96 custom definable TEXT characters. TEXT are predefined pel patterns which, when called, are drawn with a set of preselected attributes on the screen. Also important is the *unit screen* which represents the virtual display address space within which TEXT characters are deposited and all PDI are executed. Horizontal (X), vertical (Y) and depth (Z) dimensions are defined, the latter only in three-dimensional mode. The unit screen concept is presented in Figure 19.2.

A basic notion is the presentation protocol data unit (PPDU). It is made up of two parts: presentation protocol control information (PPCI) and the presentation service data unit (PSDU).

Figure 19.1. ASCII alphanumerics.

ROW/COLUMN	10 2	11 3	12 4	13 5	14 6	15 7
0	SPACE	0	@	P	`	p
1	!	1	A	Q	a	q
2	"	2	B	R	b	r
3	#	3	C	S	c	s
4	$	4	D	T	d	t
5	%	5	E	U	e	u
6	&	6	F	V	f	v
7	'	7	G	W	g	w
8	(	8	H	X	h	x
9	)	9	I	Y	i	y
10	*	:	J	Z	j	z
11	+	;	K	[	k	{
12	,	<	L	\	l	|
13	-	=	M	]	m	}
14	.	>	N	∧	n	_
15	/	?	O	—	o	■

ASCII ALPHANUMERICS

Figure 19.2. Unit screen concept.

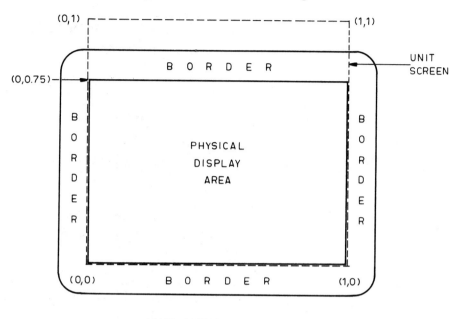

UNIT SCREEN CONCEPT

There can be either a data PSDU or a management PSDU. The syntax used inside a data PSDU is specified in:

national data syntax standards (ANSI X3.4)

the International Reference Version (IRV)

North American PLPS (which in this text is referred to as PLP)

CEPT Videotex.

This syntax is designed to be compatible both with the ISO 2022 Code Extension standard and the ISO Open Systems Interconnection. It is intended for character-oriented systems where each character is examined by the receiving presentation process, and bit-oriented systems where the use of a length field in the header is common practice. Commands may occur in any order within a single management PSDU and are interpreted in the order in which they occur.

Unless otherwise indicated, each type of management command may either be absent or have one occurence within a single management PSDU. When a command is absent, the aspect of the presentation process that it controls remains unaffected unless indicated otherwise in the specification.

Parameter values are assigned starting at decimal value 0 for each command. The 0 value is also the default value for a command when a presentation process is

Figure 19.3.

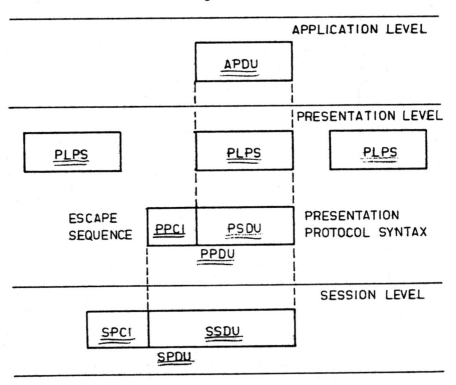

APDU   APPLICATION PROTOCOL DATA UNIT
PPCI   PRESENTATION PROTOCOL CONTROL INFORMATION
PPDU   PRESENTATION PROTOCOL DATA UNIT
PSDU   PRESENTATION SERVICE DATA UNIT

initiated or the presentation layer is reset using the *reset presentation layer* (RPL) management command. If a management command is implemented, the default parameter value is also implemented. If a given management command is not implemented by a receiving presentation process, the presentation semantics associated with the default value should be implemented unless indicated otherwise in the recommendation.

The default presentation process is a national data syntax using a display or printer presentation device. Many of the management commands and command parameter values are optional from the point of view of implementation by the receiving presentation process as indicated explicitly in the recommendation.

The presentation data syntax is prohibited from containing certain code combinations lest they be misinterpreted as presentation level commands. This will not cause a conflict with the presentation level data syntaxes currently supported by this

Figure 19.4.

				b7	0	0	0	0	1	1	1	1
				b6	0	0	1	1	0	0	1	1
				b5	0	1	0	1	0	1	0	1
b4	b3	b2	b1	COLUMN / ROW	0	1	2	3	4	5	6	7
0	0	0	0	0								
0	0	0	1	1								
0	0	1	0	2								
0	0	1	1	3								
0	1	0	0	4								
0	1	0	1	5								
0	1	1	0	6								
0	1	1	1	7	CØ SET		G SET					
1	0	0	0	8								
1	0	0	1	9								
1	0	1	0	10								
1	0	1	1	11								
1	1	0	0	12								
1	1	0	1	13								
1	1	1	0	14								
1	1	1	1	15								

protocol, as the presentation level coding syntax—which is based on ISO 2022—was chosen to be compatible with the presentation level coding syntax.

However, in the future, this may not be the case as more sophisticated presentation level data syntaxes are introduced. To accommodate these future data syntaxes, which require full use of the address space provided by the presentation level code, a transparent mode can be selected. While in transparent mode, the presentation level process utilizes a byte-stuffing mechanism to distinguish presentation level commands from presentation level data. The transparent mode facility is provided as an optional facility. The byte-stuffing mechanism is used to distinguish presentation level commands from presentation level data. All PPDU begin with the two-character escape sequence (Figure 19.3).

While in transparent mode, the presentation process in the sending station will constantly scan the outgoing presentation level data, seeking byte combinations corresponding to the escape code sequence. (This scanning does not necessarily need to be done in realtime.) When this sequence is detected, a data link escape control character is inserted into the byte stream after the escape sequence.

Parallel and serial mode controls both set only serial attributes in the terminal memory. Parallel mode controls apply attributes to character locations where the cursor prints a character (including space), and with few exceptions remains with the cursor when it moves between rows. Serial mode control codes insert or modify a market into the market memory and cause the attribute to be copied immediately into the attribute memory until a contradictory or complementary market is encountered, or until the end of the row.

Parallel and serial mode control codes are taken from different control sets and therefore may be unambiguously recognized by the terminal. The invocation of a serial C1 set will cause the mode of operation of the terminal to switch. The effect will be restored when the parallel mode is reinvoked. There is no special positioning dependence if the order-drawing primitives are presented. Pictures are built from a sequence of drawing commands. Each new command is superimposed over the preceding. Hence, pictures are built up in layers.

The protocol does not guarantee the registration between alphanumerics and graphics to be exact, thus permitting the standard to be implemented on various types of display hardware. In the absence of any specific character type specification, the display format will be 4 columns by 20 rows. Other display columns call for the appropriate commands to define the suitable character sizes.

Four G-sets and two C-sets are designated at any one time through an invocation sequence. The latter may be locking or unlocking. A designation sequence is used to establish a new meaning to a code set slot.

In a 7-bit environment, a 128-code position in-use table is defined in Figure 19.4. The table is structured in 8 columns by 16 rows. An incoming bit combination is either decoded according to the current contents in this table or used to change its contents. Code extension procedures increase the number of code combinations.

When operating in an 8-bit environment, 256 codes are available. They can be

Figure 19.5.

b8	0	0	0	0	0	0	0	0	1	1	1	1	1	1	1	1
b7	0	0	0	0	1	1	1	1	0	0	0	0	1	1	1	1
b6	0	0	1	1	0	0	1	1	0	0	1	1	0	0	1	1
b5	0	1	0	1	0	1	0	1	0	1	0	1	0	1	0	1

b4 b3 b2 b1	ROW	0	1	2	3	4	5	6	7	8	9	10	11	12	13	14	15
0 0 0 0	0																
0 0 0 1	1																
0 0 1 0	2																
0 0 1 1	3																
0 1 0 0	4																
0 1 0 1	5																
0 1 1 0	6																
0 1 1 1	7	cø			GL					C1			GR				
1 0 0 0	8																
1 0 0 1	9																
1 0 1 0	10																
1 0 1 1	11																
1 1 0 0	12																
1 1 0 1	13																
1 1 1 0	14																
1 1 1 1	15																

increased through code extension procedures, as with the 7-bit code. The table is organized into 16 columns with 16 rows (Figure 19.5).

A supplementary character set of accents, marks and special characters for Latin-based alphabets is shown in Figure 19.6. It reflects CCITT Recommendation S 100, but also comprises additional characters proposed by ISO and other organizations.

The PDI shown in Figure 19.7 includes:

6 geometric graphic primitives: point, line, arc, rectangle, polygon and incremental—each of which has four forms

8 color codes: reset, domain, text, texture, set color, wait, select color, blink

64 character positions for numeric data.

The PDI character set does not consist of predefined patterns, one per character, but of executable *drawing functions*. These produce an image not necessarily restricted to a single character field.

Handling Graphics

Geometric drawing operations assure the capability of drawing cycles, segments of circles, lines, rectangles and polygons. Each is specified as a series of coordinates within the framework of the supported protocol.

Figure 19.6. Supplementary graphics.

COLUMN ROW	10	11	12	13	14	15
	2	3	4	5	6	7
0	SPACE	°	⟶	—	Ω	ĸ
1	¡	±	`	¹	Æ	æ
2	¢	²	´	®	Đ	đ
3	£	³	ˆ	©	a̲	ð
4	$	×	~	TM	Ħ	ħ
5	¥	µ	‾	♪	┼	˘
6	#	₶	˘	─	IJ	ij
7	§	·	•	│	Ŀ	ŀ
8	¤	÷	¨		Ł	ŧ
9	'	ˀ	/		Ø	ø
10	"	"	°		Œ	œ
11	<<	>>	♭		Ǫ	β
12	←	¼		⅛	Þ	þ
13	↑	½	"	⅜	Ŧ	ŧ
14	→	¾	ʟ	⅝	ħ	h
15	↓	ċ	ˇ	⅞	ˀn	■

SUPPLEMENTARY GRAPHICS

Figure 19.7. PDI codes.

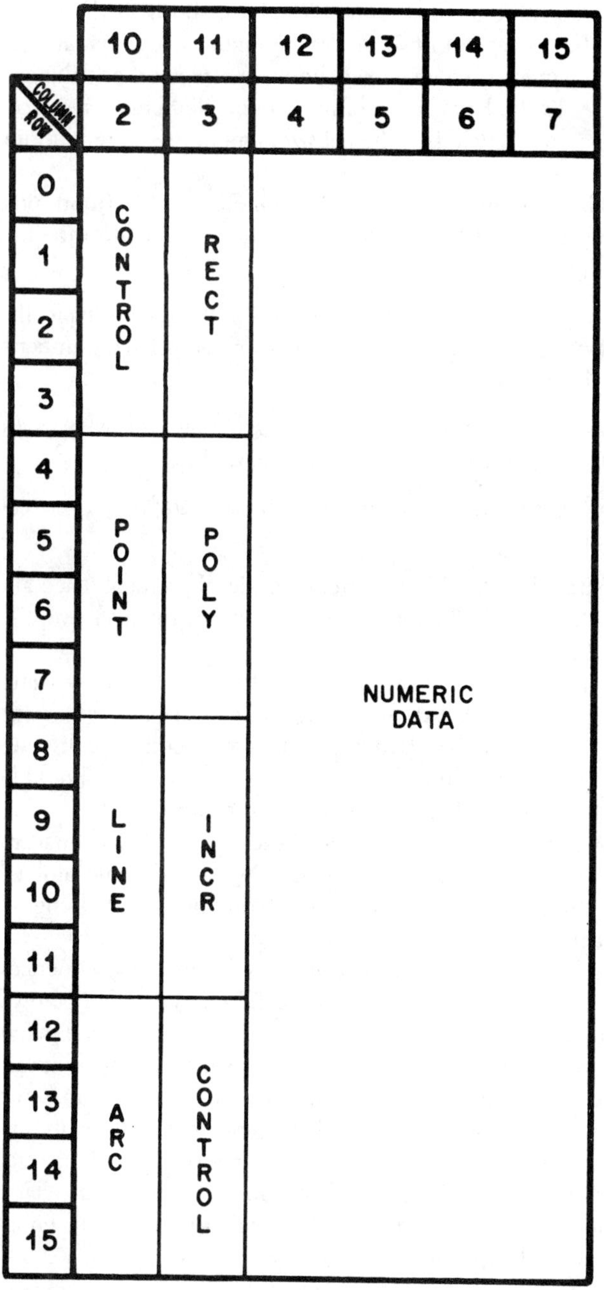

PDI CODES

Character assignments for the mosaic set are shown in Figure 19.8. Mosaic characters can be displayed in two modes: contiguous and separate. In the former, the six mosaic elements in a character should completely span the given character field at any size. In the latter, each of the mosaic elements is reduced in the horizontal dimension by the width of the pel size, and in the retrieval dimension by the height of the pel size.

Though alphamosaics were the first graphic characters (more precisely, semigraphics) to be supported by videotex, the options today are much broader. In a nutshell, they include:

alphamosaics, based on a grid-like division of the screen, typically 40 columns by 24 rows where each cell can contain any one of a fixed number of predefined graphics characters

alphageometrics corresponding to vector generation displays where images are composed of points, lines, arcs, polygons, and text

alphaphotographics implemented through raster graphics where codes for pixels are transmitted sequentially.

Remember that at the level of the presentation level protocol (PLP), another important definition is the pel, the logical presentation element, as we discussed at the beginning of this chapter.

Let's recall that dynamically redefinable character sets allow each page to use a tailored character set by first transmitting the cell display corresponding to each code and then one or more grids of codes that define complete display images. The coding techniques for dynamically redefinable character sets should be resolution-independent to accommodate developments in technology.

Alphamosaics and alphageometrics fit the objectives of management graphics at different levels of precision and cost. Alphageometrics and alphaphotographics answer the CAD/CAM requirement and bring computer-assisted engineering within everyone's reach.

Finally, macro features offer the capability of encoding sequences of presentation level codes to be executed upon command. A macro can be used by designating the macro set as one of the G-sets, followed by invoking the macro set into the in-use table and transmitting the macro code. A nesting capability is feasible.

A service reference model (SRM) outlines a set of specific implementation parameters for a particular service and defines the functionality available to an information provider and service operation for text, data, image generation and display. New features can be grouped into logically consistent classes to be employed for the definition of additional G-sets and C-sets. This enhances existing graphics and control capabilities.

International Coordination

While PLP and CEPT are good standards, they are not necessarily compatible. What has become an international norm are the presentation process commands for syntax and bit mode selection, as well as a number of syntactical aspects.

Figure 19.8. Mosaic graphics.

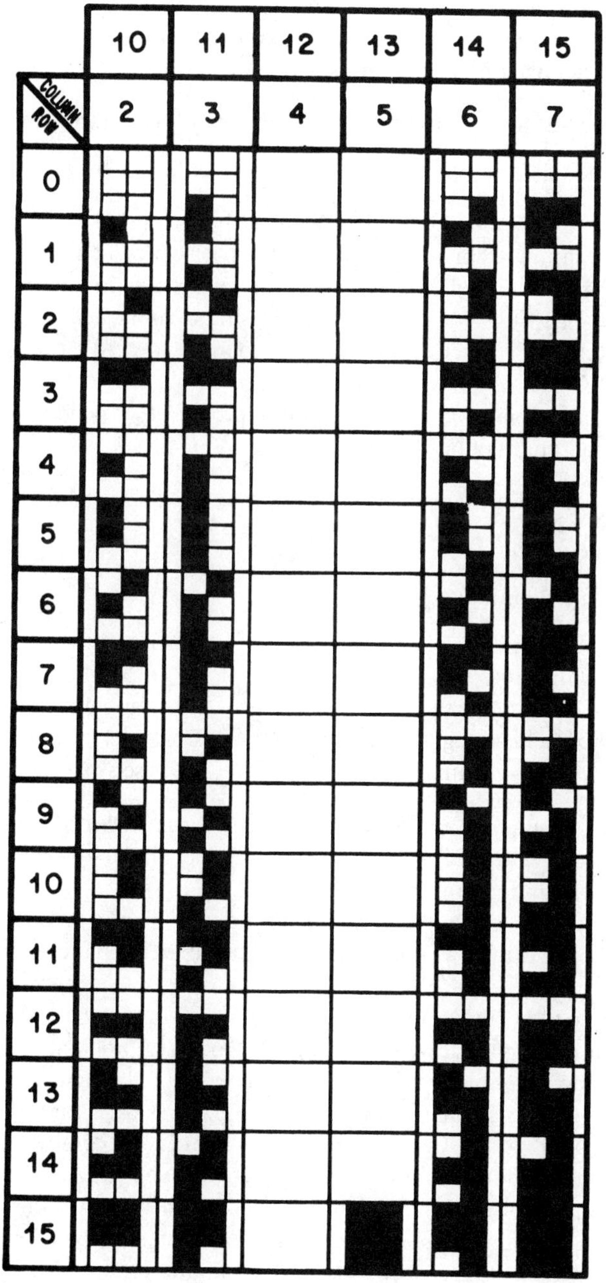

MOSAIC GRAPHICS

One function of the presentation layer is *selection of the presentation process within the terminal* that will be participating in the data transfer. Presentation processes are characterized by two parameters:

the presentation level data syntax used (national, PLP, CERT), and

the bit mode in which the data syntax is interpreted (7-bit or 8-bit).

Each type of presentation process can at most be in one of three states: active, suspended, or terminated (inactive). One and only one presentation process may be active at any time. This is the process that will be participating in the presentation level data exchange with the host. For instance, there can be an active CEPT process and a suspended CEPT process, and there cannot be an active PLP process and a suspended PLP.

Furthermore, when, for instance, the PLP process is suspended, the following display attributes are maintained:

macro set definitions

DRCS set definitions

texture mask definitions

color map contents

blink processes

unprotected fields (including contents).

All other parameters are set to their default values.

Permitting multiple PLPs allows the various groups concerned with the normalization to proceed with their work independently provided they registered their PLP with the PLP registration authority.

Each PLP working group is particularly suited to support the requirements of the body developing it, which will be responsible for the maintenance and evolution of its norms.

More difficult in terms of an international agreement has been the task of arriving at common graphic set standards. Originally, a proposal was advanced to the coordinating committee in Geneva—which labored to establish a common international graphics standard—to merge the PLP and CEPT into 11 G-sets. This rested on the fact that four G-groups in each standard were common graphics sets. However, no compromise could be reached. It was then suggested that CEPT plus PLP equal 15 graphic sets. Agreement could not be reached on this basis, either, while another argument regarded the complete code and its possible expansion.

As a result, emphasis has been placed on a higher level protocol which would allow switching between national or regional G-sets instead of changing on an equal basis among graphics on a common pool of 15 G-sets. Hence, at a lower level switching will be done equally within the 8 PLP or 7 CEPT G-sets, and at a higher level, switching will take place between standards representing whole groups of sets at the cost of three extra characters.

When switching between CEPT, PLP, and other data syntaxes, the screen must retain the old information and add the new (provided that the character field height in PLP has been explicitly set to this end). Provision for private use commands and private use parameters of standard commands should be included. (Private use coding is allocated to implementors for private or experimental use. These coding allocations will most likely never be standardized, internationally or nationally.)

Furthermore, the syntax for management commands should be general enough so that new commands can be added in the future in a compatible way such that presentation processes can be implemented that would be able to ignore them.

The solution, adopted in Geneva in February 1983, permits greater flexibility, such as adding other standards groups—Japanese characters, audio signs, and so on. Understandably, a standard along these lines greatly changes what is available today in Videotex facilities. It makes obsolete existing systems (like Prestel and Antiope), but opens the way to new developments.

Let's now examine the requirements for observing an international normalization, from character coding to protocols.

In standardizing information interchanges (for Videotex or other processes), we can consider a logical order of progress from agreement on the coding requirements to the exact presentation semantics, the coding syntax and the protocols. If we wish to apply coding techniques into a single, international Videotex norm, we have to establish a system-wide procedure. (This was the first objective in defining characters in a DRCS set.) Bit combinations from any C- or G-set may be used including C0, CI, PDI, primary, supplemental, mosaic, macro, and the DRCS set itself. Subsequently, when defining characters in the macro set, characters from any other C- or G-set may be used including C0, C1, primary, supplemental, mosaic, DRCS, and PDI sets.

Within a PDI sequence for a single command, macro characters can be employed in place of numeric operands provided they contain only numeric operand data.

With this background, it should be possible for one service to select whole character sets from others. The screen will not be implicitly cleared when switching between data syntaxes. Also, more than one PLP is not excluded in the ISO/OSI model (Open Systems Interconnection). Therefore, the recommendation for a unified presentation layer for Videotex should be independent of other OSI layer functions.

PART FOUR

Networks

20

Three Generations of Networks

The functions, capabilities, and possible implications of data communications systems can be better appreciated by taking a brief look at the origins of computer technology.

The era of the commercially available data processor, as we know it today, started with Univac 1 and the IBM series 701, 702, 650. At the time, both appealed primarily to the batch processing business machines market, and for good reason. In 1952–53 IBM and Remington Rand (in that order) controlled the punched card, accounting machines, and related equipment market.* An accounting machine of the IBM 401 type had no teletransmission problems to cope with. It simply didn't possess the facility which brings the data communications problem into perspective. This is equally true of the highly successful IBM 650 in the 1950s which employed the 401 as a basic unit for input–output.

Both Univac and IBM integrated the computer with the accounting machines product line and sold the advancement in data handling presented by computer technology† as an extension of old concepts, but not as something totally new. The early users maintained an outlook fairly similar to that of the vendors. The story of computers might have been totally different had the first machines been launched by AT&T or GTE. This situation prevailed in the early and mid-1950s in terms of applications, since in its early configuration the computer answered three needs: arithmetic calculation, logical operations, and internal storage (though limited by the fact that the early media were bulky and, correspondingly, of low storage capacity).

*Though equipment was also used, particularly during World War II, for scientific calculations, this was, firstly, a rather exceptional use and, secondly, the card programmed approaches adopted for mathematical formulas were of a totally different concept than computers as we know them today.

†Particularly the stored program capabilities (ill-appreciated at the time except by geniuses like Von Neumann and Oppenheimer) and the memory capacity of the machine.

The Early Periods

Historically, the development of computers is comprised of three periods. During the *first period*, about 1950–1957, the central processors disposed of input–output routines limited to the communication of data via classic peripheral units which were largely batch oriented.

In the 1950s we spoke of "input-bound" and of "output-bound" operations. The problem of early users was to identify and then obtain the necessary media which would eliminate bottlenecks at both the input and output ends of the system. This state of affairs is germane to the hardware components. In terms of software, it was not until 1958 that the first input–output control system (IOCS) routines start being used; at about the same time the first experience in long-distance data communications took place: a tape to tape data transmission between the Andrews Air Force Base in the United States and the SHAPE Headquarters near Orleans, France.

This experience opened the way to the *second period* characterized by the input–output control of peripheral units, by means of specially written software, and the first batch-type data communication.

Although in a way these two developments are distinct from one another, they produced a joint effect: the beginning of the *third period*, whose particularity was the development and use of special software necessary to drive terminals at long distance and, along with them, the needed interfaces with the telephone line.

This experience had nothing in common with the control of a communications network as we know it today. The terminals were extremely simple, indeed, just typewriters with a line controller. Yet, the availability of simple, unsophisticated terminals and some basic software induced imaginative minds to play with a new idea: time sharing.

Time sharing is a milestone in data communications. By 1963–64 there was evidence that users might be amenable to abandoning the old habit of batch processing; they considered sharing the facilities provided by a centrally located machine. The possibility of handling on-line data processing problems was, here and there, taking root.

The asynchronous mode had its day. But users (who quite often, if incorrectly, tried batch solutions through time-sharing terminals)* established through practice the need for more efficient alternatives. It took a few more years until finally synchronous protocols were accepted.

Point-to-Point

Point-to-point data transmission was the usual solution for these operations. Transmission was character by character, and a message was composed of as many characters as necessary. But overhead expenses also boomed as data communica-

---

*Time sharing, correctly implemented, simply means rapid access to a small amount of information. It is the negation of batch. However, many users misapply time sharing as on-line batch capability.

tions loads increased. Cost brought the need for efficiency, and this concern, coupled with the advances made in technology, led to the *fourth period* (mid to late 1960s) in computer development characterized by the advancement of synchronous protocols and the more sophisticated teleprocessing software, specific, however, to the type of terminal.

The *lack of standardization*, which characterized this period, is with us even today. As data loads boomed, gaping holes in data communications came to light. As usual, necessity spurred new research. In 1967 IBM introduced the binary synchronous communication, BSC, protocols. Synchronous communications were already demonstrating a definite advantage over asynchronous by effectively using resources.

Parallel to the developments in systems which characterized the late fifties and the decade of the sixties, we experienced an evolution in data communications equipment. One is tempted to classify the tape-to-tape devices used for batch transmission as the "beginning." As regards terminals, this "beginning" includes the largely unintelligent units transmitting in an asynchronous mode (lates 1950s, mid-1960s).

Let us recall that early computers integrated punched card and accounting machines as their input–output media. The first consoles were rudimentary; the terminals were teletypewriters and teletypes. There was no data communications industry as such. By the late sixties the situation had changed. The impact of terminals manufacturers started being felt, and the mainframe companies launched terminal product lines. Indeed, some of them, for instance, Univac, even set up a separate division.

The real-time applications of the mid-1960s (airline reservation systems, for example) gave impetus to the direction which the design of terminals should take. Video scopes came into perspective, and the term "soft copy" as opposed to "hard copy" started to be used.

The new terminals had many advantages over their predecessors. They used synchronous protocols, had buffers, and, applicationswise, became integrated into well-designed, though elementary, networks. Experiments were made with new approaches to telecommunication software, although the latter was largely machine dependent.

The First Generation

Data communications as a packet switching discipline, born with the ARPA Project, was to become one of the most dynamic fields in information technology. Earlier solutions were rudimentary by today's standards. They were private networks using the concepts of the fourth period (hence, asymmetric): centralized, starlike, with point-to-point and multidrop lines. Public networks started as an outgrowth of the private. Still, private networks are in the majority today, although inefficient as concerns the use of equipment, lines, and manpower. Economies of scale have not

Figure 20.1
Network architecture of the first generation: Arpanet, Tymnet, and Cyclades

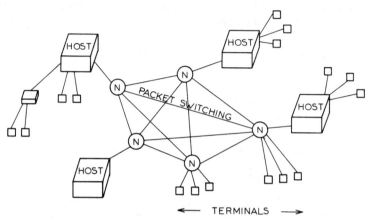

yet been realized through the use of the private networks, and, generally speaking, it is doubtful if they will be. (Incidentally, by 1973 value added public networks had already started to develop.)

they will be. (Incidentally, by 1973 public networks had already started to develop.)

The faculties of a data communications network as we conceive it now were not present ten years ago. That is why a distinction between "period" and "generation" is necessary to keep up with established practices. The word *generation* has been consistently used in literature to identify hardware developments. *Period*, as used in this text, is related to the evolution of the systems concepts which often precede (though also sometimes follow) the hardware generation.

In the late sixties, when ARPA investigated packet-switching networks,* the need for a more efficient means than BSC was just starting to be felt. The image wasn't there, and the components of the data transmission systems were costly or limited in their capabilities. Memory was still expensive, which created the need to minimize buffers. The Node (minicomputer) could only handle up to three hosts, and, furthermore, had to be located near them; layout and organization were such as to render them not as reliable as desired. The network had to be very tight; besides, there wasn't enough traffic with which to load the network. The early concepts of the first generation were shaped by machine capability—and this dictated "what could be done."

Figure 20.1 gives a glimpse of the network architecture of the First Generation. Note the clear distinction between node† and host. Arpanet and Tymnet (both United States) and Cyclades (France) are examples.

---

*A communications network which employs "packets" as the basic unit of text transmission. A "packet" is a bit string of determined maximum length which is transmitted as a whole.

†Communication equipment placed at sensitive communication spots (nodes) to which bit strings can be directed via communications facilities using a unique destination address.

Figure 20.2
Switch to public data network concept

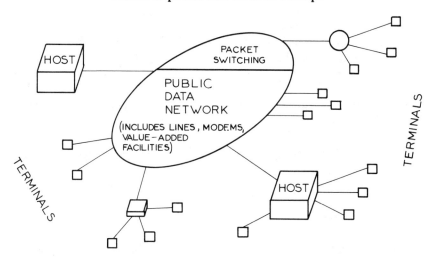

The Second Generation

With the first generation, machine capacity (host, node—individually), not cumulative network capacity, dictated what could be done. But the *fifth period* of conceptual development which started in the early seventies clearly demonstrated the need for software-controlled data transmission.* Furthermore, at the private network sites, though still behind Arpanet, users started to take an active hand in selecting the characteristics of the equipment they would employ, including the choice of components, microprocessors, memories, etc., with which they would build their own concentrators.

At the systems level, front ends started to become a favored solution. Performance made the difference—and people became aware of it.

Over a period of a few years, new types of hardware enhanced the principles which guided this fifth period. The dramatic drop in costs per bit of data storage, though just starting, opened new horizons. Memory capability was added at the terminal level.

As users became aware of a publicly offered network service, they appreciated that they could one day literally plug into a value-added carrier.† This concept, shown in Figure 20.2, is at the origin of the second generation.

---

*Typically stored at the host facility, the front ends, and the concentrator, rather than the value-added network (VAN) and the terminal itself which will characterize subsequent periods.

†Used synonymously with VAN. A communications network which employs common carrier facilities for transmission and provides in addition such services as path selection (routing), error detection, store and forward, retransmission, recovery, and so on.

Author's note: Paul Baran, of the RAND Corporation, first developed the concept of using data in packets as opposed to a continuous flow of data.

Several differences between the first and the second generations of data communication networks should be noted:

All first generation networks (with the exception of Tymnet which is private) were government financed.

Public networks,* whether run by the telephone utility or by other commercial firms, came as an outgrowth of private networks. Economies of scale were the objectives.

The second generation benefited from the basic economics. The cost of buffer space was in the meantime reduced by a factor of 10.

Nodes of the second generation can stand alone; see Figure 20.3.

Reliability in the second generation is considerably higher; 99.99 percent is the goal.

Duplex technology is used and the circuits can be highly loaded and quite efficiently at that.

The "hub" principle in data transmission has been adopted. Hub costs money, but results in better utilization of the lines.

Improvements in standards and performance are bringing data transmission costs down by factor 10.

The second generation offers store and forward facilities, and the user may attach both hosts and terminals at his discretion.

Typically, second generation networks observe the standard X.25. This is the mark of the times. Conceived in the early seventies, after the Arpanet experiences started coming into the public domain, and implemented in 1976–77, the second generation networks—Telenet (United States; commercial), Datapac (Canada; telephone utility) and Transpac (France; PTT†) were able to implement the new standards.

Merging Technologies

Among the new technologies is the virtual circuit idea. This is a point-to-point switched circuit over which data and commands (reset, interrupt, flow control) are transmitted. Virtual circuits may or may not, be a direct piece of wire, but are nevertheless a physical unit. The public network provides the routing and the flow control, giving the user a virtual circuit whenever he needs to communicate with another user. DIS implementation is thus enhanced.

Value-added networks, VAN, offer a multiple connection host interface; see Figure 20.4. This makes the private lines which came into existence with the centralized real-time approaches of the mid-1960s both very costly and obsolete. The economic trend which brought us from message to package switching has not

---

*Not to be confused with COAM—company owned and operated data networks.
†Poste, Telegraph, Telephone

Figure 20.3
Network architecture of the second generation: Telenet, Datapac, and Transpac

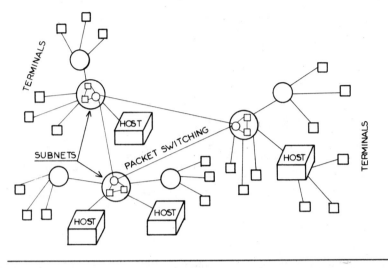

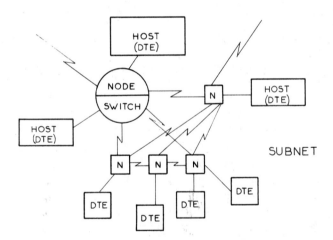

stopped. We are faced today with companies which are still living in the sixties with their centralized real-time solutions (while paying very dearly for them) while others have already moved into the eighties with DIS and VAN. The distributed information system thus has its roots in dollars, cents, and efficiency. By bringing data entry, computing, and storage to the point in the organization where the action takes place, distributed data systems have a much greater impact on information processing and on the architecture of the data system.

To summarize, the early to mid-1970s saw a fantastic expansion in private

Figure 20.4
Multiple connection host interface

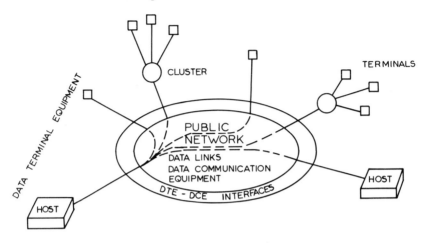

communication networks. The special software by type of terminal (or concentrator) became commonplace, while users started questioning the wisdom of emulating (usually IBM's line) communications software by type of device. To a very large extent, this was followed by small manufacturers who wanted to carve a share out of IBM's huge market.

Yet, no matter what the origins may be, this emulation of hardware opened new horizons and along with them the *sixth period* which, with minor exceptions began in the mid-1970s and is still gaining momentum. This is the time of distributed intelligence served by value-added carriers (Tymnet, Telenet, etc.) rather than through the private telephone lines of the third, fourth, and fifth periods. Beyond a doubt, the future telecommunication networks for data handling will be value-added: carriers with improved capabilities for error detection and correction, store and forward, and related data services.

Parallel to network structures and system architectures, users want, and manufacturers are on the point of producing, new hardware and software characteristics to be imbedded into the communications equipment now being projected. Typically, such terminals will incorporate a microprocessor, be very intelligent, and integrate in a telephone network, which follows the protocol X.25. The transition will take some years to settle down, and even in the late eighties there may be asynchronous terminals still in operation.* (Until the early sixties, IBM derived more income from punched card equipment than from computers). This, however, does not diminish the importance of being in the foreground of technology, to learn from the cost effectiveness of technological advancement. The producers of data systems should only be satisfied with leadership. The users should miss no opportunity to gain from the new horizons which technology is opening up.

*Indeed, today the asynchronous terminals form the majority.

Figure 20.5

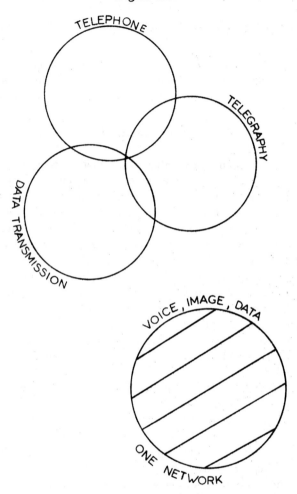

The merging of telephone (voice), telegraphy, telex, and data transmission into one single network (Figure 20.5) providing data, image, and voice facilities will have a colossal impact on the evolution of communications. It will bring about increased reliability, speeded up services, and drastic reductions in costs. This transition will present challenges both at the manufacturers' and at the users' sites. Telegraphy is a redundant process and is not even very reliable. Data transmission must be correct; it is better not to receive a message than to receive an erroneous one. On the other hand, data transmission is ten times more efficient than voice communications.

The merging communications technologies will open up tremendous capabilities:

1. *Teleconferencing* ("communicate—don't commute")

2. *Optimization of resources* (Use computers globally. When it is 7:00 P.M. in London, it is 10:00 A.M. in Los Angeles.)
3. *Serving the man with the problem (bringing the equipment capabilities to him, and not vice versa)*

It is obviously far more efficient to have common development and maintenance of the general-purpose communications facilities than to still have artificial (and obsolete) subdivisions because of the way systems have somehow developed.

Network Interfaces

We spoke earlier of coupling of intelligent terminals directly with value-added networks. This will have significant consequences for both users and manufacturers. The "pulling" of the network intelligence back into the terminal will open a new era of applications: remote batch, order entry, and point-of-sales credit verification. These are but a few of the possibilities which exist. Home computers will help optimize the use of lines (data, voice), and microcomputers will manage each distinct operation, including the lines themselves.

At the network level, VAN will take over many faculties which normally the individual user today must personally watch. Whether they are private or public, emphasis is on the words *value added*. This comprises functions such as monitoring, routing, journaling, error detection and correction. Such functions are a must in telecommunications. If the network does not provide them (and at present it does not), then we, the users—albeit in a more elementary way—must see them through and at a higher cost.

Monitoring is vital. It can be achieved both through hardware and software, distributed throughout the network. Actual monitoring is usually accomplished from one or a few control centers. By intelligent use of automatic remote checkout logic, including remote sensing of component failure, degradation,* and out-of-service conditions, failures may be detected and personnel dispatched for either node or channel repair. Statistics may be generated to measure the internal performance of the communications network, for instance, queue lengths, message sizes, line loads, time-up, overall response and routing, to aid in tuning the system and providing fault detection and correction. Many of these functions have been developed with the presently operating VAN. Others are currently under study.

Naturally, lessons learned from the first generation were applied both in the second and in the third, and although the basic concepts have changed, first generation networks are still going strong. Tymnet is a successful commercial operation which, among other firsts, has to its credit the concept of on-line maintenance; Arpanet helped build the very fine community of data communications scientists which exists today.

But the first generation also plays the vital role of the test bed on which some of the most advanced concepts are developed. One of these concepts is the integration

---

*Gradual deterioration in performance.

Figure 20.6

Basic modes of host–terminal access. Packet BSC and asynchronous DTE are accepted. Network transmission is X.25.

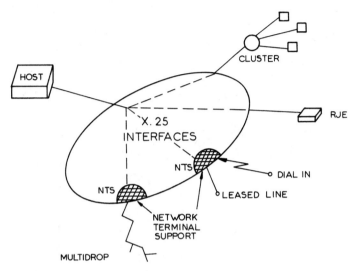

of synchronous and asynchronous transmission together with packet switching for the reasons discussed in the preceding pages. The economies of synchronous transmission are basically the same as those of asynchronous but protocol conversion and local cost of communications are primary factors in making the choice.

It is so much better to have VAN facilities to which we can admit asynchronous, synchronous, and packet switching disciplines by providing the right ports for each; see Figure 20.6. Interfaces can be assured. The problem of polling is solved by hub polling and contention. Dial-in capabilities and automatic calling by terminals with significant local memory will open new horizons at the user's site.

All this is more than just distributed information systems. The high-speed memory, and quite likely the auxiliary memory as well, may no longer reside with concentrators, but with the terminal. The terminal will, in essence, be a minicomputer or microcomputer. The successors to Intel's 8080 (8088, 8086, 80186, 80286) offer large-scale integration arithmetic, logical, and control functions on a chip. SDLC/HDLC will be on a chip and likewise the X.25 protocol. Terminals will necessarily be designed to support the network functions, augmenting the user's data communication abilities. The telephone set could be a microcomputer, and it will become difficult to distinguish a telephone set from a terminal.

On a macroscopic level, internetworking disciplines must be developed which will permit users of one network to communicate with those of another. Simultaneous multiple connections are needed and new standards permit internetworking.

Figure 20.7
Network architecture of the third generation

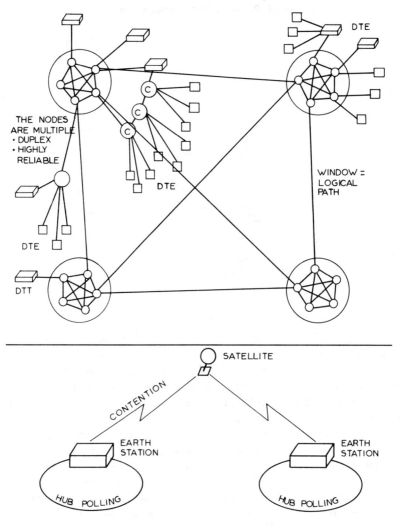

The Third Generation

The concepts which will characterize the third generation of data communication networks (Figure 20.7) are already being developed today.

Satellite communications play a vital role.
Distances play only a secondary role; tarriffs are volume based.
Contention control and token passing are the prevailing disciplines.

Figure 20.8
Solution to the problem of rigidity

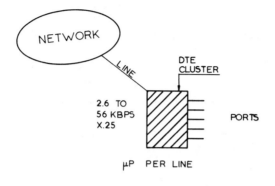

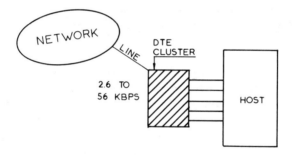

Networks keep track of the "windows" (logical paths; availability to receive) of the data terminal equipment, DTE, which it serves.

The DTE has ample buffers, with PC contesting in this process.

Transmission lines will be characterized by high reliability.

Each line will have its own microprocessor and memory.

Communications systems will be highly modular: start small, then add new nodes and clusters.

Nodes and clusters will be of a different architecture in different parts of the network.

The user's DTE will specialize according to type and level of requirements.

Attached devices will range from nonintelligent terminals to PCs, minis, and mainframes—with personal computers taking the lead.

The breadth of services will steadily increase beyond the first offerings (electronic mail) to include Videotex and other facilities.

IBM's Information Network and AT&T's Net 1000 fall into the category of the third generation. At the same time, local area networks constitute the best example of subnetworking.

Third generation VAN-like Net 1000 can accept inputs from local digital loops, and is mediated by a digital common carrier without the intervention of modems. It will be some time before such services are generally available to end users.

Meanwhile, developments in network diagnostics and control are featured in the new offerings. Especially important is the ability to pinpoint problems—determining if they are related to hardware, software, or lines, and then narrowing the area of search.

In the foreseeable future, third generation networks will generalize an X.25 technology which has by now reached maturity.

As previously discussed, a protocol—the basic configuration of a packet switching network—is a block of serially arranged data (bit, strings, or bytes) exchanged between two terminals, or between a terminal and a node. The packet protocol calls for a flag, a direction field, a control field, the information proper, a check done through a frame check sequence and a closing flag. (The frame check sequence (FCS) is usually two bytes. These two bytes are referred to as CRC).

The information field may not be present in certain packets which are known as supervisory frames (S) and unnumbered frames (U). They address themselves to the data link control whose goal is to enclose the data packet in an XDLC structure and its transmission on the network.

The supervisory functions are utilized to effect a control on the link: acceptance of the packets, requests for the transmission of packets, or requests for a temporary suspension of the transmission.

There are four system parameters defined by the X.25 protocol at the data link level, known as T1, N2, N1, and K. T1 is the time limit established for the principal timer. When it is exceeded it is necessary to transmit an acceptance command. N2 is the limit established for a counter which is incremented every time a command is transmitted because of exceeding T1. N1 is the maximum number of bits in a packet. It depends from the maximum length of the information field. K is the maximum number of sequential packets which a DTE or node can have in suspense. That is, at any given moment, transmitted but not yet accepted.

While these are general characteristics, there are many packet switching networks today which vary in terms of functionality and the organization of their services. Some networks, like the Canadian Datapac, do offer a permanent virtual circuit which does not necessitate calls to establish a connection and is continuously available.

A different line discipline, the datagram, does not require the establishment of a virtual circuit of any type. It simply poses a packet on the communications line, and this requires no calling procedure. The transmitted volume, rather than the length of the transmission, is used for billing purposes.

Practically all packet switching networks support packet assembly/disassembly (PAD). The use of PAD is specifically oriented to asynchronous terminals. It brings together or separates multiple signals which the network accepts, then transmits. A function of PAD can be that of a concentrator which brings together start/stop devices on a single X.25 line. The CCITT protocol standards X.3, X.28, X.29 are simultaneously used to define a PAD interface.

DTE clusters can serve a host through multiple lines (Figure 20.8) which is a good solution to the rigidity problem: Modularity must be applied to the network's interface.

Which are the most important factors for an optimum design?

1. Start with objectives.
2. Choose the transmission facilities.
3. Establish the switching methods.
4. Choose the topological layout.
5. Select the DTE equipment.
6. Settle on the protocols.
7. Establish the interfacing.

"Select the DTE" means to choose from alternatives. DTE clusters connected to the network become commonplace. What is still to come are *intelligent lines* using microprocessors and RAM to better service and cut costs in a way similar to the evolution which took place with computers.

21

Competitive Offerings and International Standards

International standardization efforts usually start after a certain product or process reaches a given degree of maturity, and this for two good reasons.

First, it is the wrong time to imply controls and norms right after an idea is born. The risk is high that they would stiffen a primitive product and ossify its hopes of development.

Second, the people who are supposed to be the standard setters don't have at such an early time a clear image of what the norms should be.

This has happened with a variety of products. By the early 1920s, for example, the architecture of the automobile became standardized. It has not been altered significantly for 60 years.

If we check other technical marketplaces we will see that this same phenomenon has occurred. At their beginning, a wide variety of design elements was developed. Then design ideas were assimilated and adapted until the architecture ceased to change.

From 1920 to 1925, the automobile had already experienced a good quarter century of growth. This is the situation today with computers—though not yet with networks. (Product maturity, incidently, is followed by a large and expanding market, as Figure 21.1 shows.)

Computer-based intelligence is one of the vital components of the network. The wisdom of computers and communications integration suggested, by the early 1970s, the desirability of subordinating different inhouse developments to the discipline of vendor, national, and international standards. In regard to the first, IBM's System Network Architecture (SNA) and DEC's Digital Network Architecture

Figure 21.1.

GROWTH INDUSTRIES

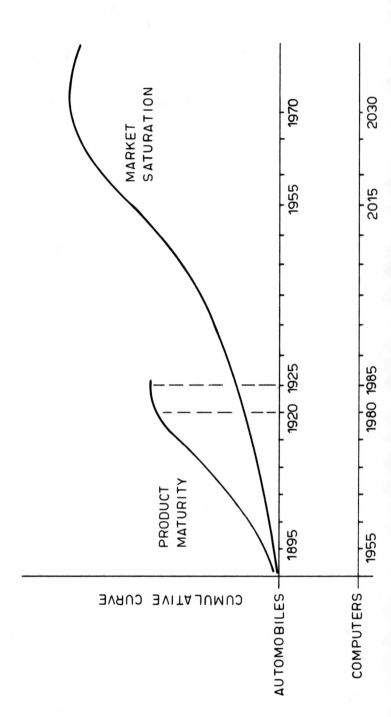

(DECNET)—both dating from 1974—are two approaches to the problem of facilitating interconnectability within a given range of products.

Both SNA and DECNET provide for the networking of terminals and host computers, including distribution of processing functions. But these proprietary architectures, of which a large number are now in existence,* do not directly address the problem of universal interconnectability.

Yet, universal interconnectability of computing machinery is a requirement the broader development of information technology has brought into focus. Equipment from different vendors should be compatible through the network, beyond the level of plug-compatible devices.

In the late 1970s, the International Standards Organization (ISO) put forward a seven-layer model of network architecture, known as the reference model for open systems interconnection (OSI). This reference network architecture is not concerned with specific hardware implementations. Its goal is to structure the protocols needed in data communications.

The ISO/OSI Model

The layers in the OSI reference model are associated with different levels of interaction. The protocols are communications rules, for each of the seven levels, between different parts of the communications system. As Figure 21.2 illustrates:

Layers 1 to 3 are concerned with data transmission and routing.

Layer 4 provides end-to-end control of transport. This serves to make the communication mechanism transparent to the user.

Layers 5 to 7 arrange the user/process dialogue, support format conversion, and interface to user processes.

As a recommended standard, the reference model of OSI provides a common basis for the coordination of systems interconnection and also allows existing standards to be placed within a common framework.

ISO/OSI is concerned with systems comprising terminals, computers and associated devices and the means for transferring information between these systems. But the model does not imply any particular systems implementation, technology or means of interconnection. Rather, it refers to the mutual recognition and support of the standardized information exchange procedures.

Furthermore, Open Systems Interconnection is not only concerned with the transfer of information between devices, but also with the capability of these devices to "interwork" on a common, distributed task. This includes applications processes within an OSI environment, any communications connections permitting information exchange, and the systems themselves.

*An estimated worldwide 12,000 to 15,000 for SNA and roughly half that number for DECNET.

Figure 21.2. The iso/osi standard.

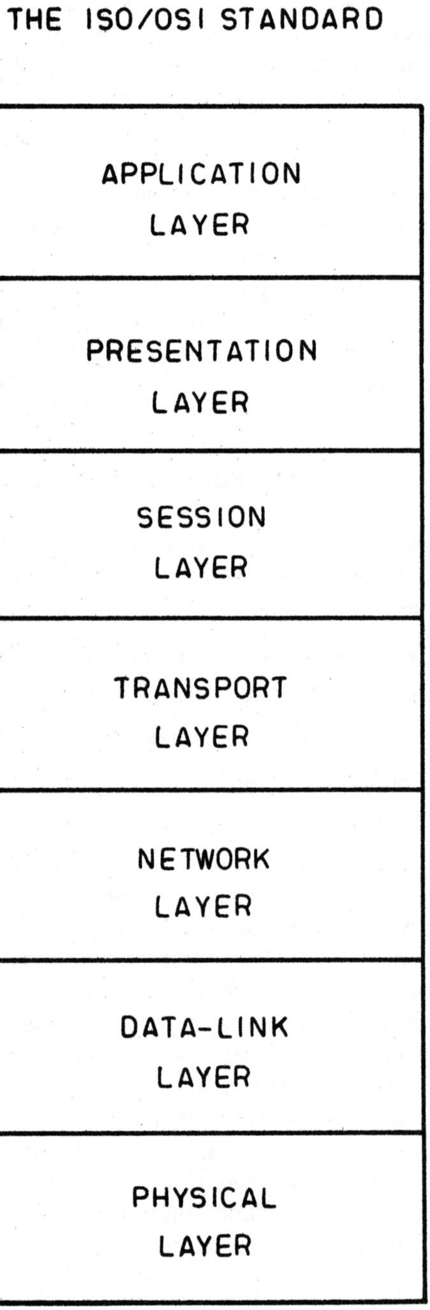

THE ISO/OSI STANDARD

APPLICATION LAYER
PRESENTATION LAYER
SESSION LAYER
TRANSPORT LAYER
NETWORK LAYER
DATA-LINK LAYER
PHYSICAL LAYER

In the ISO/OSI standard:

1. The *physical layer* describes the electrical, mechanical, and functional interface to the carrier.

Communications with distributed access control depend on this level. In a local area network, the carrier (transport medium) and the media access unit are the sublayers.

More precisely, the physical layer provides mechanical, electrical, functional and procedural characteristics to activate, maintain, and deactivate physical connections for transmission between data-link entities (possibly through intermediate systems). Each relaying bit transmission falls within Layer 1.

2. The *link layer* looks after data flow initialization, control, and error recovery.

The data link handles channel addressing, error detection, and transmission control. (With LAN, media access control and logical link control are the sublayers.)

Generally, the purpose of the data link layer is to provide the functional and procedural means for activating, maintaining, and deactivating one or more data link connections among network entities. Functions supported by this layer help detect (and possibly correct) errors which may occur in the physical layer. In addition, data-link conveys to the network layer the capability to request assembly of data circuits within the physical layer—that is, the capability to perform control of switching.

3. The object of *networking* is routing and switching through logical circuits.

End-to-end addressing, routing, and datagram services are part of this level. The network layer provides the means to establish, maintain and terminate connections between systems containing communicating procedures. It also supports the functional and procedural means to exchange network service data units between two transport entities over network connections.

4. The *transport layer* assures a reliable flow control.

Supported services include congestion control, logical circuits, the management of windows, and other transaction oriented features.

More precisely, the transport layer provides the transport services in association with the underlying functions assured by levels 1 to 3. This includes the transparent transfer of data between session entities. The transport layer relieves the transport users from any concern with the detailed way in which reliable and cost/effective transfer of data is achieved. To do so, its software must optimize the use of available communication resources, and provide the performance required by each communicating transport user at minimum cost. This optimization is achieved within the constraints imposed by considering the global demands of all concurrent transport users and the overall limit of resources available to the transport layer.

Since the network service provides network connections from any transport entity to any other, all protocols defined in the transport layer will have end-to-end significance, where the ends are defined as the correspondent transport-entities. The transport functions invoked in the transport layer to provide requested service quality depend on the quality of the network service. The quality of the network service depends on the way such service is achieved.

5. The *session layer* involves the management of logical communications paths between two users (men or programs).

Session control handles name-to-address mapping, network monitoring, and other control services. It also provides the means necessary for cooperating presentation entities to organize and synchronize their dialogue and manage their data exchange. To do this, the session layer supports services able to establish a session connection between two presentation entities and to assure their orderly data exchange interactions. To implement the transfer of data between the presentation entities, the session connection is mapped onto and uses a transport connection.

6. The *presentation layer* provides the programmatic interfaces necessary for data formatting, encoding, decoding, and encryption.

Other services are virtual terminal management, entity identification, format translation, and presentation. The specific purpose of the presentation layer is to represent information to communicating entities in a way that preserves meaning while resolving syntax differences. This layer handles the internal attributes of the virtual resource and its manipulation functions. The external attributes of the virtual resource and its manipulation functions exist in the application layer.

As of February 1983, with the international accords on presentation level protocol, the functions of Layer 6 are well defined. This cannot be said, at the present time, about Layer 7—hence the interest of discussing a boundary between the two layers by way of elaborating on their functions.

7. The *applications layer* addresses itself to a number of services and procedures which can be arranged as sublayers—applications, DBMS, file access, end user interaction, and end user presentation.

The user interface is very important. Most available protocol standards today do not include these 5 levels. Yet, the applications layer is the highest one in the reference model of Open Systems Interconnection. Its goal is to provide services to the users of the OSI environment, not to the next higher layer.

In principle, the application layer should serve as the window between communicating users of the OSI environment through which an exchange of information occurs. The user is represented by the application entity to its peer.

The National Bureau of Standards estimates that it will take at least until the mid to late 1980s before a unified application level standard emerges. Table 21.1 shows the 7 layers of ISO/OSI, their objectives, the origins of their standards and the development of their protocols.

Let's recapitulate. The open systems architecture is structured in layers. Each is

Table 21.1.
The layers of osi.

Layer	Object	Origin of Standards	Development of the Protocol
7	Applications	Users	User Protocols (for the time being)
6	Presentation control		
	* File transfer	ECMA/ISO	In process of definition
	* Virtual terminal	ECMA/ISO	In process of definition
5	Session control	ECMA	In process of authorization
		ISO	In process of definition
4	Transport control	ECMA	ECMA-72
		ISO	In process of definition
		CCITT	S.70
3	Networking	ISO	X.25-3
		CCITT	X.25-3
2	Data link	ECMA	ECMA 40, 49, 60, 61, 71
		CCITT	X.25-2
		ISO	ISO 3309, 4335
1	Physical connection	CCITT	V.11, X.21, V.24, etc.

composed of an ordered set of sublayers. Adjacent layers communicate through their common interface.

The operation of a layer is based on cooperation between the entities it includes. It is governed by a set of protocols specific to that layer.

The services of a layer are provided to the next higher layer, using the functions performed within the layer and the services available from the next lower layer. An entity in a layer may provide services to one or more entities in the next higher layer and use the services of one or more entities in the next lower layer.

The ISO/OSI model is having a strong impact both on the development of standards for the control of interactions at the different levels and on software/hardware implementations. The appeal of broad interconnectability is causing computer manufacturers to structure their product lines accordingly.

A System Network Architecture?

SNA is currently managed by an architectural maintenance board which meets every month to discuss interpretations, extensions, and implementations. Other vendor supported network architectures seem to have nothing comparable. Besides, IBM's weight is felt in the drive to make SNA the de facto industry standard.

When first introduced, SNA was an hierarchical structure. Successive releases have softened the rigidity of central control.

The first model of SNA was working at IBM in 1972, and the first installation came two years later. In the intervening 12 years, not only radical changes were made conceptually and in the software but also the products were made to be compatible with the SNA.

Initial releases of SNA were oriented around a single host. Then, about 1977, changes were introduced to allow multiple hosts to communicate as peers. These changes have been amplified since then, both in scope and in terms of supported capabilities. Also, IBM has recognized the problems inherent in centralized approaches and is working on solutions.

Whether we talk of SNA or any other architecture we should expect there will soon be a terminal on every desk, so we must address both dynamic and passive network management. *Dynamic management* primarily concerns problem solving, and *passive management* is the planning function that lets users know when the system is reaching its maximum utilization level. Passive and dynamic management overlap at many points: When we get a message that response time is degrading, solutions must be searched in terms of dynamic management. At the same time, this is a signal that we need to reconfigure our network for more communication power.

Fundamentally, SNA is doing what computers and communications professionals have been saying for years is wise course of action: Relieving the overworked mainframes to develop a distributed DP/DB/DC environment. By downloading application programs onto remote units—which then access and enter data and programs—the functions of the host change radically, but the host is not eliminated. As cannot be too often repeated, the main theme with distributed information systems is to bring processing power, data entry, and database query access to all locations—specifically to the end user.

The main benefit from this transition is the higher productivity of managers, professionals, clerical personnel—and a better decision-making capability at the executive level. Other benefits are that transmission costs from remote WS to hosts are lowered, and computing power can be added or subtracted as needed without expensive large-scale changes.

To answer in a factual and documented manner how well a systems architecture provides the needed supports, we must:

analyze its set of rules, or protocols,

define the functions of each network component, and

evaluate the means for communications between components.

Such evaluations must be objective to elicit valid measurements. Yet, subjective issues cannot be weeded out altogether. As one user remarked, "SNA's Synchronous Data Link Control does provide better network management than BSC, but it is not without problems. For instance, with SDLC we can only pump a small amount of data across lines and then wait for a reply—while we would rather have liked to pump lots of data to make maximum use of private lines."

Sometimes the adoption of a network architecture is forced upon the user because of solutions adopted in datacomm issues. As another user commented,

"When we switched to IBM 3278 interactive terminals, it became necessary to implement SNA. The BSC system was limited in two respects: the number of terminals that could be linked to the host, and network management capabilities."

These two statements are not incompatible. First, let's recall that SDLC (though an IBM offering) is in no way radically different from ISO's HDLC and the other XDLC designed to support Layer 2, the data link, and these XDLC dialects are the best protocols we have available today for data link connection.

Second, though SDLC can be and has been criticized on several counts, it is more efficient than BSC (and let's not talk of start/stop). As a result, it should help shorten response time from other available alternatives.

But it is just as true that a change to SNA (or any other *private* network architecture) will require a huge financial outlay to upgrade all terminal equipment in order to support it in the right way. Here again the options are not many—as several organizations have found that the costs of increasing their bisync capability and migrating to SNA are about equal.

Two alternatives have to be given careful consideration. One is the use of services provided by value added networks. (We spoke of them in the preceding chapter, and will return to them in a following section.) The other is the adoption of X.25 "rather than" XDLC.

Arguments based on this latter reference involve quite a bit of misunderstanding. XDLC is *not* avoided. It is included in X.25. Rather, what this reference refers to is that X.25 offers compatibility to a growing range of efficient devices (one offered by SESA being an example).

SNA Compatibility and User-Oriented Supports

A problem with SNA, which should not last long, is the existence of a still-limited number of SNA compatible products. Such products have consistently improved in speed and number.

PCM compatibility will turn SNA into an open architecture though it began as a closed network approach. As other computer manufacturers and electronics equipment suppliers adopt SNA, or provide interfaces, IBM proprietary networks will move out of the *closed* category into something of an *open* one. (A closed network is offered by one supplier and only the products of that supplier can be attached to it. Many mainframers and mini manufacturers have used this approach to lock-in their customers. An open network uses international standards to allow the products of many manufacturers to be attached to it.)

Through its rules governing packet switching network services, X.25 establishes a common ground, allowing different offerings to work together. But the SNA/X.25 issue can have many solutions. IBM itself offers X.25 support through the 8100 and other items; independent vendors present devices which, as network interface adapters, convert SDLC protocols to and from X.25 communications protocols; other mainframers and mini manufacturers offer gateways between their networking systems and SNA (Honeywell and DEC are examples).

Digital Equipment makes available a dedicated computer system linking its Digital Network Architecture with SNA. This Decnet/SNA gateway allows PDP-11 and VAX computers linked by Decnet to communicate with IBM's networking system. Honeywell has a set of communications software facilities to enable its DPS 6 and Level 6 computers to operate as satellites on SNA networks. These consist of SNA RJE facilities, SNA interactive terminal (3270) software, and SNA transport facilities that handle most low-level SNA protocols.

Through its 1980 Statement of Direction, IBM encouraged the formulation of an international standard to serve as the basis for interfaces to public data networks. Also, in 1981, IBM introduced products that allow SNA units to communicate using data-transmission services based on X.21 and X.25.

As a matter of fact, IBM is forging ahead in this direction, integrating its PC into SNA as a vital tool, and has already announced packages and hardware products that allow its Personal Computer to be connected to an IBM host through SNA. The 3270-emulation and RJE-support software permits the IBM PC to act as a terminal that can communicate with a host in one of two modes, supporting either SNA 3270 or 3770 RJE. The 3101 package provides emulation of the 3101 Model 20 display terminal, including its ability to transmit ASCII format files to and from the host computer and local diskette storage. This package also allows conversion of ASCII format diskette files to and from binary format.

The Encryption Standard

Let's take a closer look at the NBS data encryption standard (DES). Its object is to define the encryption of 64 bits through cipher text. A 56-bit key is used for coding, and since it is determined by the user, it is at the core of security. To decipher data, a user must know the key used to encipher. Theoretically, with 56 bits to define a key, there are more than 70 quadrillion different keys that can be used; that is, variations of the encryption algorithm.

In practice, this is different. First, if a key is obtained by an intruder, the system loses its security. Second, following the pronouncement that it would take the most powerful mainframe decades to decipher the DES, it was said that a teenager working on a PC broke it.

It is paramount that encryption algorithms be updated at the discretion of whoever commands the network (or the subnetwork). This must be done in a dynamic manner and offer a multikey hierarchy—with one or more keys defined by the end user.

A good example of this approach is the Home Banking solution adopted on the Videotex (Bildschirmtext) offering in Germany by the Verbraucher Bank. For client identification purposes it supports:

the account number and personal identification number established by bank management, thus creating 2 levels

up to 3 keywords set and changed by the end user (adding up to 5 levels)

a *virtual check* discovery whereby the bank supplies through a different channel (post) numbers to be used only once with a telebanking order or payment (6th level).

Over and above such a structure can be employed, for instance, Motorola's MC 6859 with its two-key hierarchy. A primary key is written to the device and stores, and a secondary key is written to the device. The secondary key can be encrypted using the DES and the primary key by writing the secondary key to a specific address in the microprocessor. When the secondary key is encrypted, that value will be used as the key for coding the data that follow. Hence, an encrypted secondary key is the basis used to code or decode data.

A key hierarchy allows versatility in system design. One authorized person can generate and control one key, another handles the second key. But, as stated, keys alone don't make a system. A network-wide view is necessary, and the architecture should support it.

Using Value-Added Networks

We have spoken of network architectures, XDLC and X.25. Many executives in charge of value-added networks have opted to go along with the X.25 network interface for packet-switched networks using an HDLC or SDLC protocol. A key feature to this solution is the gateway processor.

Several companies have (or are about to make) subtypes of a universal gateway processor. This is in response to demand for devices able to connect a user to a public data network such as Tymnet or Telenet.

As discussed in Chapter 9, the latest multiplexer developments include the increased use of the statistical multiplexer; the linking of stat muxes to local networks; dynamic allocation of stat mux channels; the handling of a wider range of protocols; wideband stat mux trunking; the incorporation of both port contention and switching capabilities; and the use of stat muxes as gateways to X.25 networks. We have already shown that gateway functions are becoming increasingly important to network users of all types. Different solutions are bound to show up. The particular requirements of individual users are different and require different implementations. Engineering firms are coming up with possible design elements that can be combined into existing architectures.

A stabilized design perspective redirects creative energy toward a better-focused goal: the improvement of the design elements, their interdependence, and the services which they offer.

To be effectively attached to a VAN offering, some users require black-box protocol converters; others, standalone gateways; still others want these functions integrated into the software running on their existing front-ends or message switches. The demand for a variety of solutions continues because the user needs to implement that which makes better economic sense.

Value-added networks offer significant enhancement to the standard use of telephone wire for data transmission. These include:

1. error protection
2. acknowledgment disciplines
3. transfer of data from one character set into another
4. changes in data transmission rates
5. increase in data flow without compromising integrity
6. terminal-to-CPU communication through a variety of protocols
7. rerouting as a function of link availability and/or congesting
8. multiplexing of data from a number of sources
9. packet switching capabilities.

A value added network's adaptive routing capability makes a flexible and easily available communications link. Adaptive routing allows nonadjacent nodes to communicate and eliminates the need for direct physical links between two communicating nodes. Messages are automatically routed through the network over the most effective path. Adaptive routing also ensures that if any line in the network is disabled, the data being transmitted are automatically rerouted through another path in the network in a way which is apparent to the user.

The VAN monitors activity on all network nodes, accesses statistical and error information, and isolates hardware and software problems. In turn, such features enhance network flexibility, reliability, and ease of use. They also contribute to financial savings as VANs are managed without personnel—while they can amortize their own personnel expenditures among many users.

Stated differently, the use of LAN facilities can result in appreciable savings in time, effort, and money—while the fact that all of the organization's departments are connected with each other on-line can reduce paperwork and speed communications.

While financial savings are a probable outcome if we contrast the use of private line to the services of a LAN—compared to using the mails or a specialized delivery service—the latter can eliminate the time delay and inconvenience involved in transferring data between systems via magnetic tape. (Magnetic tape was the traditional way of accomplishing data transfers in the recent past, and is still used in a surprising number of cases though costly in both system and operator time.) Furthermore, with a LAN there is no rigid network topology and no prerequisite host processor. The user's DTE can be added or deleted without disrupting local functions, so that *his* network can easily be expanded or reconfigured to meet changing requirements.

There are also prerequisites to be observed. To capitalize on the above advantages, the user must have a clear aim of his project at the outset. The aims of such a project should include: First, specific DP/DB/DC goals; second, the ability to measure performance and gather traffic patterns for a variety of applications; third, the knowledge of how to manage and maintain such systems, including hardware, software and resource management.

The user organization should investigate the problems in using value-added networks for traditional computer-to-computer and computer-to-terminal interactions; examine in a factual manner their utility for business communications; and adopt appropriate components and protocols. The organization should also be prepared to monitor the reliability of the network; establish where better local systems design or redundancy would provide higher dependability; and examine traffic patterns to be gathered directly from the networks where possible, and also from hosts, terminals and interfaces.

In this manner, advantages to the end user will grow as new offerings come to the market. For instance, AT&T's Net 1000, when it does become fully available, will be a communications processing service that provides not only data storage and transmission, but also necessary translations of the various protocols used by data processors. Like other common carrier packet networks, it will be used to transport data among the various service points. Access to the service point can be via either analog or digital transmission. As with all VAN, the approach is not to process the information but to handle it as expeditiously as possible from one end to the other.

22

Toward Local Area Solutions

Current trends in network architecture and protocols point to new concepts. Designers are now separating the communications and networking functions from applications characteristics. They dedicate a set of processors to network functions and keep the databasing requirements and processing applications separate.

Designers are also integrating separate networks to reduce the redundancy of communications facilities throughout the organization. At the same time, they focus on *personal computing* power, bringing computers and communications to every desk.

The last two issues find their expression in local area networks (LAN). Such networks typically operate up to 1 km for baseband and up to 10 km for broadband, and are able to support individual workstations and gateways to long haul and file servers. The more versatile LAN support a variety of processors and terminals operating diverse applications.

Designers are also maximizing architectural and protocol compatibility to make these diverse elements work together. One way to manage diversity and change is to set up a generalized network with application orientation accomplished through layers of terminal hardware and control protocols.

Successful utilization of a network largely relies on the method in which a device gains access to the communications medium, including

communications controllers,

communications channels,

communications disciplines,

switching elements, and

distribution elements.

Communications controllers are software oriented, dedicated to communications control: front-ends, remote concentrators, network monitors. Communications disciplines aim to provide an efficient usage of existing physical facilities. They do so by subdividing communications channels (FDM and TDM being examples).

Switching functions are performed through one of the methods we have been describing. Local distribution is accomplished by means of coaxial cables, optical fibers, laser links, and radio links. Wide area data distribution is also performed by undersea cables and satellites.

As the functions, methods and media interleave and interact with one another, the network architects are becoming involved with a wide range of physical and logical devices to form grand designs.

Assuring Connectivity

Let's assume that the choice has been made to use a packet switching methodology. The communication functions will typically include:

store and forward,

routing,

switch monitoring,

line concentrating,

reliability and availability,

redundancy evaluation, and

error handling.

Another characteristic of computers and communications is response time, while functionality includes information display, priority handling, security assurance, statistical loading calculations, and customer billing, among other issues.

Which are the specific technical issues the network architect must resolve? The technical issues requiring solution include:

- First, the issue of connectivity.

Typically, the connectivity (number of line ends per node) of first generation packet switching networks has been between two and three. However, a higher connectivity is desirable to provide minimum transit delay through the network and to ensure a higher reliability.

The early Arpanet design called for a connectivity of 2.23 (1972). Arpanet connectivity was increased gradually, reaching 2.75 by 1978, and is now well above 3.0. This is primarily to provide sufficient reliability, but also to assure that there is no contention which can lead to undue delays.

However, added connectivity, higher reliability and low contention has a cost, typically a network utilization of about 30 percent during peak periods. This is not as bad as it seems. It represents the level at which a typical voice grade network becomes clogged.

- Second, terminal support.

If we support low-speed terminals and dial ports directly from unduplexed computers, we obtain a high level of unavailability. This is unacceptable to most users. It is therefore desirable to support the terminals through duplexed solutions—but to duplex all computer ports is economically unwise.

Hence, low-speed ports are first concentrated by means of Time Division Multiplexing (TDM) onto a high-speed line. For instance, low-speed ports may be switched to a standby computer if the primary computer fails. This results in high port availability without unnecessary duplication of terminals ports.

The subject solution also provides the option of extending the service to small users outside the cities served with computer-based packet switches, at only the cost of a duplexed TDM and one or two access lines back to the large city. Topology and utilization would dictate the fine tuning of a system solution.

- Third, the prevailing topology.

The topology of modern packet networks can be a two-level hierarchy. The nodes of the top-level net are small, highly interconnected packet switching subnetworks. Due to this and standby computers at each site, the switching nodes are very reliabile. Evidently, the network topology must answer subscriber needs. This leads to microprocessor solutions that assure users and potential users of hook-ups to the network.

Among the basic configurations we distinguish small asynchronous concentrator(s) and host interface concentrator(s). The former is an inexpensive statistical device permitting multiple asynchronous ports to be concentrated onto a higher capacity line. It is primarily used in small cities, host computer interfacing, and terminal clusters.

A host interface unit can concentrate asynchronous host computer ports onto one or more synchronous access lines using, for instance, the X.25 protocol. Primary use is for interfacing host computers to the network when the host does not support X.25 directly.

The packet switching node supports many varieties of terminal and host computer protocols including packet assembly and disassembly functions. The node interconnects with the rest of the network using the X.25 protocol via multiple network lines.

The microprocessor hardware consists mainly of line cards. Each line card has 4 or 8 asynchronous and/or synchronous ports, a microprocessor, local memory and connection to two data transfer busses. Each card has sufficient processing power to handle the line protocol (X.25, BSC, polled, asynchronous) for all its ports and to assemble or disassemble buffers of data. It then transfers the data blocks to a large buffer area in main memory, and dual microprocessor CPUs then route the data to the output line card and take care of connection management and other supervisory tasks.

The dedicated processing power and memory available on each line card ensures the responsiveness and reliability of the system even with heavy loads, complex protocols, and large numbers of lines.

- Fourth, the network organization.

The availability of the microcomputer switch has two primary impacts on the network.

First, a completely redundant multicomputer-based packet switching node supporting the full range of port speeds and protocols costs less than half that of its minicomputer predecessor. It can be installed more extensively in smaller cities. Where the full packet switch is uneconomic, the small asynchronous concentrator can be used, producing error-controlled, concentrated access at less than half the cost of multiplexers or minicomputer-based concentrators.

The second impact is the high reliability of the redundant multimicrocomputer design and the ability to interconnect the switches into the network, creating a third level of hierarchy.

Benefits from a Packet Switching Network

Computers are recognized as the major element in any sizeable information system. However, distributing and dispatching the information cannot be handled by the computer as we have known for over 30 years.

Between the user of the information and the supplier, an adequate distribution channel must be provided. This is the role of a data transmission network. From the beginning, the distribution of computerized information has used the infrastructure of other distribution processes. Thus, printout from a computer can be mailed by regular postal services; magnetic tapes containing millions of characters are regularly airmailed across the world; new services (the so-called teletext system) make use of the television network to distribute computerized data.

The telephone network is the most obvious network to be used in data transmission. Almost any computer can transmit and receive data over a telephone line. A similar statement can be made about replacing messengers in a building by using local area networks, workstations and the facilities which they support.

In the case of wide area coverage, faced with providing remote access to an interactive computer system, the data communications planner typically takes a look at the amount of usage expected from various remote locations. He then compares the economics of building a leased private-line network vs. using conventional public circuit switching facilities.

The public packet network is technologically superior in many respects to a private line network because of:

1. Its ability to adapt to changing and often unpredictable terminal communication requirements: new locations, increased traffic load; new types of terminal equipment; new applications.
2. Higher quality service than is possible in the typical private line network.
3. Reduced direct costs for communications as well as better utilization of the company's computers, terminal, and human resources.
4. Elimination of many of the housekeeping chores associated with network management, such as selecting equipment with multiple vendors, maintaining the system, and monitoring network utilization and performance.
5. Ease in handling peak traffic loads through a larger (though shared) bandwidth; better sequencing; controllable delays; reduced error rates; broadcast or point-to-point capabilities; multidestination; capacity allocation.
6. Ability to add terminals to new locations without system restructuring requires no major effort at all on the user's part.
7. Greater flexibility. Typical private networks offer access to only one computer center, but the public packet network permits any terminal to access any computer system on the network.
8. Higher availability and quality of service, coupled with powerful error detection and correction techniques.
9. Economic factors from original investment to operations.
10. The ability to extend long haul packet solutions into internal company networks serving local environments.

Practically everything we said of a long haul solution through packet switching holds true in terms of implementing the same technology in a local area. The main difference is in ownership: A satellite, fiber, or radio link-based value-added carrier will be a shared resource. A LAN is dedicated to the company which employs it.

A second difference between LAN and VAN is in the planning requirements and resources to be dedicated. The design, implementation, operation, and maintenance of a nationwide private data communications network requires a considerable amount of company resources. It is necessary to:

forecast less-than-certain traffic volume

recruit data communications specialists

consider various network design alternatives (modems, multiplexers, minicomputers, programmable concentrators)

evaluate different procedural solutions (roll call, hub polling, contention)

incur significant capital investment costs for equipment.

Network management costs for such tasks are sometimes as large as the direct costs for network line facilities. A public packet switching network performs these functions on behalf of the user. It is designed to operate in the real world where phone lines fail, and "standards" are not standard at all: Current packet switching technology guarantees no more than 1 bad bit of information over 4 billion bits transmitted—a bit error rate of better than 10^9.

Broadband local area networks implemented through protected coaxial cable can match that BER. Baseband LAN typically use twisted pair, flat wire, or unprotected (flexible) coaxial and their BER can be lower by 2 orders of magnitude from the reference just made—but still many orders of magnitude higher than many voice-grade lines where 10^{-3} to 10^{-5} BERs are quite common.

In the VAN and LAN structures the most significant services are:

1. Error detection and correction—hence, dependability
2. Adaption of or choice among a great variety of terminal devices, transmission codes, protocols, speeds
3. Security/protection
4. Complete accounting and statistical information
5. The development of quality databases and remote diagnostics
6. Store and forward for VAN; pipelining for LAN
7. Gateway capability.

Among all characteristics of a gateway, flexibility is probably the most important. A gateway must cope with actual and future requirements in terms of capacity, handling of various protocols, interfacing, and speed.

Service goals should also be examined. Performance characteristics—functional and applications-wise—should be identified. A pre-choice of transmission media, bandwidths, media access protocol, interfacing must be made. This involves the analysis of physical transmission paths, choices among types of uses, and methods of obtaining a good communications service. The choice of methodology to be used is closely related to that of the media. It involves both physical and logical aspects, and it has cost aftermaths as it impacts the usage and sharing of the transmission paths in the data communications network.

Specifications should be developed for each of these issues by defining performance requirements, topology functions, equipment and interfaces. Protocol design is intimately related to the functions to be assured, and so are the interface characteristics.

The ability to handle mass data transfers such as occur between computers, between high-speed terminals and computers, and among workstations comes from increased node processing speed. To remove this factor as a network limitation, it is necessary to implement a design that can modularly cluster these nodes; interconnect as many as are appropriate; achieve a bandwidth objective through an appropriate transfer mechanism; and make the cluster behave like a multiprocess computer operating on a single memory.

The Local Area Network Concept

A valid way to look at a LAN is as a local extension of VAN software capabilities providing for inhouse communications. Connected through long haul facilities, local area networks can support up to a thousand nodes, but they also offer an entry option. We can start with as few workstations as we wish and add more as they are needed.

Both LAN and VAN are datacomm engines. Both give us the flexibility to add or remove nodes quickly and easily without disrupting ongoing communications and without redesigning or reconfiguring our entire network.

There are also differences. Perhaps the least evident is that a LAN is owned and operated by the company using it. The VAN is a public service. Another not immediately evident difference is that (barring satellite long haul links) a LAN offers much more bandwidth than any long haul solution. Let's repeat what we already said about bandwidths:

typically, broadband (being analog in nature) supports up to 300 or 400 MHz

baseband (a digital service) supports from 1 to 10 MBPS

modern long haul lines work at 56 to 64 KBPS.

Here we have a couple of orders of magnitude in difference, in terms of line speed.

Broadband and baseband are the terms that describe different varieties of coaxial cable used for local area networks. Actually, this is misleading, since broadband and baseband are signaling techniques which are independent of the physical medium. These names have been tagged onto the most commonly used varieties of coaxial cable for those two signaling techniques.

Coaxial cable* has become a popular medium in local area networks because of its large capacity, low error rates, and configuration flexibility. A variety of taps, controllers, splitters, couplers, and repeaters are available that enable the cable to be easily extended and branched off to reach user locations for connecting user devices.

Integrating DP, DB, and DC—something essentially both LAN and VAN do—is a task largely related to the more strategic and still poorly defined issue of how offices will be working in the next 5 to 10 years. Yet, the experience of the last 3 years of LAN implementation suggests that solutions will involve local area networks. They are destined to play a key part in the overall network of the corporation.

IBM contends that SNA has provided the general structure that will accommodate all the necessary services for distributed information systems, including that of interconnecting the locally established LAN. This is a direct reflection of the fact that IBM is committed to SNA, and its communications products will be based on SNA. Expansion and enhancement will be developed with this philosophy in mind.

IBM's philosophy on LAN and SNA will necessarily have an industry-wide impact. Local databases, supported through file servers, have been so far an integral part of LAN offerings. But by all indications, IBM has no plans to put a local database on its LAN.

To the contrary, starting with the XT, IBM will support hard disc at the PC level.

---

*Twisted wire is an alternative carrier for baseband solutions; optical fibers for broadband.

Access to a central database will be assured through protocols linked to minis and mainframes. If so, the IBM LAN will surely need to integrate into SNA, and it will not be a self-sustaining structure (a *real* LAN with full facilities).

Indeed, the IBM strategy most likely capitalizes on the worldwide LAN drive to enhance its thousands of SNA networks. This will not inhibit concentrating—at the WS level—on user-friendly solutions such as the graphic tablet, mouse, joystick, and touch sensing screen. (The mouse is employed in the most recently announced PCs; graphic tablets and touch screens can be added to many microcomputers. A still more friendly access method is voice input.)

A Relative Standardization

If the local database run by the LAN is substituted by PC-based microfiles, what's the possible impact on the evolution of LAN technology? To answer this question, we must first look at the definition of a LAN.

By slightly adjusting the definition advanced by the IEEE 802 Committee, we can say that a LAN is:

1. A datacomm system allowing independent devices to communicate directly with each other.
2. These devices fall into two broad classes: WS integrated one per desk, and servers assuring functions.
3. Three types of servers must be distinguished: database or file management, gateways toward other communications facilities, and printer/plotters.
4. LAN address themselves to communications problems confronting geographic areas of moderate size. (Distances run between 300 meters and 1 kilometer for baseband, and 1 to 10 kilometers for broadband.)
5. The communications rates (as stated) stand between 1 and 10 KBPS for baseband and up to 300 and 400 MHz for broadband.

Here is where, I think, Project 802 has made an understatement. These data rates are not "moderate" by any standard.

A LAN offers its users specific advantages:

Cognizance of the ISO/OSI standard

Media and topology independence

A functional flexibility to be implemented as low as possible in the architecture

Direct party-to-party communication

Coexistence and interchangeability

Fairness criteria in the use of the communications resources.

Such fairness criteria are put in action through the implementation of an access algorithm: Carrier Sensing Multiple Access with Collision Detection (CSMA/CD) and Token are the two most popular protocols.

Though designed for long haul communications, ISO/OSI is just as applicable with LAN, with the only exception that the physical layer is split into two sublayers: a carrier, or transport medium, and a media access unit (MAU). The data-link layer is divided into media access control (MAC) and logical link control.

Within the framework of this definition, distributed information systems can be viewed as a set of users and servers. A user wishing to employ a server first consults a directory to find its address and then uses that to send a message to the server. Messages contain sufficient information that the server can reply to the user. In a local network environment, the user should follow the same procedure irrespective of whether or not the service to be accessed is on the same LAN.

Within the LAN architecture, the nodes are identical and are connection points to the carrier. The ports are logical entities.

In a baseband network, the node will typically have one port and will be connected one-to-one with the WS or server. In a baseband network, the node is the bus interface unit (BIU) and generally has 2, 3, 4, or 8 ports—each port being in a one-to-one correspondence with the workstation or server.

A link between the sending WS and receiving WS must be established prior to carrying on any data communications. As stated, protocols perform that function. They formalize information transfers between different points and represent handshakes between two devices.

A variety of different protocols are available to LAN users according to the particular architecture they have chosen. But each LAN, like each long haul network architecture, uses one and only one protocol. Thus, if there is no file server on the LAN, protocol compatibility will oblige that the WS, the LAN, and the long haul network architecture obey the same disciplines.

Between the local and central resources, communications will be assured by the gateway. It recognizes the requested service as remote and "knows" the topology of the appropriate database. Similarly, remote databases can act through their gateway until the destination network is reached, down to the destination node and port number.

Also, while hard disc-based microfiles at the WS level are a good idea since they help minimize LAN traffic and accelerate response time (as compared to floppy discs), there are functions common to more than one WS on the LAN. For these functions, the local database is mandatory. Its absense will render file update unduly complex.

In conclusion, implementation perspectives for PC and LAN will be that much brighter if we abide standards: from physical interfaces to protocols and design characteristics, and keep the system flexible, polyvalent and open to change.

Cost/Effectiveness with LAN Solutions

DEC presents an interesting case for cost/effectiveness with a LAN solution. The contrast between alternatives is shown in Figure 22.1 and 22.2.

Figure 21.1 presents the local, on-site connection of two VAX and two PDP-11

Figure 22.1. Ethernet DECNET with comparative advantages.

FIRST BANK SYSTEM

VIDEOTEX NETWORK

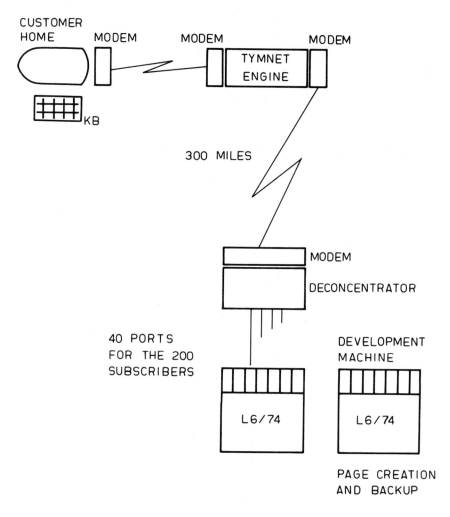

computers linked together. These are connected to two different remote locations through modems. On-site, they communicate through one 56 KBPS and four 9.6 KBPS lines. Interfaces are provided by DMR, supplied by DEC at the cost of $4,400 per unit. For 10 DMR, the cost is $44,000.

Figure 21.2 involves the same midis and minis, but attached to an Ethernet LAN. The interfaces toward long haul connections are the same, but on-site

Figure 22.2. Typical DECNET: local and remote.

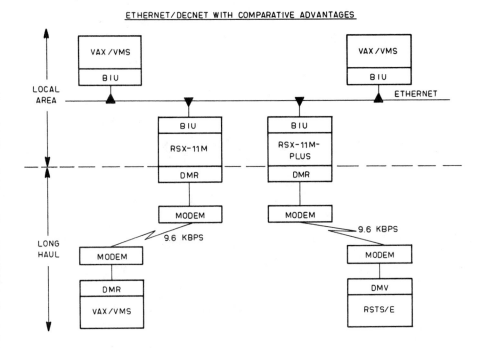

ETHERNET/DECNET WITH COMPARATIVE ADVANTAGES

Ethernet assures data transport capability. Two alternatives are suggested by DEC. Until mid-1983, DEUNA (designed for unibus attachments) would have been the choice. Since that time, DEQNA is the better choice—at least as far as costs are concerned.

So, using for BIU the DEUNA device, 4 units at $3,500 per unit will cost $14,000 (vs. $44,000 for the classical solution). But with DEQNA (including the H 4000 transceiver of DEC) the cost will be 4 units at $1.100, or $4,400.

The difference between $44,000 and $4,400 is a saving no company can miss. Further notice that Ethernet works at 10 MBPS while the best connection in the classical solution was 56 KBPS.

23

Backbone Operations

Network topology information is necessary for the nodes of a distributed computer and a communications network to communicate. Furthermore, since nodes and links sometimes crash, a scheme is needed to update this information.

The pivot point, and at the same time one of the major constraints in providing and upkeeping topology information, is the protocol. A topology information protocol must be quite general and remain unaffected as new nodes (hosts and switches) are implemented on the computer network.

Topologies can vary in their basic characteristics, depending, among other factors, on the area which they cover. As Table 23.1 demonstrates, we can distinguish among wide area, limited area, and internal computer structure. The latter will increasingly resemble a data communications network.

A different way of presenting this three-way classification is to distinguish among the following:

Remote Computer Networking	Local Networking	Multiprocessing
Aloha	Ethenet	Illiac, etc.
ARPANET	Spider (Bell Labs)	

Area-oriented classifications became important as computer communications grew from earlier implementations barely distinct from one another: real time RT, time sharing TS, telecommunications, and multiprocessing. Multiprocessing led to networking. Networks allow distributed multiprocessing.

Experience has demonstrated that substantial remodeling is necessary to achieve reliability, availability, modularity, and a reasonable compromise between good throughput, low delay, and good quality service as the network becomes increasingly complex.

325

Table 23.1

The network concept must be seen at three levels:

1. WIDE AREA

   Say, 100 to over 5,000 kilometers, characterized by

   Multiplicity of data communications media

   Synchronization

   Repeater problems

   Lack of direct control

2. LIMITED AREA

   Say, 500 to over 7,000 kilometers; typically

   Factory

   Office building

   Apartment building

3. INTERNAL COMPUTER STRUCTURE

Topological Description

Let us begin by looking back at the fundamentals. A typical computer and communications network is a collection of host computers connected by a communication subnetwork. This is a constellation of minicomputers (the switching nodes of the network) interconnected by bi-directional links (usually telephone lines).

A topological description of a network specifies the nodes and the links. But a general description, though necessary, is not sufficient. The other pillar is the procedural definition. It addresses itself to the routing of calls through the network, and in its most basic form it boils down to two alternatives: star or loop. Typically, in a star structure connections are made between links via the switching node. Whether the transmission equipment* (links) is cables, waveguides, radio bridges, or any other, the links radiate from the center. In a loop, there is a series connection. This results in a remarkable reduction in links and route lengths, while providing the possibility for many useful services. Examples are fault monitoring and control functions.

*The transmission system connecting switches to other switches and to terminals is commonly referred to as the "transmission plant."

Whether a star or loop solution is preferred, geographically separated networks must be interconnected. This is done in a hierarchical (tree) structure or in a horizontal structure. The latter has been the preferred solution, but this is changing.

Since the early years of telephony, concentration has been effected through tandem switches and links. The tandem switches have always been considered as "higher levels" in the network. The risk in a tree structure is that the time-out of a high level link will interrupt the traffic of the low levels feeding into it. Reliability is, therefore, reduced.

In an horizontal (loop or ring type) organization, signals can circulate around through alternate paths. Such an arrangement helps reduce congestion, increase traffic capacity, and, most importantly, provide for reliable solutions. As networks expand and grow, starlike, centralized solutions become bulky and prone to errors and inefficiencies. The assurance centralized solutions can provide is, very often, far less than satisfactory. Both technical and economic factors point to the wisdom of horizontal approaches.

Modularity: Horizontal networks have a significant impact in the implementation of modular solutions. While hierarchical approaches are optimized for a given level of traffic, horizontal approaches allow steady growth as the load and user requirements expand.

Software implication: A large centralized facility is very dependent on centralized control. The software is complex, difficult to maintain, and very costly.

Data base handling: A fair amount of data base activity will be provided by the architecture. The stumbling block with network solutions is the management (update, pruning, synchronization, protection) of data bases. Distributed implementation might ease the burden. (Notice, however, that data bases is the area where the jobs of the network and of the system architects interleave and interact. This is a demanding and challenging field. The communications job is not nearly as complex as data base handling.)

*Efficient journaling:** A good journal must be accurate, timely, and complete. The data must be recorded before answering processing requirements and must be available to serve reference purposes, restart, recovery, and checkpoints. The record kept must provide for checks and double checks. Procedural safeguards should assure that the record is whole, not partly written. And checks must be sufficient to weed out the junk.

Topological Solutions

The purpose of a network is to interconnect host computers and terminals so that a user of any of the DTE (or one of the entry points) has access to all other DTE on the network.

Figure 23.1
Topology solutions

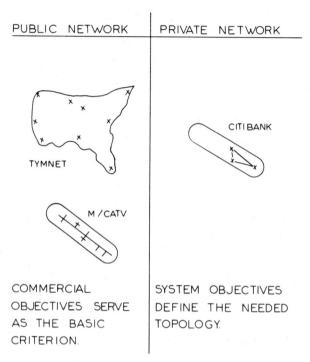

PUBLIC NETWORK	PRIVATE NETWORK

TYMNET

CITIBANK

M /CATV

COMMERCIAL OBJECTIVES SERVE AS THE BASIC CRITERION.

SYSTEM OBJECTIVES DEFINE THE NEEDED TOPOLOGY.

The design of a topological layout has two important prerequisites. The first is to start with the objectives. A topology is designed with specific objectives in mind; see Figure 23.1. The second is the appreciation of the interactive nature which exists between the topology of a network and the protocols which serve it: protocols (different by type) presuppose a topology (there is *no* standard topology) and must be chosen to *support* the topology and not to defy it.

Since the early first generation of computer networks, the switching nodes were essentially invisible to the user. As horizontal networks evolved from vertical networks and were influenced by their problems, one of the reasons for having that extra hardware was to reduce the host software costs. Without the nodes it is necessary to interface every host computer with every other host computer and to install telecommunications support in every host. With them, it is only necessary to interface each host with the node switch minicomputer and the identical minicomputers with each other, thus creating the *backbone* of the network.

By creating a backbone structure, the entire network would act as a single *data bus*. This is the solution used by Arpanet, Telenet, Tymnet, Datapac, Transpac, and Citinet. The backbone structure will care for all switching operations, including store and forward, error control, and other value-added services. It will provide the means to connect foreign devices to the lines (not available on traditional circuit switching links). It will ensure controlled redundancy to increase reliability, and will handle the generalized communications functions.

The following system elements constitute the backbone:

1. *Node switches* (usually minicomputers)
2. *Links* (bidirectional physical connection between the two nodes X and Y)
3. *Neighborhood (subset) principle* (node X is a neighbor of node Y if both X and Y are operational and connected by a physical link)
4. *Route* (This route should not be confused with the physical link. Between the nodes K and L the route is a connected sequence of operational links and nodes, starting with link K and ending with link L.)
5. *User* (a process or a job in some host)
6. *Record* (the unit of user-generated information that the network conveys from DTE A [node K] to DTE B [node L])
7. *Message* (a network-generated piece of information that travels from node K to node L)
8. *Topology change* (any one of the following events or any combination thereof: a link going down [ceasing to function]; a link coming up; a node crashing; a node restarting [by this is meant the node minicomputer, not the host])
9. *Service change* (are subject to fluctuations due to congestion control)
10. *Network control center*

Networks must be managed, that is, their operations planned, directed and controlled. Their overall performance will depend on the choices which are made in terms of planning and control.

There are no universal solutions to this subject. Some network architectures are highly centralized, for instance, IBM's SNA in its original version. Other network architectures distribute the planning, directing, and controlling functions; an excellent example is ARPA. Still other architectural solutions seek a compromise route; for instance, Tymnet has a central control point for its coast to coast network in the United States, but there are two stand-by control centers in other parts of the country, each ready to take over in case the primary one is down.

Figure 23.2 identifies the alternatives which exist between centralized and distributed environments. The alternatives bring into evidence the impact dynamically managed service tables can have on network performance.

Sender and Receiver

Topology information has a major influence on design characteristics In a network of some size, it quickly becomes quite impractical to have a direct connection between every two nodes. Thus, in order for the network to route records between nodes X and Y, it may be necessary to route these records via nodes X, U, V, and Y.

Figure 23.2
Routing table

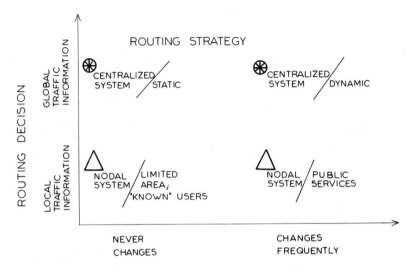

This implies that node X (the sender) must know enough about the network topology to determine that in order to get the record to node Y it should send it to node U. Node U (the intermediate) must recognize that the record is not destined for itself, but for some other node. Furthermore, node U must also know enough about the network topology to determine that in order to get the record to node Y it should send it on to node V, its neighbor. When the network topology changes, some scheme must exist whereby these changes are made known to all nodes in the network. However, the occurrence of topology changes should be invisible to the users of the network.

A DTE at node X communicating with the computer at node Y should be totally unaffected by changes (which occur while the session is "on") in the route between nodes X and Y, as long as such a route continues to exist. But if all routes between X and Y are down, the user's connection will be automatically closed and the user should be informed of what happened. The necessary information about the topology of the network is stored in routing tables. The nodes in the network inform each other about topology changes by sending each other special messages (housekeeping or netchange). All network architectures provide routines that send and receive housekeeping messages and make the appropriate changes in the routing tables.

Compared to the possible complexity presented by the overall performance of a large computers and communications network, this particular task—the actual process of record relaying (or record switching)—is a conceptually trivial one. The sender and intermediate nodes merely consult their routing tables to determine which neighboring node to send the record to. The interesting part is the scheme used to make network topology changes known to all nodes in the network. This is the job of the housekeeping protocols. Thus the problem is to design a correct topology information maintenance control and implement the protocol in question.

Because networks can get unwieldy and complex, a sound and often-used policy is to work at the subnetwork level. In order to correctly relay a record, a node does not need to know the complete and exact topology of the network. All it must know is what direction to send the record, that is, what link it should transmit the record on. In other words, it should know the identity of the first node along the route between itself and the destination node. If there are alternate, feasible routes, it needs to know the relative lengths of these routes. Length is measured in terms of "hops." Thus a route with two intermediate nodes in it is three hops long. This information can be stored in tabular form in a "distance table," which has a column for every node in the network (mapped into the node in reference). Each node has such a distance table, and it should be clear that each node's distance table is different from that of the other nodes'.

Sharing tasks

The backbone of a distributed computers and communications network is designed to take maximum advantage of available resources by sharing tasks. Sharing the communications tasks and distributing the data processing and data base requirements increases the profitability of the resources. Smaller computers working together in a distributed network can provide high responsiveness at each local computer and large system power at a reduced cost. In addition to speed and cost advantages, this type of network gains by its modular construction. Any increased need can be met directly, without necessarily upgrading other network parts.

With high-speed, broad bandwidth data communications available, the system itself will determine how and where processing is done and storage maintained. Operators will make fewer decisions as "secure" operating systems take complete control of the system resources.

Ease of use is perhaps the number one objective and can be attained as the Arpanet, Tymnet, Datapac, Cyclades, and Citinet (among others) experiences demonstrate. In turn, these facilities see to it that more on-line communication oriented systems will evolve as these facilities become easier to use, privacy and security concepts are proven, and systems become more reliable and dependable.

Five characteristics in support of end-user objectives in the coming decade can be distinguished.

The first is distributed special-function processors, including instruction stream processors, file processors, communication processors, event processors, and supervisor processors.

The second characteristic is interpretive processing capability both for end use and for developmental activities. For the program development environment, high-level microprogrammed minicomputers will execute source code (such as PL/1, Cobol, Fortran, and APL) directly.

"Native node" minis and micros will be available for performance-conscious, production-oriented users. Indeed, this may become a competitive strategy both for computer manufacturers and for major users.

Memory hierarchy is the third characteristic. Most hosts and DTEs will utilize their own private high-speed cache (buffers) as well as up to 256,000 characters of integrated main memory, and will be able to share a larger (over 100 million characters) secondary or bulk storage. Communications will be increasingly bit oriented. (In this context, it should be noted that the word bytes has been dropped from most IBM 370 documents, and new system characters may be defined on a dynamic basis, i.e., consisting of 4, 8, n bits, depending on the function to be performed.)

The fourth characteristic is that high-speed, wideband bus will be the basic medium, probably as optical fibers. No one thinks anymore of making a star connection. All the local system resources will exchange data and communicate with each other via a unique wideband, multiaccess bus.

The fifth characteristic is that input–output interconnections will take new forms. A single, multiplexed wire (coaxial cable) or loop (dual loops will be optional for redundancy) operating at a very high speed will probably replace today's numerous cables. This loop system will also permit, in effect, replacing the "channel" function with special integrated input–output processors.

At the network level, monitoring centers will be provided, with the functions to support diagnostic information and inform on error conditions. The services to be offered include line quality monitoring, remote tests, control of configuration, and remote control of software.

New facilities will evolve, such as port sharing and port selection. Communication equipment has a cost proportioned to the number of ports; hence, we don't wish to dedicate ports to suppliers.

High-speed bus adapters will probably be the means by which mainframes will connect to front ends and peripherals. Internet gateway computers will also be provided and this represents a whole *new* type of technology.

Datapac—An example of Network Service

The Canadian Datapac—one of the first packet-switching networks to come into service—is internally structured as a number of distinct layers. Each of them provides a set of communication facilities.

The outer three layers are packet subnet, virtual circuit (or liaison) process layer, and subscriber access (or interface service) layer. Protocol choice and message handling are shown in Figure 23.3.

The packet subnet provides facilities for a process in one node to send or receive packets to or from processes in another node. This layer uses the internal nodal trunks, together with a routing strategy and a defined packet format. The packet

Figure 23.3

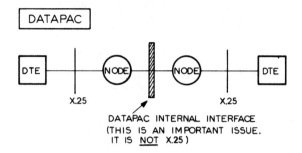

DATAPAC INTERNAL INTERFACE
(THIS IS AN IMPORTANT ISSUE.
IT IS <u>NOT</u> X.25)

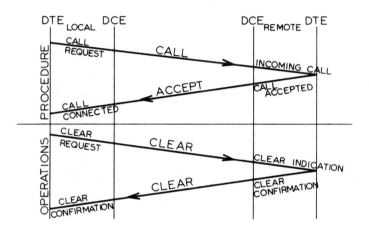

subnet does not guarantee that packets will be delivered in sequence without loss or duplication. It does, however, guarantee that the data field of packets that are delivered is correct. The properties of the packet subnet arise from such factors as the use of alternate routing for packets between nodes when there are parallel facilities or, in cases of failure, retransmission (when errors are detected). The trunks employ a link protocol designed to detect errors in transmission and invoke packet retransmission when any errors are detected.

The main function of the virtual circuit layer is to set up flow control and end-to-end error control schemes to handle the traffic between pairs of processors or processes. Flow control is achieved by the receiver controlling the "credits" that it sends to the transmitter. This is determined by the rate at which packets are "consumed" by the receiving terminal. End-to-end error control is responsible for resequencing, duplicate detection, and recovery from packet loss. Recovery is effected by the sending node holding a copy of each packet that it has sent until an acknowledgement is received. When a packet is sent from the local node to the

Figure 23.4

Alternative 1 (*e.g., may be a program which makes the MF look like a terminal—Case Datapoint/6600)

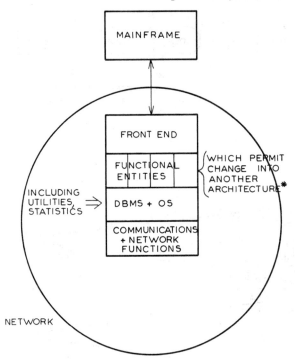

remote node, a copy of the packet is kept and a timer is started. If the remote node receives the packet correctly, it returns a positive acknowledgment. If the acknowledgment is not received before the timer expires, then the local node will retransmit the packet. After a specific number of retransmissions, the call is aborted.

Finally, the subscriber access layer leads into session and presentation control.

Gateways

An important service of Datapac and of all advanced user-oriented data communications networks is the capability to interface disciplines other than the primary one which they support, for instance, asynchronous and bisynchronous within a packet-switching environment. Datapac does that with the so-called network interface machine (NIM). Stated differently, the user's DTEs (computers, terminal controllers, terminals) may be connected directly to the Datapac network using point-to-point links. DTEs not capable of implementing the Datapac protocol, for instance, point-of-sale terminals, would be connected to the NIMS.

Present data services are based upon providing a physical data channel, a

Figure 23.5
Alternative 2

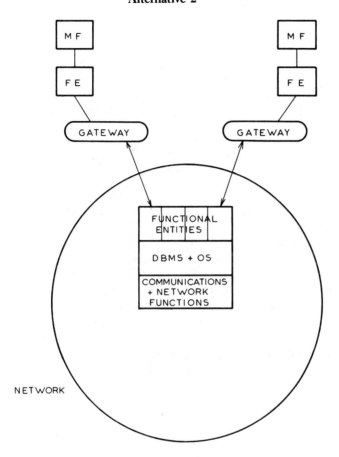

dedicated bandwidth. This may be permanently leased as a private line or periodically accessed as a switched offering. But the crucial issue is the provision of gateways which permit different line disciplines to be attached to the network.

The Datapac solution is one possible alternative. In general, publicly offered data communications services must choose between two alternatives, as presented in figures 23.4 and 23.5, respectively.

Alternative 1 calls for the network to provide a wide variety of services from front ends to mainframes. This is seconded by internal gateway capabilities (functional entities) and by the other services the network must offer. Stated briefly, a gateway is a path offered between two information processing systems with dissimilar protocols. It provides the necessary transformation from one protocol to the other—and thus allows the exchange of information.

Alternative 2 leaves the front ending to the client, dividing the gateway between

Figure 23.6

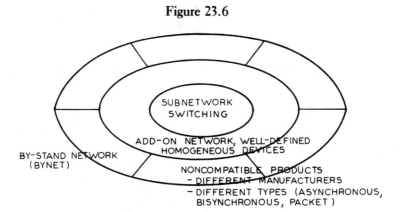

an internal and an external part, the former being the more important. Point-of-sales equipment, for instance, can be front ended by an intelligent concentrator whose functions would include the conversion of an asynchronous protocol to that of the network, though the network may also choose to offer some of these conversion functions.

A third possibility is to project the network in three layers; see Figure 23.6. The central one, subnetwork/switching, will be the true backbone. This is the case of the CIGAL subnetwork in the Cyclades network. An external layer will basically consist of gateways. It will be built up as user requirements develop. Between the internal and the external, there is an intermediate layer which is dedicated to the service of well-defined, homogenous devices conforming to the network's dominant protocol.

24

Basic Definitions for Architectural Design

As applied to the framework of distributed information systems, an architecture is a set of functions, interfaces, and protocols. It provides a structure and a framework to do task-to-task, end-to-end, job-to-job, and the overall data communications processes with accuracy, adaptability, and reliability. To accomplish basic aims, the architectural design should consider the topology, the applications environment, the hardware to be used, and the software which is available or under development. Invariably, the architecture will have to provide for (1) device-sharing—integrating machines (hardware) and running routines; (2) file-sharing—including data base management system DBMS) aspects; and (3) the operating systems functions. This is what the architecture of Arpanet, Telenet, Tymnet, and other data communications networks operating at the moment is doing.

Overall, the architecture will be divided into communications, networking, and applications. To cover its functions it must account for control actions to be applied to messages, transport, paths, links, and errors. The architecture must also contribute to the data base and applied programming routines, including file access, DBMS, programming library, operating system functions, and possibly encryption. Such functions clearly underline the fact that the development of a systems—or a network—architecture calls not only for *concepts* but for a *whole mechanism* as well to be put into action.

Systems and Network Architecture

Why is there a distinction between "systems" architecture and "network" architecture? Because functional differences exist between them.

337

In terms of architectural design a distinction must be drawn between network architecture and distributed systems. The network architecture will start at that point and go into the environment. This architecture, which might support 1,000 terminals or more, is *outside* the "internal" module devoted to processing purposes.

It is possible to enlarge the framework presented in this specific example by establishing a definition which can pass the test of time as concepts evolve and new systems develop. A systems architecture for DIS may cover distributed processing and, to a substantial degree, distributed data bases, but it does *not* need to provide a network solution. Two facts characterize this approach: (1) The minicomputers (say, the work stations) at the periphery (and even at the headquarters) will not necessarily be linked together into a network projected and implemented by the user—including its nodes, lines, and software support.* (2) The on-line operation between work stations will take place sometimes during the day but *not* continuously—a condition which would have required a network approach.

The solution which Paribas has adopted is a cost-effective one using the state of the art in systems technology to the best advantage and is an example of systems architecture.

The solution Citibank has chosen with its privately owned CITINET is an example of network architecture. (Citibank hired a specialized firm to build the network as a result of the experience of ARPA.) Public networks—Telenet, Tymnet, Datapac, Transpac—have to go through network architecture, but not all users need to follow Citibank solution. Value-added carriers will, to a very large extent, make this unnecessary.

A network architecture is the only one that can ensure distributed operating systems, on-line maintenance, and end-to-end encryption. But not all users have the expertise to set up the system on their own, and most manufacturers are still in the developmental stages of this advanced discipline.

Not only is it important to distinguish between network architecture and systems architecture, but also the user must be brought into the picture from the start. The information-centered computer and communications systems we have been discussing make this a necessity. In Table 24.1 ten critical issues are outlined, and user interaction with the network and with the systems architects is shown for each of these issues.

Within a systems architecture it will be required to specify all the functions that exist at the level of the projected DIS implementation. Generally, it will not be necessary to design the interfaces between functions, say, of the same node of the network, since this should be provided by the network architecture which the user will adopt.

The systems architect must bear in mind software configurations, equipment selection, operating system explosion into discrete modules specific to certain functions, procedural developments for implementation, compatibility and transparency in application modules, and maintainability of the same—and of the

---

*Though the latter may be provided by the computer manufacturer.

Table 24.1
User Interaction with System Architects and with Network Architects

User's Viewpoint	Systems Architect	Network Architect
1. Structural description	←————————→	
2. Applications overview	←————————→	
3. Network overview	←————————————————→	
4. Potential systems development	←————————→	
5. Actual examples	⇐————————→ ←————————————————→	
6. Effects of commands on network behavior	←————————————————→	
7. Communications issues	⇐————————→ ←————————————————→	
8. Efficiency characteristics	←————————→	
9. Design impact: changes aftermaths	←————————→	
10. Costs	←————————→	

network—in terms of on-line tests and on-line dispositions. In this sense, systems architecture is what tomorrow's user will need most. However, to project DIS systems effectively, the user must know the data communications jargon (even its fine print) and must understand how a network works.*

The Nodes of a Network

The pivot points of a network architecture are the *nodes*. By definition, a node is any of the computer equipment connected by physical links. *It is an addressable entity.*

In other terms, all computers are nodes, independently of the function they perform. A node may be a switch, host, or terminal concentrator. A *switch* is a node which serves only the routing function. A *host* is a node able to support application programs; it is an information processor which provides supporting services to users, communicates with users, communicates with other nodes (switches, hosts), and

---

*In different terms, the know-how on a network architecture must be available even though the user may limit his design at the level of a systems architecture.

Figure 24.1

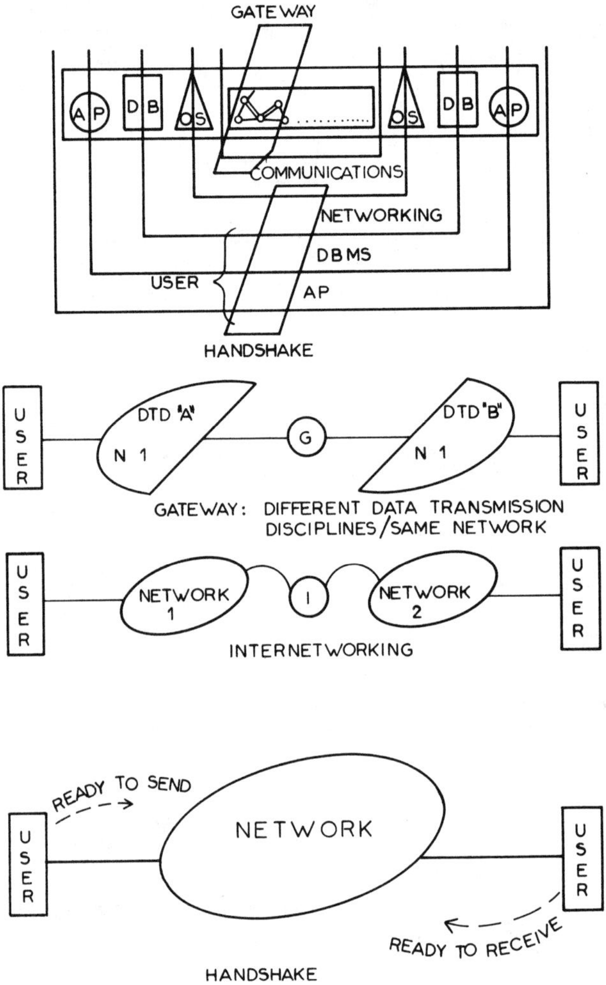

GATEWAY

COMMUNICATIONS

NETWORKING

DBMS

USER

AP

HANDSHAKE

GATEWAY: DIFFERENT DATA TRANSMISSION
DISCIPLINES/SAME NETWORK

INTERNETWORKING

HANDSHAKE

offers supporting services to other hosts when necessary. A terminal concentrator is a minicomputer or microcomputer whose job is to coordinate a number of terminal devices.

Let us also add that the physical placement of a node within a network does not determine what its function is. The function is determined by what it does.

Other subjects which need to be defined in terms of network architecture are the following:

Protocols and interfaces (transparent or virtual)

Handshaking and gateways

Figure 24.2

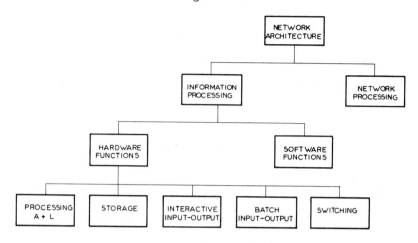

Virtual (or logical) circuits and datagrams

Streams and windows

Rejection and abort procedures

Native commands and network primitives

Downline loading and upline dumping

Balanced (symmetric) and unbalanced (asymmetric) networks

Topological layout

Performance criteria and standardization

Basic Definitions

The most critical issue following the definition of an architecture is that of protocols. Protocols interest the network as a whole, the communications subnets, and the subscribers, and they must be respected by all parties. A *protocol is a formal set of conventions governing the format and control of data.* It comprises well-defined procedures clearly understood by all parties. The data communication rules established through a protocol are applicable between similar processes. (In contrast, an interface establishes rules for communication between dissimilar processes.)

A *transparent protocol* sends data through the system without particular constraints from low-level details.* The user can't see it, but it *is* there. With a

---

*That is, protocols and standards interesting lower levels, such as the data communication equipment (modem).

Figure 24.3

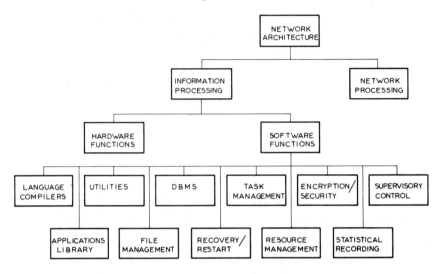

virtual protocol there is a sequence to be observed. It is better to have transparent protocols, but is is not easy.

The interfaces, too, can vary. They may be virtual or real.

A handshake is a controlled transfer of information between the sender and the receiver. It is ready to send and ready to receive (Figure 24.1), and as such it involves data, receipt of acknowledgments, sending completed, and completion of acknowledgment.

A gateway is a path provided between two different data transmission disciplines, within the same network, with dissimilar protocols. The object of the gateway is to allow the exchange of information by providing the necessary transformation from one protocol to another.

A virtual circuit is a point-to-point switched (or permanent) circuit over which data, reset, interrupt, and flow-control packets transmit. It is also referred to as "logical circuit" or "logical path." It is correct to observe that the virtual circuit concept defies the known principle of Euclidean geometry—that "the straight line is the shortest path between two points." Within a data communications network the shortest (or best) path is the one which is reliable and available at the same time.

A datagram is a section of a message (typically of 256 or 512 characters) individually routed through a packet-switching network. Datagrams are used to split long packets into smaller units. However, as compared to long remote batch transmission types (as we know them today), datagram service charges are two to four times the corresponding cost of bucket transmission because of the cost of headers, tailers, and routing. Such costs may become increasingly substantial.

A stream is a virtual circuit application (particularly used with reference to satellites, going through a single broadcast.)

A window is a logical path to be opened between two processes before data can be passed. It is used in flow control management.

The *rejection* and *abort* procedures to be adopted are very important in data communications. *Abort is invoked by the sender causing the recipient to discard (and ignore) all bit sequences transmitted by the same sender since the preceding flag sequence.* Aborting should be followed by retransmission. A good retransmission strategy is to wait a while, and if nothing comes back then retransmit. The alternative to this is to send the receiver station a NAK (*no acknowledgment*). NAK has its own problems, though, for instance, loss of its own data.

The next definition is that of *native commands* which means *native to the particular set, or subset, of an operating system.* Another way to look at native commands is to say that they are supported by an operating system, that is, they are the normally visible instructions.

Network primitives are the set of basic commands characterizing the network architecture and its subsets.

We said earlier that the implementation of a network architecture calls for a whole mechanism to be put into action. Downline loading and upline dumping are two gears of this mechanism. *Downline loading means the load of programs for immediate or deferred execution on a minicomputer or generally a network component. Upline loading, or as it is usually called, upline dumping, means sending information upline not for execution but for analysis purposes.* Both terms stem from the traditional hierarchical networks with a host (master) to satellite relationship.

We have just mentioned the traditional host (master) to satellite relationship. *A protocol which supports master/slave (or primary/secondary) computer operations is called unbalanced or asymmetric.*

Figure 24.4

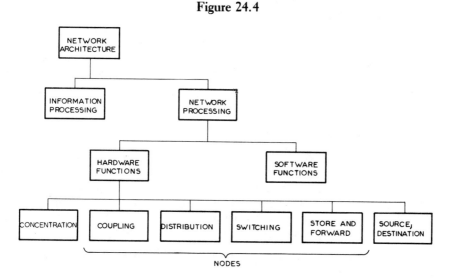

Figure 24.5

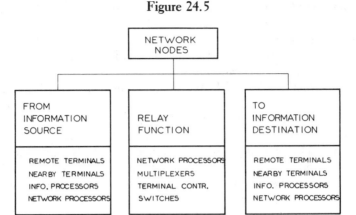

A protocol is balanced or symmetric when there is no master/slave relationship, that is, the network is horizontal. This is the new approach in networking, reflected in the X.25, LAP "B".*

A further definition necessary for a good understanding of how a network acts is that of the *topological layout*. This is an important prerequisite inasmuch as a topology is designed with specific objectives in mind. Protocols presuppose a given topology.† (There is *no* standard topology as such).

Projecting an Architecture

We said that within the framework of DIS, a architecture is a set of functions, interfaces, and protocols. Designing the architecture means to specify the functions that must exist at every node of a distributed information system. It also means projecting the interfaces between two functions of the same node. Usually functions interface through a protocol. This brings up the need for establishing or adopting protocols and for integrating them with the architectural framework. For instance, when we deal with programs which are able to exchange messages, we are faced with a *message protocol*. A *link protocol* is one whereby two functions exchange information on the physical lines, and so on.

Throughout the architectural perspective emphasis must be placed on long-term support of DIS developments, just as we appreciate the need for superior design and manufacture of computer products. This basic philosophy of a systems and a network architecture must be such that the user can rely on complete assistance to maintain the system at peak efficiency. A DIS must be backed by multiple resources, from efficient protocols to field service, training, and documentation. All important parts of a system must be subjected to highly detailed attention.

*Adopted in mid-1977 by the International Standards Organization. LAP stands for "line access protocol."

†Even if IBM's SNA and Digital Equipment's DECNET, etc., are more or less generalized.

Figure 24.6

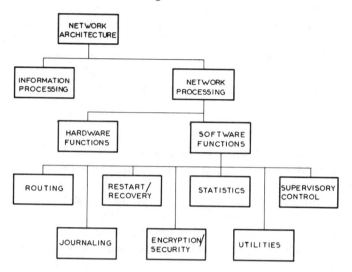

The architectural design must ensure, specification of requirements, reasonable cost, reliability and availability, and overall efficiency. The principles of design must be such as to enhance control action and to assess quality while it guarantees maintainability.

Complexity may be controlled through visibility—the process of making completely visible to project management all the constituents of the activities over which it is necessary to exercise direct control in time to promote systems simplicity.

Simplicity can be assessed by means of measurements—the need to measure, with great precision, progress toward well-defined design goals in terms of the observance of standards, the avoidance of intricate solutions, and the attention to established timescales and to performance criteria.

Simplicity helps quality. Mounting pressure to meet user needs, as expressed by the user and according to his own priorities, should not overshadow the requirement for quality results. Quality costs more, but in the final analysis offers the maximum benefit to all concerned.

Quality, in turn, promotes maintainability. The need to produce systems that have long useful lives, lower total life cycle costs, and sufficient flexibility to meet changing user demands is one of the indisputable basic facts in data communications.

Conclusion

The objective of an architecture for DIS is to provide an ensemble of instruments which permit the user to (1) proceed with an effective distribution of his hardware resources (device sharing); (2) put into action an optimal software distribution (program and procedure sharing); (3) effect the correct approach to a distributed data base network; (4) use high-level languages in approaching communications problems; (5) make full use of front-end and rear-end capability; (6) work in internetworking through the gateways; and (7) eventually implement distributed operating systems, on-line maintenance, encryption, security, and privacy. In order to competently help the user as far as the foregoing faculties are concerned, an architecture must be characterized by some specific capabilities inherent in its original design.

Device independence. The ability to utilize peripheral units of any type.

The ability to control remote peripherals as if they were local. Specifically, a program on remote computer or concentrator should be able to write directly into a disc of the higher level.

Program distribution. This characteristic permits the transmission of programs via a communication line to remote systems and subsequent execution. Such a faculty is important to remote equipment which does not have mass memory but is able to manage applications by means of requests posed to programs in other systems of the network.

Execution of system directives on remote equipment. This permits the activation or close down of programs between two remote computers, as well as downline loading and upline dumping.

Management of remote data bases. If the distributed system includes distributed data bases, it is necessary to provide for the management of a networkwide data base system. Such provision must account for the use of heterogeneous equipment.

The orderly approach to the design of the architecture would separate information processing from network processing, then integrate into a working ensemble the hardware and the software aspects. Figures 24.2 through 24.6 demonstrate this approach. The hardware and software functions are clearly distinguished. Each is crucial to the efficient and continuing performance of the network.

25

Functions and Objectives in Network Architecture

The architecture of data communication networks has evolved to a point where a common philosophy on functions and objectives is now emerging. The philosophy reflects a certain structure: the division of the networking functions into discrete modules and the layering of these modules such that higher layers or levels are built on the functions provided by the lower levels.

In order to structure the framework and to define the functions to be performed, it is advisable to divide a network architecture into communications, networking, and applications. Such layers are hierarchical, each one building on the abilities of the preceding or lower layers. The communication layer creates error-free sequential links from the physical channels connecting the network computers. The networking layer uses these links to route data from source to destination and create virtual circuits or Datagrams between the communicating programs or system resources. The application layer uses this communication path to control input–output devices, access files, and transmit application program data.

Most current network architecture use this layered structure. Within each of the layers a protocol is designed to perform the functions of that layer under the constraints and capabilities of the lower layers and physical equipment. This is the basis on which the concepts are developed. The network processing software, as it evolves, will necessarily reflect the design we have outlined.

Layered Solutions

One of the most important tests of a network architecture is that it is layered, and that the principle of independence between the layers is observed. This is fundamental since network architecture by its nature is a complex undertaking. The user needs layers and the concept of independence among layers to protect against

Figure 25.1

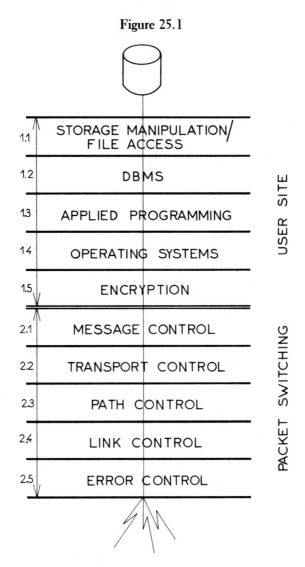

upheavals when changing successive functions or developing and inserting new ones.

We have distinguished information processing from network processing. The former is done at the user's site, while the latter is the object of packet switching. As Figure 25.1 demonstrates, each is divided into a number of subsets or constituent parts. For some of them, computer users already have well-established notions. Others, like encryption and path control, are still being developed.

At the user's site the overriding need is for terminal control. Assuming that in the future intelligent terminals will be commonplace, users will need to be assisted

Figure 25.2

SECTION	OBJECT
TRAILER	ERROR CONTROL
FRAME	LINK CONTROL
PACKET	PATH CONTROL
ID FRAGMENT	DTE OR CLUSTER CONTROLLER

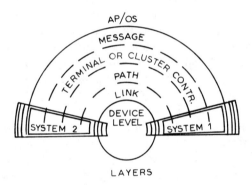

LAYERS

with DBHS and file access systems which would be available not just at a given central processing location but throughout the organization wherever a terminal exists. Record access protocols are necessary and these include user identification, file attributes, requests (open read; open write; delete), acknowledgments, data, and control functions.

At the applications level we must observe terminal access, network control, and remote system loading. Services to be provided within the packet-switching area will be overseen by the organization of the packet, which contains corresponding sections for each function to be performed; see Figure 25.2.

This explains how a layered solution helps two DTE (terminals or computer systems) communicate with each other. Within each layer, programs are written independently of the hardware reference, i.e., of the precise equipment which will be used.

We should also notice the role played by message control. The logical relation supported through the APs (applied programming) is independent from the physical relation of the nodes within which packet switching will be executed.

This leads to the idea of the maximum service a network architecture will provide; the network architecture offers the overall view on how the systems representation will be made. A logical organization, a physical organization, control and flow of information, and representation, interpretation and transformation of information—functions reflected since the original architectural design—are at the disposal of the user. The user's objective can thus be specified: to ensure that the faculties inherent to an architecture are used to their fullest extent.

Duties of the Network Architect

To make the network architect's job manageable, a sharp distinction must be made between architecture and implementation. The latter is the user's job. The network architect must confine himself scrupulously to (1) development of an overall concept, the definition of what it can do, and the examination of whether or not it answers the performance demanded; (2) evaluation of the project's ability to balance requirements with resources—putting the resources to work to the fullest extent; (3) spelling out the design specifications for further implementation; (4) testing needed to assure that the developing architecture respects the prerequisites in general and, in particular, the layered approach; (5) inclusion of standard protocols and the development of efficient interfaces; (6) making a comprehensive instruction text which is simple enough for less skilled people to use.

These are precise responsibilities to be performed step by step. Take, as an example, the functions of the networking layer: (1) *routing*—moving of data from source to destination; (2) *congestion control*—a global network problem; (3) *virtual channel management or Datagram solution*—inside this function we should distinguish: (a) *call establishment*, including message ACK, connection/disconnection, sequentiality, and flow control, and (b) *message segmentation*—the task of breaking messages into packets. Some of these functions will eventually be enhanced through international agreements, but this is not yet always the case. X.25, for example, still does *not* offer a true end-to-end ACK and flow control mechanism which means that either the network architect has to provide his own mechanism (hence, a minilayer), or accept the possibility of scrambling. The job is big, and it will necessarily have to be tackled by a team, which should be organized like a surgical team where one does the cutting and the others give him every support that will enhance his effectiveness.

The network architect and his team will have to analyze the functions performed by level. Take the communications level as another example. Physical link, error detection, recovery, sequentiality (order in/out), and link management should all be examined. The last must ensure the mechanics of the operation: if there is more than one transmitter, there should be multiple control and ownership of the link by one transmitter at a time. Indeed, if we look at the interface to the communications layer, we see a *sequential* throughput: a multipoint link can be assimilated by many point-to-point hook-ups. These bring about the need for protocols. If there were many point-to-point connections—not a multidrop one—

Figure 25.3

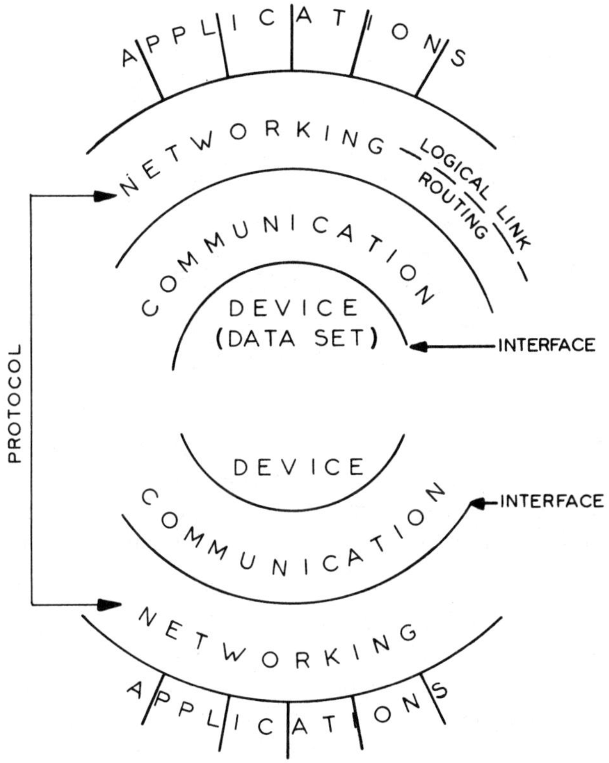

and *if* the total system were error free, we would not have needed the use of protocols for anything except framing.

Network architecture, however, does *not* really include the requirement of protocol design.* What it includes is the layers, the function definition *within* the layers, and the interface *between* the layers. These issues should attract the architect's attention.

Protocols and Interfacing

We have said that in order to handle its distributed data problems a network has to provide the solutions for interfacing (between layers) and protocols (between sender and receiver). Figure 25.3 demonstrates this relationship. The layers of communications and networking interface together. Within one layer there will be sublayers; for instance, link protocols break down into three functional components:

*In fact, it is better free of protocols so that protocols can be changed as new standards develop.

Figure 25.4

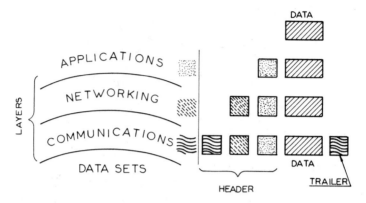

1. Framing—finding "beginning" and "end" of a message block
2. Data exchange—passing correct sequential data over the link
3. Link management—performing functions such as addressing receivers and selecting transmitters in the case of multiple transmitters and receivers

There follows the very important concept of "protocol purity." It means don't mix the protocols of the different layers, and don't use overlapping patterns. Figure 25.4 demonstrates how each layer adds to the packet its own reference. The header and the trailer are like brackets around the data. The header includes flags (mainly message priority), destination, and source. The trailer includes the control data.

Differences between protocols can exist all over, for example, in framing, where HDLC and SDLC versus DDCMP (digital data communication management protocol). The difference is in bit staffing even though both are synchronous disciplines. A need for special hardware results from the differences in question.

At the data exchange level, protocols are very similar regarding positive acknowledgment, retransmission and time-out occurrence. But they differ in efficiency.

Finally, the reference to link management concerns polling, tributary stations, contention, and symmetry. More precisely, it concerns whether there are primary/secondary solutions or whether all stations within the network are equal. Link management determines *when* a station sends a message, not *what* the station sends.

The Grand Design

Let us say that all problems relating to protocols and interfacing have been settled, and that the network architecture has been made to work efficiently and dependably.* What comes next? Let us assume that the network is a public service or, more

---

*Which might be a fact within four to five years.

Figure 25.5

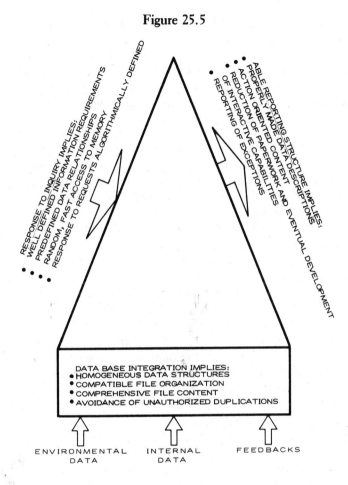

DATA BASE INTEGRATION IMPLIES:
- HOMOGENEOUS DATA STRUCTURES
- COMPATIBLE FILE ORGANIZATION
- COMPREHENSIVE FILE CONTENT
- AVOIDANCE OF UNAUTHORIZED DUPLICATIONS

ENVIRONMENTAL DATA   INTERNAL DATA   FEEDBACKS

precisely, a value-added network. This is by far the most interesting development for a large number of industrial and commercial enterprises and financial institutions. The following, then, might be the grand design.

First, the availability of an efficient and dependable VAN would transfer to this Network most of the communications-related functions that are now performed by front ends, multiplexers, concentrators, and remote controllers. Among other functions, it would provide network control, flow control, code coversion, error control, terminal polling, message routing/rerouting and formatting.*

A high-level data communication language would allow the user to specify communications process requirements in standard form. Data, the most essential element in this new kind of system orientation, will become the center. The so-called arithmetic or central processor units will no longer be central—they will be auxiliary, away from the center or on the periphery of the system.

*In IBM terminology, the system would exclude access method (VTAM), but include network control program (NCP).

We emphasize these facts because they herald a different epoch in information system design and orientation. From a central processing unit-centered organization in 1950, we moved into a memory-centered system in 1965, and into a data-centered network in 1980. Organizations wishing to advance, not only keep up with but also profit from the evolution of technology, experience a major conceptual change. This is a 15-year cycle, and largely engulfs three generations of computers. Furthermore, the real growth of information systems will not be the amount of data—although this will grow substantially—but rather the use of that data. Control over data should be another prime subject of optimization.

The answer to the question of what to improve is that computer manufacturers should dedicate at least part of the greater processing engine power to providing easier, faster access to data, rather than using it merely as a means to house ever larger collections of data.

Another key function to optimize in systems to be delivered in the early 1980s concerns the format of the data whose access we seek to make more efficient. Still another refers to the data base management systems and their ability for ease of use, responsiveness, flexibility, and modularity. The input-output channels or their equivalent processors will also have increased data rates. Main storage will undoubtedly be substantially larger and faster with more functional designs, for example, hierarchical storage structures.

Both in business and, eventually, at home, the increasing business opportunity of information electronics will continue to displace other modes of control, reaching into nearly all aspects of our lives. The R + D money invested in this field will ensure that industry makes more sophisticated functional elements at ever decreasing costs. (These references are not made only in respect to data communications networks. Examples from everyday life abound. Mechanical elements of the calculator and the watch have been displaced by integrated circuits that are less expensive but more flexible. In the near future the automobile will be controlled by a microcomputer with a consequent improvement in efficiency.)

All these developments are extensions of the traditional application of electronics to the task of information handling in measurement, communication, and data manipulation. By the mid-1980s the number of electronic functions incorporated into existing products each year can be expected to be some fifty times greater than it is today. Correspondingly, the cost per function will decline by then to between 1/15 and 1/20 of that of today, though in some areas where cost reduction during the last decade has been slow, the ratio might be much more impressive. Data communications is a specific case. As we stated earlier, with optical fibers, satellites, the multiplexing of voice, image, data, and the mass economies made possible through VAN, communications costs are projected to decrease by an impressive ratio, somewhere between 1/40 and 1/50 of where they stand today.

Impact at the Workplace

Developing an electronic mail service, expanding the data base and making its contents more accessible, providing interactive man-machine communications, disseminating knowledge for educational pruposes, and performing many of the clerical tasks in an office are tangible results to be expected from the exponential proliferation of products of data communications and of microelectronics.

The real evolution will be manifested in office routine. But how? An announcement made in late 1977 stated that the Firestone Tire and Rubber Co. was in the process of switching to a distributed processing system. The firm planned to split the data base and install both a terminal-based and a minicomputer-based system. Now we shall make the hypothesis that a VAN in operation was chosen to link the Firestone factories and sales offices, relieving the company from having to project its own network—as has been the case with Citinet. The decision to use

Figure 25.6
Decentralized applications

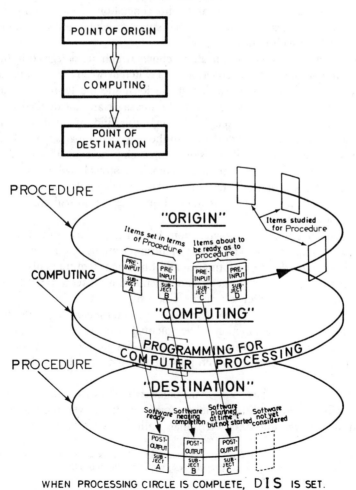

WHEN PROCESSING CIRCLE IS COMPLETE, DIS IS SET.

existing data communication facilities changes the perspectives of the study. The problem is dimensioned from network architecture to the level of a systems architecture.

With the network services taken care of, and provided that the user's analysts understand both the dynamics and the mechanics of data communications,* the salient problem of the user is that of the distributed data base. Over the last quarter of a century, the basic reason for the failures of computers was that the users were paying for big data processors but were only taking out of them the power of accounting machines. Let us not repeat the same failure with the networks.

Figure 25.5 brings this problem into focus: data base integration—*then* segmentation—response to inquiry, and able reporting structure are the three key issues. These will establish the requirements. The hardware study for the remote sites comes next. (And remember the rule for system architecture: dimension the equipment for the job to be done—not vice versa.)

The existence of VAN services may suggest the local use of intelligent terminals (see the discussion on the second and third generation of data communication networks. This system solution does *not* necessitate much buffering or complicated terminal switching techniques.

Relieved of the data communications chores which are delegated to the VAN, the local minicomputer can effectively act as a switch between the terminals and the data base. This solution requires that at the local site the terminals themselves queue-up the messages. In other words, the messages are *not* queued inside the computer but at the terminal level. A solution of this kind, incidentally, can just as well be used in a bank or in industry. With the new technologies where 16 kilobits and eventually 64 kilobits will be stored on a chip or two, a, say, 32-kilobyte memory is no obstacle. In fact, it's half a chip. The obstacle will be, as usual, the procedural study; see Figure 25.6. This is a known but rarely appreciated fact; we have to give it our most careful attention. Equipment is no real challenge today. The system architecture is.

In conclusion, in a given organization, the existing telecommunications skill, the age of the equipment, and the nature of the applications determine in a substantial part the general design performance and functional requirements for the new system—the more so as new systems and functional units require radical redesign of the old structures in order to give the best results.

The systems architect will deal with physical and logical supports, topology, applications, and systems functions. The potential of networks—their perspectives and facilities challenges—varies with the overall design, the number of terminals attached to them, the distance which must be covered, and the use to which they are put.

There is a score of large important organizations in banking, transportation, manufacturing, merchandising—not to mention the governmental services— which think of upward of 10,000 terminals online.

---

*Which, as we shall not fail to repeat, is a *key issue* and must always be kept in evidence. If one does not know data communications well, it is better not to work with the subject.

26

The Tradeoffs

Computers and data communications literature quite often fails to divide between network architecture and systems architecture. The difference is subtle but important. A network architecture is made up of a number of modular functions. Its goal is to simplify the task of description and implementation of a distributed environment, specifically one oriented to data communications. These functions may be implemented in hardware, software, or by human action. There will be a communications area—the backbone of the network—and a control area the network architect must provide for. These are not necessarily visible to the user. However, there is an applications area with which the user will interface; see Figure 26.1.

The general requirement of a network architecture is to provide networking capabilities across the broad range of functional uses. An architecture must be developed to support a wide variety of signal carriers, a broad range of processors, different operating systems, different data bases, and user interfaces. Because it is developed to operate within a transaction-oriented environment, the network architecture must ensure such supports on-line and through a complete interconnectability. This means supplying a mechanism where any pair of processes or devices can communicate.

The network architecture must use well-defined protocols and software facilities to achieve the desired ability to interconnect. It must also allow for future technological advances to be incorporated into the design and implementation with minimal upsetting of operations.

Trade-offs have to be made. Several of them relate to data representation. Will the communications system support only one data type or code? Two, three? What will be the format of the messages to be exchanged—fixed length and fixed fields? How much of a restriction will this be on the different applications to be handled on the network?

Figure 26.1

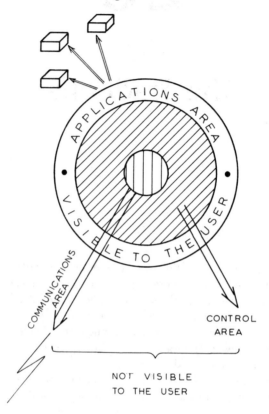

Trade-offs extend all the way into the applications domain. Should the communications system deliver the messages in a transparent manner, or should it provide a certain amount of data conversion? Of code conversion? Should it provide a certain amount of interpretation of the content of the messages, as electronic mail systems may require?

Which applications will be supported? Which hardware? Which software? Will services be provided to integrate existing hardware and software? Must the existing protocols be supported? What if the main current protocol is an old one that was designed for a limited application only?

Network Requirements

The line protocols to be supported and their impact on network control, network access, protection and security, response time considerations, error rates, and throughput are among the issues involved in a network planning study. Every factor to be studied involves trade-offs. Trade-offs among conflicting ends cannot be made intelligently unless the requirements have been established. Network requirements include:

1. Provision of a reasonably good network performance for each type of utilization
2. Assurance of a mechanism for connection to other networks
3. Support of functions necessary for protection and security
4. Assurance of correct accounting and billing procedures
5. Ease and efficiency in maintaining operations
6. High degree of availability

These are stated in generic terms; more specifically, the requirements will relate to the job. Do we wish to integrate voice, data, and image? Control the information and voice flow? Prepare statistics on the use of the system and on billing? Create network interfaces and gateways? In Figure 26.2, for instance, the circuit switching area is the telephone company's. The user has to think of PBXs and of terminals, of connection to the nearest port the backbone offers, and of cost and performance. And what about tomorrow—how will the unavoidable expansion be made?

The need for systems planning is evident. The network services will be developed over a number of years, but they must operate much longer. Continuous evaluation and maintenance are crucial issues for a successful life cycle. It is better to pay more capital cost in the beginning than a very high price during the whole life cycle.

One of the increasingly significant problems facing the designers and planners is the timely and accurate definition of systems elements, activity interrelationships, and their interfaces. A specific issue within a network environment is "sockets." The

Figure 26.2

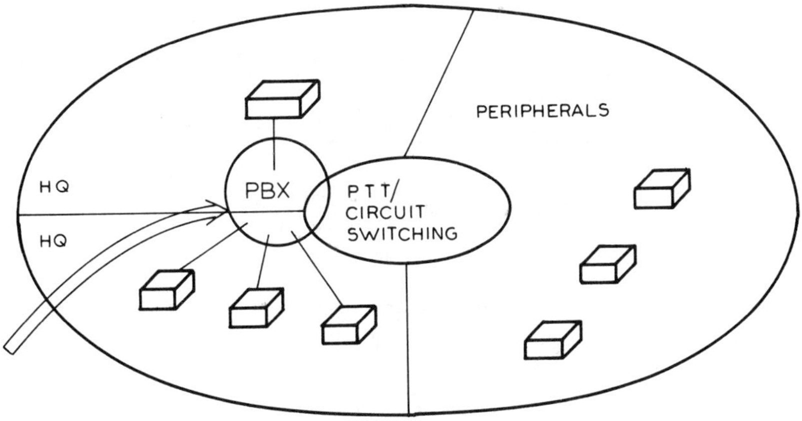

definition of sockets is important in process-to-process communications and connection procedures, both establishment and rejection; see Figure 26.3.

Assume that processes have input–output ports whose names are peculiar to operating system implementation. Processes themselves may be identified in different ways in various operating systems. Imagine that the host-to-host protocol must provide a uniform name space so that a process in one system can effectively "connect" a local port to a remote one by reference to the common naming conventions. Assume that the common naming conventions will be translated into local conventions by the host-to-host protocol program. We will refer to the implementation of a host-to-host protocol as a control program, (CP). The common names for ports will be sockets and these will implicitly identify the host and process

Figure 26.3

This multilayered structure is necessary to ensure that data do not get lost. The ports are defined locally and are idiosyncratic. The socket reflects a uniform, standard name space.

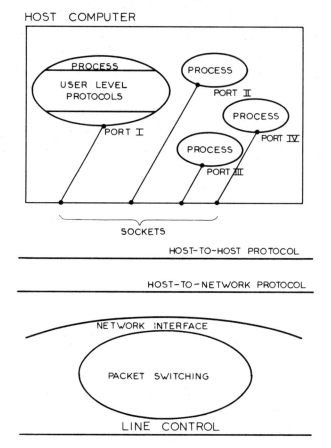

Figure 26.4
Criteria for choosing networks: error protection, available protocols, gateways to other networks, speed of transmission, store facilities, parametrically defined functions

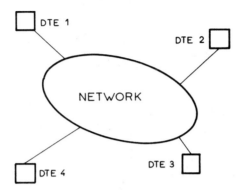

owning the port. A process can range between COBOL (or any language) program, a library, a file system, a whole data base, a peripherals handler (e.g., printer) and its software, and a rear-end machine.

Processes need both hardware and software resources to be run and sockets through which to communicate with their environment. In a remote communications network, the communicating objects are typically terminals and processes—the latter usually being unaware of the physical location of the former. Indeed, the location of the device, file, or program is usually unimportant as long as it is accessible. As far as the user is concerned, the location is determined by the functions which are performed, while accessibility is assured by the network.

The Seven Basic Steps

Lack of internal expertise in many companies creates the situation where they are asking for a network for data communications without specifying whether the need is for inquiry–response, interactive problem solving, transaction-oriented requirements, bulk data transfer, or other possibilities. Alternative solutions, for example, facsimile, could answer the needs. These alternatives have very different kinds of requirements in terms of the parameters of choice.

As Figure 26.4 demonstrates, criteria exist for choosing networks, and these are largely user oriented. Choices have to be made. To satisfy user-oriented requirements—both current and future—many techniques may be employed which center around the structure and the protocols.

The first technique is *layering and modularization*. The functions to be performed by the network architecture may be divided into modules and structured in a layered manner. We shall talk of layers in the following section. Here, it is

Figure 26.5

A total mechanism showing a network with different levels of transmission speeds and usage

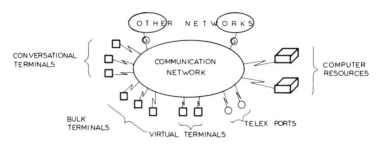

- TERMINAL-TO-TERMINAL
- TERMINAL-TO-COMPUTER
- TERMINAL EMULATION
- INTERACTIVE AND BULK TERMINALS

- AUTOMATIC TERMINAL RE- COGNITION
- HOST AVAILABILITY
- TERMINAL/HOST ROUTING
- PROTECTION/PRIVACY

- ERROR DETECTION AND CORRECTION
- STORE AND FORWARD
- ALTERNATE PATH SELECTION
- NETWORK RELIABILITY

sufficient to remark that high-level layers use the functions provided by lower layers in a strictly hierarchical ordering. This creates a flexible architecture and ensures efficient implementation. It has, however, a cost, namely, interfacing (between layers) and implementation overhead.

Architectural design and subsequent implementation may structure each layer as a separate task or process, provide the communications link between them, or combine several layers into a single process (using subroutine calls to pass information and control). The implementation must make use of the logical solutions available within the system. Hence, an architectural design must project and provide from the beginning for such techniques.

Always keep in mind that trade-offs extend into all three areas of a network: the physical (nodes, communications links), the logical (rules, commands), and that of the subscriber (to use the physical facilities, these subscribers must observe the logical constraints). From among the conflicting requirements the designer faces, he must strike the right balance.

A second technique, *layered abstraction*, is a basic characteristic of layered solutions. A level of abstraction is created by each layer in the structure to the layer above it. A simpler way of saying this is that functions (and sometimes structure) specific to a given layer are used within that layer; they are not passed to layers above. A lower layer, for instance, manages the data link control. Such functional characteristics are transparent to the next level which manages the routing function. In turn, this is transparent to the next level which addresses itself to virtual circuit service.

The functional mechanism technique follows the overall design and also complements it. Such a mechanism must ensure that functions specific to a given application or use of the system are, as far as possible, moved to the user level; additions, deletions, or changes in specific uses do not affect the networking portion of the architecture; any function can be moved to a higher level without affecting the complexity of the interfaces or the basic structure.

Because we are still at the early stages of architectural developments, we should avoid making systems rigid. Today security protection, and the information required, may be handled by the same layer. Tomorrow one layer might provide the information necessary for security and protection, but the mechanism proper could be the object of a higher layer.

Figure 26.5 shows a total mechanism. It lists functions whose objective is to provide a network with the broadest appeal to the user. Therefore, different levels of transmission speeds and use have been incorporated.

In the *protocols within protocols* technique not only are the network functions layered, but the corresponding protocols are structured one inside the other. This is known as nesting of protocols. Each functional layer should look at the protocol envelope which concerns it directly and should not involve the other protocol layers. This approach—handling protocols only at the architectural layer to which they correspond—gives the flexibility to add or subtract new protocols.

The *layers within layers* technique designs the layers of a network architecture and the corresponding protocols with sublayers (or subsets). This ensures flexibility in future expansion or upkeep. To some extent it also makes feasible that part of the whole system might adhere to the structure of another architecture. Indeed, this is the course new architectures have followed. Table 26.1 documents this by comparing the layered approach of three architectures: Digital Equipment Corporation's Decnet, Hewlett-Packard's 3000, and IBM's SNA. This table also presents the terminology used by each of the three manufacturers—notice that it is not standard—and, correspondingly, the terminology the reader will find in this book.

In the *resources and their use* technique reference is made to system resources and functional modules for communication and identification. This can be done using a global "object type" descriptor, mapped locally into the process to which communication is addressed. It is necessary to ensure that each system, subsystem, and process knows about its local characteristics—whether or not it is needed to pass this information to other parts of the network.

Let us recall what was said of processes and sockets. Figure 8.6 shows a multiprogrammed maxicomputer operating in a typical banking environment. This is a resource at the user's level, but at the network level it is a data load. Serving equipment calls for resources and requires interfaces. A computer gateway needs to be provided.

A final technique is to take a *long hard look* at the network architecture. It must be designed so all nodes operate within a given structure. The functional use of a node depends on its physical location in the network and the user-oriented functions it is designed to perform. The architecture treats nodes either as switches or as local intelligence. The latter may be hosts, front ends, terminal concentrators, or terminals and will be handled identically from a network perspective.

There will be many design issues to consider. One of the most important is that of the trade-offs, for instance, between line efficiency and processing optimization. Further, the design of a network architecture for general-purpose networks must

Table 26.1

Common Carriers (CCITT* recommendation X.25)	Decnet (Digital Equipment Corporation)	3000 (Hewlett-Packard)	SNA (IBM)	Corresponding Terminology used in this book
Users' level: referred to as level 4	Dialogue layer	User protocol User interface Host services	Function management	Users' layer, divided into several distinct levels
Level 3	Network services protocol (NSP layer)	Distributed system monitor Network system	Transmission control Path control	Networking/virtual circuit or datagram Networking/routing
Level 2	DDCMP (digital data communication management protocol)	Protocol driver (communication)	SDLC	XDLC communications layer (data link control, link management)
Level 1	—	—	—	DCE DTE

*International Telephone and Telegraph Consultative Committee

Figure 26.6

Multiprogrammed maxicomputer operating in a banking environment

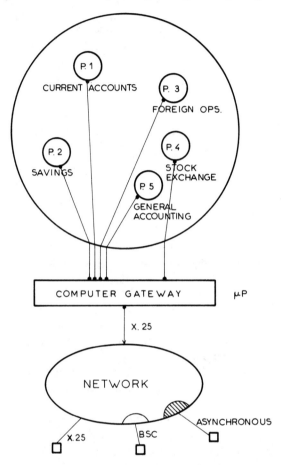

account for the variety in the kinds of messages to be transmitted. An effort should, therefore, be made from the start to accommodate large as well as small messages in the most efficient manner. Tymnet, for instance, worked on this solution.

Finally, with internetworking it will be necessary to have a multiaddress scheme. Small networks use a single-part address, while larger ones can expand into multipart addresses. One way is to make addressing hierarchical.

Layered Communications Principles

Protocols and processes may be layered and ordered so that the higher level assumes that the functions provided by the lower level exist and are ensured in an able manner.

Figure 26.7

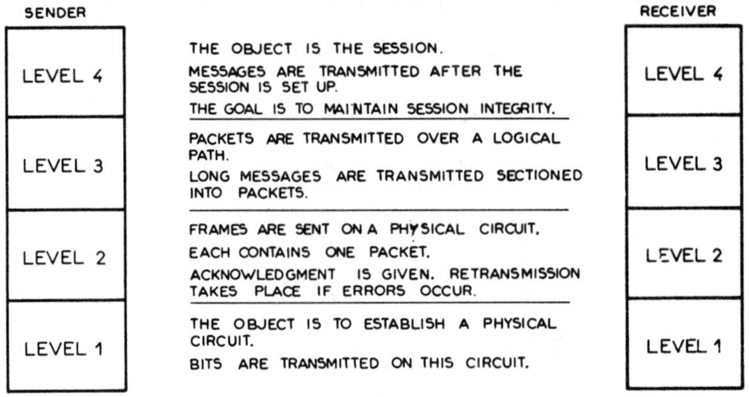

SENDER		RECEIVER
LEVEL 4	THE OBJECT IS THE SESSION. MESSAGES ARE TRANSMITTED AFTER THE SESSION IS SET UP. THE GOAL IS TO MAINTAIN SESSION INTEGRITY.	LEVEL 4
LEVEL 3	PACKETS ARE TRANSMITTED OVER A LOGICAL PATH. LONG MESSAGES ARE TRANSMITTED SECTIONED INTO PACKETS.	LEVEL 3
LEVEL 2	FRAMES ARE SENT ON A PHYSICAL CIRCUIT. EACH CONTAINS ONE PACKET. ACKNOWLEDGMENT IS GIVEN. RETRANSMISSION TAKES PLACE IF ERRORS OCCUR.	LEVEL 2
LEVEL 1	THE OBJECT IS TO ESTABLISH A PHYSICAL CIRCUIT. BITS ARE TRANSMITTED ON THIS CIRCUIT.	LEVEL 1

The architecture centers around functions which are well defined within the layer, and if redefined will not necessarily touch other layers.

The interchangeability of component layers is considered in terms of functionality within the network.

Specific implementations of the architecture may be tailored.

Internetworking interfaces may be more easily provided since only some components need translation to the client network's code.

Future design changes may be implemented without upsetting the total structure or the unchanged portions.

Further layers may be added as the network technology develops, particularly layers at the user level where developments are still weak.

Figure 26.7 presents the now classic division into layers for a packet-switching network. It identifies both the object and the functions.

Several technical requirements must be answered to ensure layered solutions. Layered communications involve a clear definition and separation of tasks, the dedication of a layer to each major task (data link, routing, and so on), the ability of adjacent layers to communicate via interfaces and of equivalent layers to communicate via protocols.

Protocols and interfaces must be supported by a sound software (or firmware). These reside in each processor in the network, or, if distributed, they are accessible by each processor as the need arises.

Each layer must answer the prerequisites of a communication mechanism. This involves both the processing of data and the control of the communication system and its components.

Components of communications systems are the devices and their software, conversation establishment, the routing of messages, flow control, error detection, and so on. Every one of these components serves the purpose of the network

Figure 26.8

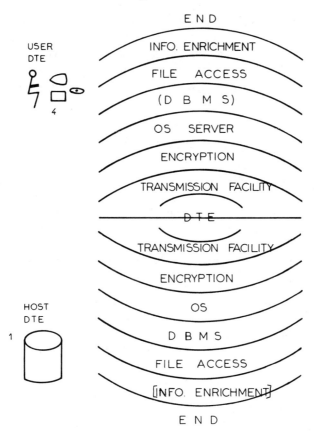

architecture, namely, the transfer of data between applications or processes, operating on different systems using data links between the systems supporting the processes. Emphasis is on the processes, and it is in this regard that the end-to-end reference should be made; see Figure 26.8.

The data being transferred may be a single character, an entire file, a program to be executed, or an entire library. The DTE (terminal, hosts) used in the network may be of different families, with a variety of operating systems, using different data types and structures. The links between systems may be permanent and stable or temporary (dial-up). They may be of different speeds, synchronous or asynchronous, and use a variety of protocols.

Whatever solution is chosen it should not alter the way the user communicates at a high-level protocol. Between the bit-level data access and the user's dialogue there is room for many layers of protocols.

Let us recapitulate. The layered communications concept must be supported end-to-end in a topologically independent way. At all times, the communications mechanism must allow objects (DTE, processes) to carry on a dialogue. The processes must agree to conduct the dialogue by undergoing a connection (session establishment) procedure though they may not perform a direct object-to-object communication, which is particularly true of devices. The general communications mechanism thus consists of three parts: establish, conduct, and disconnect the process-to-process dialogue. Each layer within the communications system has a role to play in each of these functions.

Implementing a Layered Solution

The communications mechanism ensures data exchange between processes residing in the system. Programs, data files, input–output devices, and terminals exchange information over communications channels. The functional requirements of the communications must be supported, and this calls for both physical and for logical resources.

These components of a layered communications process may be divided in the following way, starting from the lower level:

1. Hardware interfaces (data set, modem DCE)
2. Communications (physical link particularly concerned with call establishment, data integrity, and control)
3. Networking/routing (the prerequisite for the logical link layer, dialogue control)
4. Networking/virtual circuit or datagram (establishing the logical link)
5. User/application level (oriented to device control, applications, data base) which may be subdivided into a number of layers

As Figures 26.7 and 26.8 also demonstrated, in an end-to-end solution the first layer is concerned with physically moving digital information from one geographical location to another. It may include (and most likely will) equipment from different manufacturers: modems, interfaces, and lines.

The second layer guarantees the basic parts of a communications mechanism: data link establishment and link control. Among it functions are specific dialogue faculties such as error control. This layer takes care of the maintenance of data integrity and sequencing across a signal carrier which connects two or more processors and/or devices. Correcting errors typically introduced by signal carriers, and the addressability of DTE are also handled by this layer.

The third layer controls the flow of information, guarantees sequential data delivery within the network, and controls end-to-end communication. It is also concerned with the location of services, the guarantee that a topologically connected network is virtually connected, and the optimality of the paths that messages take through the network—in brief, the routing component.

Figure 26.9

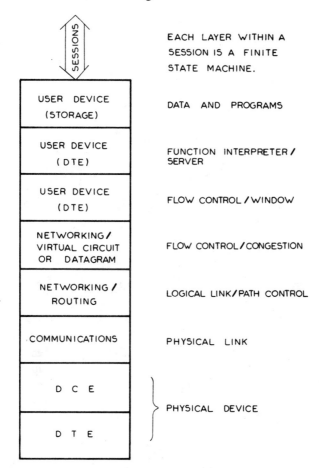

The fourth layer addresses itself to provision of generic services obtainable in the network. They include a user (application) program, a task or process loader, a file system, a printing device, an operator's console, and so on.

Figure 26.9 shows three user layers prior to reacing the objective establishing a session. Each performs a distinct set of functions and presents a level of abstraction to the higher layer. Such functions and their implementation are reflected in a protocol.

27

Circuit, Message, and Packet Switching

This chapter digresses from the coverage of network architecture and looks more closely into the PTT/AT&T area of lines and switches identified in the preceding chapter (see Figure 27.2).

The discussion of trade-offs has not yet ended. Indeed, one of the biggest issues is the choice of switching technology. Let us look at the fundamentals. Switching choices essentially mean a decision on how to share the communications facility. With point-to-point operations the alternatives are multiplexing and switching. With multipoint (broadcast, multidrop) approaches we have a choice between polling and contention. They all involve line switching. There are three basic switching disciplines available for line switching: circuit, message, and packet.

Circuit switching is the oldest and the most used. This classic approach provides a "total path." There is a setup time for call establishment; call termination results in the circuit being dropped. Circuit switching may have many different aspects and offer a variety of service levels.

With message switching, one user talks to the other while a record is kept, for instance, on disc. The message can be controlled for errors. Other services are offered, such as store and forward. Hence, while with circuit switching one user talks directly to the other, with message switching all messages transmit via a processor (for instance, minicomputer) which registers prior to transmitting. This has opened up extensive possibilities, since the minicomputer can link to other minicomputers with different protocols, elaborate the text it receives, check for "passwords," and provide inquiry capabilities, to mention only a few services.

Packet switching is a newer, more elaborate form of message switching.* It presupposes data transmitted in discrete quantities. Messages are created as individual blocks or packets which "hop" from node to node. The transmission

---

*This statement can be controversial. Not everyone accepts it. But we shall see the reason for it in the more detailed discussion which follows.

Figure 27.1

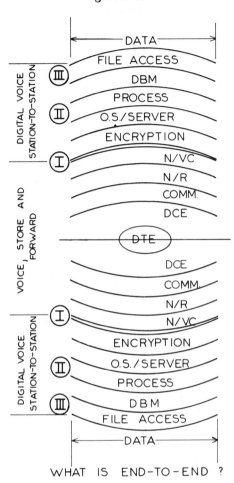

WHAT IS END-TO-END ?

facilities are shared all the time. A packet is a unit of information with predefined length. Its very special characteristic is that it is *not* oriented to a specific application. To the contrary, message switching *is* oriented to the application. This is a basic characteristic to which several references will be made.

Notice that all three methods allow resource sharing which is fundamental to any data communications system. And all three methods accept data and voice communications capabilities; see Figure 27.1. Data and voice can coexist up to a point—the logical path. This opens tremendous horizons for voice communications since it makes available store and forward capabilities. With this perspective there are three levels of an end-to-end reference the reader must follow (identified as I, II, and III in the figure).

The problem to which the following sections are addressed is this: Given the

Figure 27.2

Circuit switching (S = sender; D = destination; A and B are nodes over which messages travel)

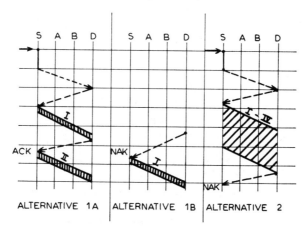

possibilities of alternatives, what are the relative strengths and weaknesses of each method?

Circuit Switching

The best example of circuit switching is the dial telephone network. The user dials the desired number. The network switches assign a circuit from source to destination, but the lines may be busy and delays result in setup. If answered, the circuit is established. In multipoint, a primary station authorizes a secondary station to transmit—thus assigning a circuit. This circuit remains assigned to the call until the call is terminated. During the communication time, the circuit is dedicated to this particular operation, whether or not data is transmitted.

The basic characteristics of circuit switching may be outlined as follows: First, it involves the establishment of a total path at all initiations. This results in significant inflexibility, given the way in which current voice-grade networks are implemented. Second, the circuit is established by a special signaling message which threads its way through different switching centers. Third, this circuit (being a total path) is subject to the speed and code limitations of the slowest link. As stated, the total path remains allocated for the transmission, regardless of utilization. Call termination results in the circuit being dropped, each line and switch returning to a pool of available circuits. Figure 27.2 is an example of circuit-switching data transmission.

Circuit switching has three advantages:

1. Circuit routing is simpler.
2. The discipline is the most widespread today.

3.   There is the possibility to attach terminals with different characteristics.

There are, however, many disadvantages:

1.   No automatic retransmission
2.   Inefficient use of circuits
3.   Switching failures fatal to the traffic
4.   Inefficient to "bursty"* traffic
5.   Voice-grade lines
6.   No record-keeping
7.   Long setup time (with traditional circuits)
8.   No speed- or code-matching capability
9.   Relatively high error probability

Errors filter through since there is no particular preoccupation with error control in circuit switching.

It must be emphasized that many of the problems of circuit switching—connect times, bandwidth, conditioning, voice and data imcompatibility—are common to current networks. With the new technologies the entire way of handling communications traffic will change—and circuit switching will be able to stage a comeback. Intelligent terminals will be doing speed change, buffering, editing, and the like. Use can then be made of circuit switching's relative advantages over other network solutions: its widespread acceptance† and the fact that circuit switching can handle traffic *without* preallocating resources. With other methods, for instance, store and forward, this cannot be done.

We may use a circuit (and the circuit-switching discipline) to connect two stations, T1 and T2—and only these two stations (Figure 27.3). This is known as point-to-point. It has been used in the past and is still used extensively, but it is an inefficient solution for long distances and large networks. When terminals do not transmit to the central computer (or through the central resource to each other), the line is idle—and lines are expensive.

An improvement would be to put more terminals on the same line, but now we run into addressing problems. We have to solve them and program our solutions. Or, we may adopt network approaches, and let the network do the job. This is what packet switching, for instance, does.

Let us repeat what we have said. If point-to-point communications media are chosen, the system may be organized at the host level around multiplexing or switching. However, if multipoint (multidrop or broadcast) is used, polling and contention are two alternatives for resource sharing.

In *contention*, communication can be initiated by either the terminal or the computer, if there are messages to be sent to the computer and vice versa. Either can start up transmission sending a signal to the other to reserve the line. A typical contention procedure carries out the following phases: the unit, ready to operate, asks for the go-ahead to transmit; the receiving unit gives the go-ahead; the

*For example, when many devices enter the circuit at the same time.
†17,000 exchanges in the United States alone don't need to change.

Figure 27.3

POINT-TO-POINT/OWN LINE, ONE SOLUTION

SWITCHING CENTERS/MANY SOLUTIONS

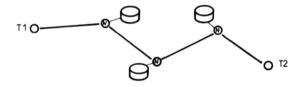

- POINT-TO-POINT
- MULTIDROP/DEDICATED LINE
- MULTIDROP/FIRST PRIORITY
- DATA NETWORK

ALSO MANY TECHNOLOGIES
1. SPACE DIVISION
2. FREQUENCY DIVISION
3. TIME DIVISION

NETWORK APPROACHES/ ONE SOLUTION

transmitting unit starts transmission; the receiving unit signals correct message reception; the transmitting unit closes down the transmission process.

In a contention system each subscriber attempts to communicate information to a central computer. This takes place at the time the information becomes available or at a locally determined time soon thereafter. Stated differently, systems transmit whenever they wish and resolve collisions of two systems transmitting simultaneously by means of variable delays and retransmission. This procedure can jeopardize the behavior of the two units in the following cases: (a) the receiving unit does not give the go-ahead for transmission; (b) the transmitting unit does not receive the transmission go-ahead within a certain time limit; (c) the receiving unit signals that the message has been received incorrectly, but the transmitting unit does not receive the signal; (d) the characters for message reception do not reach the transmitting unit.

Additional features, such as carrier detect, may be added to reduce the collision problem. (As with any scheme, times are necessary to recover from outages. Link management information may be lost and recovery action is necessary.)

Figure 27.4
Polling

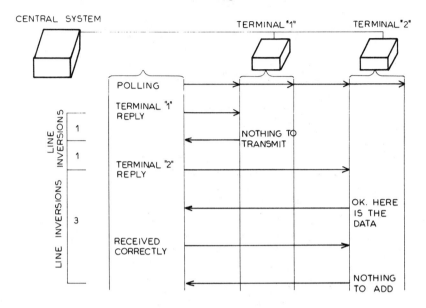

Contention has, however, many advantages. One of them is not using the computer's resources, when there is no traffic present; because of this it is used by several networks, Ethernet and Alchanet being examples.

Polling is a technique for controlling the use of lines by agreed protocols between devices trying to share a common transmission path; see Figure 27.4. By means of polling, the user places the terminals in a "speak only when spoken to" mode (as contrasted to contention). While all terminals will sense a given poll, only one will respond to it. The terminals must be rigidly controlled, given that all of them use the same principal line.

There are two types of polling disciplines in common use: roll call (or bus) and hub (or distributed).

Roll call polling is governed by the central computer which sends a control message to each terminal in turn, inviting it to transmit a message. The terminal replies either with transmit message, or with a control message indicating that it has nothing to report. One system—the control—polls or invites tributary systems to transmit, maintaining central orderly control of the link. Polling carried out in this way obtains reasonable flexibility because the computer may recognize the order of polling should it become necessary. On the other hand, a high proportion of control messages have to pass through the network and this tends to make it inefficient. Furthermore, among the disadvantages is the delay resulting from the larger number of line inversions; see Figure 27.5.

Figure 27.5
Roll-call polling (each call is often made λ times (λ ≅ 3); then multiply by λ)

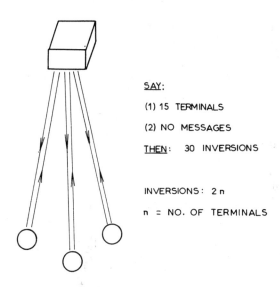

SAY:

(1) 15 TERMINALS

(2) NO MESSAGES

THEN: 30 INVERSIONS

INVERSIONS: 2 n

n = NO. OF TERMINALS

In hub polling the control system creates a poll command, which is then passed along the path of a multipoint circuit. The computer invites the first terminal to send a message; if none is ready, the first terminal passes the request to the second terminal and so on. This is particularly efficient when the terminals are inactive and lines are very long; see Figure 27.6. Whenever a terminal replies with an information message, the computer deals with it, and then resumes the polling sequence by inviting the next terminal to proceed. In this way an active terminal near the beginning of the circuit is prevented from monopolizing the attention of the computer. At the completion of the cycle—with all resources connected into the loop interrogated—the host regains control.

Another technique of polling when concentrators are used is to allow each remote concentrator to poll the terminals connected to it. This is more efficient than polling from the central computer because each multiplexer operates in parallel and there are fewer control messages involving the computer itself.

Polling is typical of party-line configurations, but may also be employed in point-to-point. Several types of messages may exist, however. A terminal may reply "failure" to the control characters which authorize transmission. Faulty message reception sent by the terminal or central system may call for repetition. Reception failure on the part of the terminal (or central system) of the control characters sent by the central system (or terminal) will initiate a whole error routine.

Selecting is employed for the transfer of messages from the central system to the terminals or other remote devices. As such, it forms an integral part of a polling and

Figure 27.6
Hub polling. Advantages: rather than 15 "empty" polling, only 1. Need:
intelligent terminals

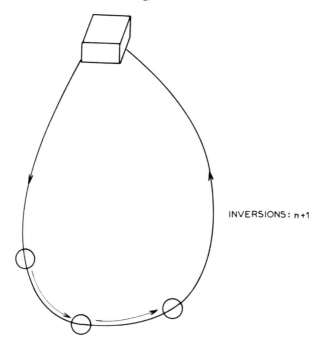

INVERSIONS: n+1

selecting procedure. In polling and selecting, whether transmission comes from terminal to computer or vice versa, it is always the computer which puts the proceedings into motion.

Message Switching

Message switching developed from the tape systems originally used for telegraphic switching and Telex. Figure 27.7 gives an example of a message-switching application. This method is also known as "traffic dispatcher" and "message router." With message switching, the messages are small—64 to 256 bytes—and are not decomposed into small elements by the network because they are oriented to the application.

The contrast to circuit switching is interesting. While with circuit switching one user talks directly to the other, with message switching all messages transmit via the central unit (minicomputer) which registers the messages prior to transmitting. Furthermore, the minicomputer can:

Figure 27.7
Message switching (S = sender; D = destination; A and B are nodes over which messages travel)

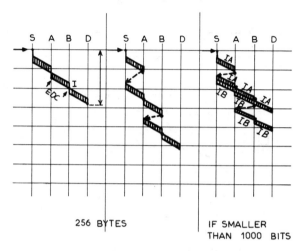

256 BYTES   IF SMALLER
                             THAN 1000 BITS

1. Link to other minicomputers with different protocols
2. Elaborate the text it receives
3. Check for "passwords"
4. Provide inquiry
5. Handle multiaddress traffic
6. Distinguish priority traffic
7. Provide for error control and recovery
8. Allow code conversion as the subscriber passes messages to a subnetwork, which accepts messages from or sends messages to distant terminals
9. Analyze headers for destination, special processing, etc.
10. Take responsibility for delivery

In brief, with message switching one user talks to the other but there is a record kept, e.g., on disc, and the message can be controlled for errors. Message switching will *not* pass the message to the terminal until it is assured that it is complete and error free. This may result in delays since messages are not decomposed into smaller elements.

Store-and-forward techniques—originally developed for message switching—provide greater throughput. Indeed, the emphasis of a switching application is on fast transmission (as in the case of packet switching) or greater throughput. Store and forward may include peripheral storage systems such as magnetic discs or drums. It is useful with link protocol conversion, code conversions, message monitoring, message recording, etc. Buffer and queue delays frequently are long so that interactive delay requirements cannot be met.

Figure 27.8

RIGID CONNECTIONS

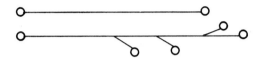

MESSAGE- AND PACKET-SWITCHING
SOLUTIONS

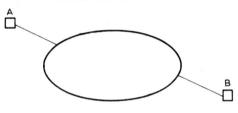

WITH STORAGE CAPABILITIES

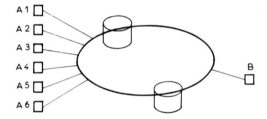

The impact of storage capabilities is shown in Figure 27.8. The old, rigid connection has ceased to exist, and points A and B communicate through the network facilities. Adding storage capabilities at the nodes disassociates A from B. Now many A's can communicate over the same line—without B feeling this multiplex—for any practical purpose.

Store and forward messages are typically terminal to terminal or unsolicited host output messages stored on disc and routed to the destination. They involve a wider variety of destinations than core-switched traffic and require more extensive routing capabilities.

For core-switched traffic, routing functions are necessary: extraction of the destination logical identifier, determination of the destination line and station tables, completion of the control block for output with the appropriate routing data, and queuing the control block for output.

Similar functions are necessary for disc-switched traffic: edit: extract the routing data from the message content; route: use the routing data to determine the logical identifier and then the line and station tables; tag build: complete the control block

Figure 27.9
**Packet switching. The message is divided into three packets of nominal size;
each travels independently to destination.**

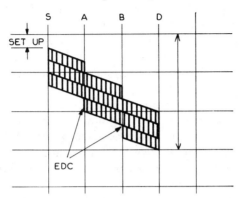

and build additional control blocks as required for multiple deliveries; queue: queue the control blocks, send message acknowledgments, and write logs as necessary.

A typical queueing program writes the control blocks to the appropriate output queues in disc. It also updates the queue pointers retained in core, sends acknowledgments when required, sets the flag for output service action, and may perform logging. A typical output queue service program reads the control block entries from disc queues, reads the message segments from disc, and interfaces with the appropriate input–output routine to initiate output.

Store and forward permits a tremendous capability applicable not only to data transmission but also to voice and image. Briefly stated, the sender and the receiver are decoupled. No longer is there a one-to-one correspondence of the wire circuit type or its equivalent.

Two, three, or *n* senders may be hooked up on the same node, same physical facility transmitting messages through time-division multiplexing (TDM). The messages (more precisely, their parts) are stored, then forwarded, in the most efficient way the network permits at speeds which made this process hardly noticeable or, more often, not noticeable at all.

Packet Switching

Packet switching is a block of data organized for transmission with both a minimum and a maximum length and which obeys packet protocol rules. It had its origin in message switching, but it is not applications oriented. A record or message longer than the maximum must be split into submessages. The maximum is 1,000 to 2,000 or up 8,000 bits. If the message is longer, it is divided into packets of nominal size and each travels independently to its destination; see Figure 27.9.

Packet switching transmits data in discrete quantities. Messages are created as individual packets or groups of packets (i.e., decomposed into small elements by the network) which "hop" from node to node. Transmission facilities are shared all the time. There is no prerequisite of secondary storage (the original packet switching could also be seen as message switching without secondary storage). Packets are routed independently (pipelining), and message delay is typically a fraction of a second. Systems allow for effective use of circuit bandwidth and of intelligent switches. The network establishes the responsibility for queuing the messages in the right sequence.

This requires powerful minicomputers and more storage (disc) capacity at the nodes. In the late sixties and early seventies minicomputers were marketed at low prices and offered a high cost/performance ratio, making packet switching economically feasible. The price made it more economical to assign dynamically costly transmission capacity by the packet than to preassign a fixed bandwidth (end-to-end) subchannel to each call or session.

Packet switching is characterized by the routing of data through a network in discrete quantities at bit transmission level. Each packet includes a header, information, and a trailer. Messages are created as individual packets or groups of packets, within the specified limits. Packets, in transit at all times, "hop" from node to node. They are error checked, queued, routed, and stored and forwarded. Packet switching provides line and data concentration. Facilities are shared at all time, and traffic is active and instantaneous. One result of great potential impact is the disconnection between sender and receiver.

Advantages of packet switching are the following:

High transmission facility utilization

Flexible network routing

Flexibility of message handling irrespective of the type of message

Minimal network transit delay

Low degree of susceptibility to many types of network failures, hence, high reliability and very low error rates

Output terminals buffered by the network from the input terminals

Flow control minimizes network or nodal congestion, journaling, statistics

Packet switching also has its disadvantages. Among them are an elaborate setup, the need for software support, and a rather costly network which must be used as near to capacity as possible.

As a final note, let us discuss briefly pacuit switching, hybrid version of packet switching and circuit switching. Pacuit creates packets of information at different points, then uses the techniques of statistical time-division multiplexing. It provides packet creation and switching at source and destination nodes, while it follows circuit switching technology at all intervening nodes.

Table 27.1
The Three Types of Switching Contrasted

Criteria	Circuit Switching	Message Switching	Packet Switching
1. General purpose	x		x
2. Physical connection	x		
3. Logical connection		x	x
4. Real time (classical)	x		
5. Secondary storage		x	x
6. Easy saturation	x		
7. Rerouting		x	x
8. Long setup	x		
9. Cumulative delays		x	x
10. Error control		x	x
11. Speed conversion		x	x
12. Code conversion		x	x
13. Multiaddress		x	x
14. Throughput		x	x
15. Good line usage		x	x
16. Diversity of devices	x		x
17. Flexibility		(x)	x
18. Growth possibilities			x

The division is good for 1979–80.

Circuit pre-establishment is required. As a result, pacuit does not offer instantaneous routing flexibility (hence, no true interactivity), but it does ensure the delay minimization features of circuit switching. The fact of using circuit switching approaches ensures that pacuit does not provide end-to-end electronic data communication or store and forward between nodes, though it does ensure error protection from DTE to node and from node to DTE.

Pacuit allows for lower speed transmission links between nodes than does packet switching. Rather than building queues, it builds time-slot links via a software table. The DTE-to-DTE communication is through virtual circuits.

Comparison of the Three Basic Methods

Having discussed the basic characteristics of packet switching, we can now outline the primary features characterizing this procedure. The features may be regrouped into twelve major points: (1) principal line control protocol for recent teleprocessing products; (2) two-way simultaneous transmission of data (full duplex); (3) transmission of code-independent (including character length) information; (4) full information transparency; (5) higher throughput rate than earlier protocols. Some of the technical features regard flexibility: (6) can be extended for satellite communications; (7) applicable to existing common carrier facilities; and (8) can be utilized primarily in polled networks, asymmetric networks which include one primary station and one or more secondary stations, and symmetric networks. Then there are the dependability and efficiency characteristics: (9) full error detection; (10) automatic retransmission ability; (11) piggyback implied acknowledgment; and (12) ability to interleave information, programs, and supervisory control messages.

We said that packet switching has been an evolutionary process largely influenced by message-switching experiences. Table 27.1 uses 18 criteria to contrast circuit, message and packet switching in a brief but comprehensive manner.

Finally, Table 27.2. presents the year of availability of dedicated datacomm networks in the United States and in Europe.

Table 27.2.

Datacomm networks in America and Western Europe.

| Country | Availability | |
	Circuit Switching	Packet Switching
USA	1972	1975
Austria	1980	1984
Belgium	1983	1982
Denmark	1981	1984
England	—	1982
Finland	1981	1983
France	1973	1980
Germany	1976	1982
Italy	1984	1984
Switzerland	1981	1981

PART FIVE

Messages and Transactions

28

Transaction-Based Systems

A large number of the new computer systems being installed are transaction-based, that is, they are characterized by a fast response to a limited type of inquiry. Some typical ones are the financial, retail, and airline-reservation networks. Transaction systems are human-driven, for mobile users and customers, based on a fixed set of transaction models, highly decentralized, and locally demand-intensive. They must respond to user distribution, a profile of requirements, and a range of facilities offered (e.g., credit and debit cards) and have the dual faculty of being oriented toward both customer and management.

Figure 28.1 dramatizes the difference between a batch and real-time computer environment and a data communications one. In the former the machines and data operate independently of one another. The network idea is of a different sort, and the data communications system is a network. Instead of distinct equipment there are "processes," which are files, programs, and so on. Each process is accessible to each point of the network, by means of either sophisticated or very simple units. Simplicity should be an aim of any project. Indeed, much of the value of transaction systems is that they use the DTE facilities of the most wide-spread carrier, the voice-grade telephone lines.

The Transaction Network Service

An example of transaction-based networks is Bell System's Transaction Network Service, TNS. This service is largely used for credit approval (it was started in a small bank in Seattle, Washington). It is a new, switched, common-user service designed to meet the needs of high volume, short messages, and inquiry–response applications, with attention to reliability, maintainability, and error-free performance. Its inquiry–response applications include credit verification, cheque au-

Figure 28.1

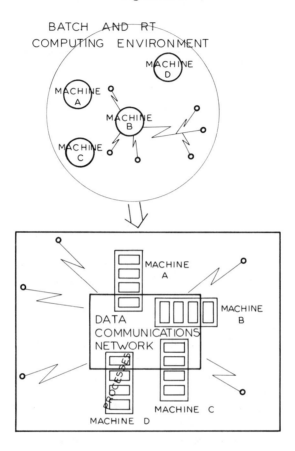

thorization, order entry, and inventory control and quotations. Customer-transaction text sizes of up to 128 characters can be accommodated.

The service has both polled and dial terminals for high-volume and low-volume customer locations. On both, customers have the advantage of a cost-effective communications delivery system with network and message control, high reliability, and low undetected-error rates. The system also has a "voice-answerback" with TNS vocabulary. Customers may select line speeds of 2.4K, 4.8K, or 9.6K bits per second and message flow options that allow for effective communications with traffic loads.

Service may be between terminals and host computer (data centers), or between data centers. Access to host computers from the network service is provided by synchronous data links, with a specified line control procedure and message format.

The most important aspects of this service may be listed as the following:

Fast and easy startup and expansion

Switching time at the millisecond level

Simpler system and software design, hence less development time

High reliability achieved by total system; redundancy within the common-user network

Good-quality maintenance ensuring maximal network uptime

Network management of the entire communications system, effecting savings in resources

Single-vendor interface for a total-system solution

No private lines, hence inexpensive

Chiefly offered to large customers

Very economical, no major investment needed

Users connected to data bases

A newly introduced data termination equipment has a one-number repertory for repeated calls to the same number. It can dial out from a private branch exchange or on a foreign exchange line. The system contains an automatic facility that tests for proper operation. It may be equipped with an auxiliary manual-entry card, so that the customer at a bank or store can enter a personal identification number when required.

The present-day transaction systems still have limitations. For instance, when the local switched network is seized, a dial tone is recognized, which results in the automatic dialing of the local telephone number. Once this connection is made, a second dial tone occurs, which permits the dialing of the security or billing number. But today's computerized private branch exchanges cannot recognize this second dial tone.

The Choice of Facilities

The foregoing section outlined the capabilities and limitations of a transaction-based system. By and large, the choice of facilities will depend on four basic factors: frequency (bandwidth), medium (cables, radio, satellite), analog or digital signals, and supplier. For instance, satellite carriers offer digital services at very low cost and very high frequency, and when such services become available, a great many companies will have to reexamine their network design.

The data communications networks of the future will offer many services that today are now obtainable only through private, sophisticated arrangements. Four trends may be observed: digital networks (the existing voice networks no longer are sufficient), value-added networks (VAN), which offer more than the carrier facility (store-and-forward procedures, error detection and correction, routing, and so on), large private networks (probably using types of value-added solutions and, possibly, value-added backbone facilities), and new tariff structures for the mass requirements expected in the next decade.

The technical requirements to be observed in all future solutions quite definitely include full error detection, error correction, recovery, fast selection, two-way simultaneous transmission, interaction (dialogue), store-and-forward procedures, and bit-oriented protocols. The last (which is beyond the scope of this book) needs more capabilities from terminals, such as new operating codes, buffered data transmission, synchronous mode of operation, error detection and correction, and address and command fields framed in a unique way. Most terminals do not meet these criteria. Other technical requirements are standardization (hope of), an extensive topology, complete code independence, and device independence. Standardization, topology, and code and device independence are suggested by the sheer size and diversity of the data communications systems to come. The following example presents an order-of-magnitude calculation of the data loads to be applied on data communications systems during the next decade.

First-class mail and interoffice memos represent 16 to 19 billion pieces, say, 17 billion; see Table 28.1. Some 54 trillion characters are the estimated annual exchange of information in United States business, with about 4.5 trillion characters a month. A typical minicomputer today holds 10 megabytes. Hence, under current conditions the aforementioned statistics would represent 450,000 minicomputers.

Table 28.1
Estimated Annual Exchange of First Class and Interoffice
Mail in the United States

Mail	Number of Characters per Page	Annual Total of Characters per Page (billions)	Annual Total of Characters (trillions)
1 page	1,000	9.86	9.86
2 to 4 pages	4,000	4.76	19.00
5 pages	10,500	2.48	24.99
			53.85

Types of Communications Links

The choice of communications facilities will necessarily be influenced by the type of link. The links may be analog or digital and may use sub-voice-grade, voice-grade, or wideband speeds.

Analog facilities transmit analog signals that have been converted by modems at each end of the link; modems convert the digital signals from terminals and computers to analog signals. Typically the facilities follow the late-nineteenth century principle of transmitting voice over wire. The circuits transmit a continuous range of frequencies; the information being transmitted bears an exact relationship to the original. Analog repeaters amplify the signal and noise. The transmitted frequencies are susceptible to distortion from resistance, thermal noise, fading, and so on.

Digital facilities are relatively recent. They transmit digital signals without conversion to analog signals and with no need of modems. In this case voice (the analog signals) is converted into digital signals for transmission. Digital circuits transmit discrete signals, and digital repeaters detect the precise signals (or bits) being transmitted and retransmit them at their original strength. That is why we said that modems (digital data sets) are required for interfacing between the circuit and the terminal (central processing unit). Digital repeater stations reduce the error rate significantly below that of analog circuits.

The speeds fall into three categories;

Sub-voice-grade, or narrowband, is used for telegraph and typewriter terminals; the channel can carry up to 600 bits per second.

Voice-grade speeds are 1,200 to 9,600 bits per second; the channels have a bandwidth of 3,000 to 4,000 Hertz.

Wideband is for speeds in excess of 20,000 bits per second; originally up to 240,000 bits per second, it now is in excess of 1,000,000 bits per second, with a bandwidth of 48,000 Hertz.

The modes of operation may be one of three types:

Simplex, which allows transmission in one direction only.

Half-duplex, or two-wire, which allows transmission in two directions but not at the same time.

Full duplex, or four-wire, which allows transmission in two directions simultaneously.

These differences have their origin in design, but their impact on applications is very substantial. Furthermore, the wires, or the radio band, may be leased, switched public, dial-up, or value-added.

Leased, or private, lines are used only by the subscriber and are available at all times; the lines are in an established routing pattern that does not change.

Switched public lines are used by many subscribers, but only one at a time. They are part of the carrier's network and are not dedicated to any single subscriber, though they guarantee access time (usually minimal) to each subscriber.

Dial-up connections are often used for temporary and relatively short periods of time. The connections are established by calling numbers, as in a regular telephone service. Inbound and outbound WATS is often used with this type of facility.

Finally, the newer packet-switching and value-added networks are private services supplied by vendors that use one or more of the above-mentioned facilities. Figure 28.2 integrates the characteristics we have been discussing.

Further factors govern choices:

1. Number of messages (or interactive sessions)

2. Distribution of message length (or holding time)

3. Urgency, allowed response time, lags, priorities

4. Peak versus off-peak volume

5. Geographical points of origin and destination of traffic (distance between points, clustering)

6. Location and access nodes on a common-carrier network

7. Pricing classification (e.g., high or low density)

8. Adaptability of network to widely varying traffic loads, both short-term fluctuations and long-term trends, without apparently affecting the response time and without maintaining excess capacity

9. Ability to take advantage of technological development in communications and switching without maintaining a large expert staff

10. Ability to link a large variety of terminals of low to intermediate speed with a number of different host computers

11. Types of terminal and host computer that must be connected through the network

12. Reliability

13. Security and privacy

14. Vendor dispersion and support (whether from one vendor or many vendors)

15. Expected changes in traffic patterns (e.g., a steady growth in traffic)

16. The fairly high cost of modifying a host computer's operating system or front-end processor, or the possible use of microprocessors

17. Terminal-to-host traffic (which many value-added carriers apparently see as the bulk of its potential market) or host-to-host connections

Notions of networks are subject to widely varying definitions, which largely depend on the subscriber's viewpoint, the service objectives per se, and the thrust

Figure 28.2

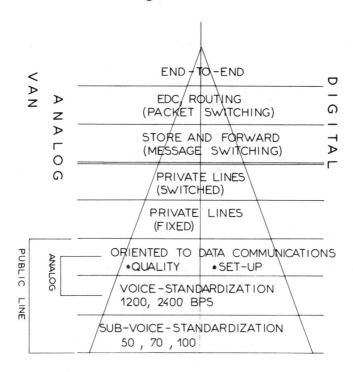

of the vendor. The designer concerns himself primarily with function, and this concern tends to mask certain physical details or questions of implementation. Such characterstics as the type of service provided by the network (switched or dedicated, point-to-point, or multipoint), the mechanisms required to invoke the service (circuit setup, addressing, or other conventions), the procedures required or available to manage the service (flow control, sequencing) and, finally, the overall reliability of the service—these are the crucial variables that define the nature, structure, and cost of the service.

Change in Structure

In the animal kingdom some reptiles change their skin when their body has outgrown the skin's boundaries; something similar is happening with transaction systems. Originally designed to serve a limited number of users, the starlike networks, with point-to-point or multidrop lines, have long passed their usefulness.

The expansion in terminal installations since 1970 has been fantastic. International Business Machines, for example, saw the 100,000 terminals it had in 1970 multiply to 350,000 by 1975. The pace is steadily accelerating; we now forecast 5 million terminals in the mid-1980s. The increase implies a corresponding one in other facilities: what often escapes attention is the fact that teleprocessing tends to produce a twofold to fourfold increment in main-memory use and a threefold to sixfold one in disc storage. More significantly, on-line terminals are giving rise to requirements of unprecedented proportions; we shall outline them in the following section.

First let us quantify the tremendous growth of teleprocessing. The following assumptions are being made. By 1981 an estimated 280 American users will have 2,000 terminals each, which, worldwide, can easily represent 500 organizations; of all the terminals 85 percent will be located at remote sites; the population of large teleprocessing networks will double by 1985. Banks, telephone companies, airlines, large manufacturers, oil companies, merchandising firms, and government institutions will be heading the list (see tables 28.2 and 28.3). This colossal investment is still below the current level of cumulative capital investments at AT&T. Besides, it is worldwide; telephone companies in the United States alone have invested $130 billion. For every 16 terminals there will be an average of one minicomputer; some 412,000 minicomputers will be needed. Probably there will be one maxicomputer (or its equivalent) for every 10 minicomputers, or a total of 40,000 maxicomputers. Finally, the number of earth stations will equal the number of maxicomputers; this means about 40 per organization. As to earth stations, we should count not only the dedicated installations but also those used by business, industry, and the public at large.

Eventually the investments in computers and data communications will exceed those in telephony. To appreciate this potential market we must remember that by mid-1978 about 500 of IBM's Series 1 computers were delivered, yet IBM had an estimated 14,000 in backlog orders, and orders were building up rapidly.

Table 28.2
Estimated Increase in Number of Teleprocessing Networks
in the United States between 1981 and 1985

Number of Firms	Terminals per Firm	Total Terminals (millions)
200	12,000	2.4
200	9,000	1.8
200	6,000	1.2
200	4,000	0.8
200	2,000	0.4
		6.6

Table 28.3
Market Estimated for 1985

	Number of Units (thousands)	Dollars per Unit (thousands)	Total Dollar Business (billions)
Terminals	6,600	3	19.8
Minicomputers	412	50	20.6
Maxicomputers	40	1,000	40.0
Earth stations	40	300	12.0
			92.4

This colossal investment is still below the current level of cummulative capital investments at AT&T. Besides, it is worldwide; telephone companies in the United States alone have invested $130 billion.

To see beyond statistics, we should note that the typical Series 1 has a raw computer power of 370/135. The use of such power at local sites will revolutionize computers and data communications.

Series 1 is no more a valid measure of formerly mainframe-based power. It is obsolete. IBM's PC matches Series 1 capacity, but there are other manufacturers of personal computers who offer more.

The statistics in Table 28.4 have been developed by a Unix consultancy and reflect benchmark results on selected equipment running with the UNIX operating system. The time is seconds indicates two simultaneous compilations of the same programs and a single compile.

System Requirements

The specific objectives to be reached by the implementation of a generalized architecture include the following. The terms are defined elsewhere in this book; here we merely have a list for a bird's-eye view.

Task-to-task, job-to-job, and process-to-process: We would not need to know the precise characteristics of the topology and hardware or software.

Device-sharing: One machine must be able to run the devices of one or more other machines.

File-sharing: On a distributed basis and with a dependable security and protection mechanism.

Downline loading, upline dumping, and loopbacks: With the use of facilities in the network, such as data, programs, and systems commands.

Table 28.4.
Benchmarking a compilation time.

Equipment	Two Simultaneous compilations		Single Compile
Plexus	20	20	18
Masscomp	27	27	10
NCR Tower	34	35	22
Altos 586	38	39	37
IBM Series 1	38	40	25
DEC micro/PDP 11	45	45	37
Cosmos	58	1:02	41

Fail-soft: For meeting the requirements networkwide, the topology and management facility must be kept dynamic.

Route-through: Neither the architect nor the applications programmer should need to know how the network routes the messages to each destination, but he must know how the mechanism works.

Virtual devices and virtual programs: Resources would be shared by operating virtual-level DTEs so that several programs might have access to dispersed devices *as if* they were local; provision would be made for optimization of resources and avoidance of duplication.

On-line network and device maintenance: Through on-line tests, histories and diagnostics of good quality would be available.

Network response: Microscopically small decisions are made, second by second, which condition the response of the network.

The network: In its overall operation it *must be immune* to noise, error, and failure; it must detect and correct errors and automatically retransmit correctly; the user must not have to be concerned whatsoever with these processes.

The accomplishment of these functions is an involved, demanding job. It is the best practical example of how far the more advanced systems may be developed.

29

Message Theory

A message is any datum that is communicated. Messages encompass exchange of information, financial documents, cheques, sales orders, billing, personnel data, advertising, and engineering documents. Messages are carried by diverse communication systems, all of which are neutral concerning the content of the information. Some, like circuit switching and packet switching, are also neutral regarding the structure of the messages, that is, they are applications independent. Other kinds of message switching are applications oriented. We shall return to these notions.

Communications theory provides one important perspective: the channel is far more significant than the device. The capacity of a communications channel limits, for the most part, the speed of the device; rarely has the opposite been the case. Channel capacity, security, and speed recently have been profoundly influenced by the convergence of communications and computer technologies. This, and developments in applications, have brought message-processing from the world of accounting and order-entry into the mainstream of business, and the developments are far-reaching. It is possible that the entire organization chart will be altered to make way for new structural relations and also positions. The trend has been developing for several years and should be accelerated by the influence of the new technologies.

Message Technology

A surprising aspect of so-called message technology is the unanticipated and unsupported nature of its birth and early growth. In the beginning messages were discrete events spaced in time; telegrams are an example. Voice communications changed this; particularly important has been the question of continuity. Some messages exchanged by voice were converted to hard copy. Then the flow of messages grew, organizations were heavily affected, and shifts were made from the postal service to the telephone to the Telex. Communication took place at electronic speed. Records of the communications were kept, and the sender and receiver were decoupled, eliminating the need for real-time channels.

The message technologies followed rather than preceded these structural changes, and they suffer from that historical fact: they evolved without planning, and they were obliged to integrate codes and equipment from different manufacturers lacking common standards. Message technology "just happened," and its early history has been more the unconscious evolution of a phenomenon than the deliberate development of a scientific discipline.

This state of affairs changed, however, as the potentials of the new media began to reveal themselves. While the procedural developments followed the new media, they took on certain characteristics. Initially messages were a simple text, but then came message-manipulation programs, in which structure was imposed, and structure meant header fields. A header field includes recipient, sender, number of copies going to recipient, time of sending, and keywords. For a while the early approaches continued to view the nonheader part as an unbroken text, but now we see that messages ought to include other information: in addition to text as such, messages ought to consist of numerical data, pictures, and other matter. In general, arbitrary objects of many types ought to be transmittable as the text of a message.

Functional layers are needed, and so is software. The logical support necessary at the terminal and host levels is presented in Figure 29.1. Conventions for interpreting the structure now permit senders to generate and recipients to distinguish the components of a message and to interpret its contents.

Other necessary information is the author, the sender, and the person to reply to, besides annotations, if any. A message is composed by an author, sent by a sender, and received by a recipient. The recipients are usually people, but they may be "roles" or computers or terminals. The author of a message has in mind one or more recipients. Among the tasks of the sender, who may be the same person as the author, is that of determining what conventions must be followed to guarantee that the message will reach the recipients. He must first select a mechanism of delivery and then determine what information and action will effect that delivery.

All this goes beyond the nineteenth-century attitude toward message-handling, which still characterizes telegrams. If a total path is to be assured automatically, every facet of the operation must be studied and detailed and the proper procedures implemented.

Principles of Message Systems

During the next ten years computer-based message systems will have as great an influence on business practices in our society as that which the telephone had

Figure 29.1
Message handling involves (1) functional layers, and (2) subsystems: data base,
applications programs, terminals, hosts, network management

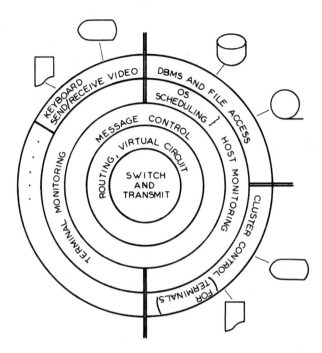

during the last hundred years. Applications usually are the factor that determines a
data communications system. Some prominent applications are the following:

Credit inquiries

Banking operations

Electronic fund-transfer

Electronic mail

Stock-brokerage information

Travel reservations and scheduling

Point-of-sale data collection

Sales order and inquiry

Inventory control and reordering

Production monitoring and control

Accounting and finance

Management information

Document cataloguing and retrieval

Hospital and medical information

Home-sector applications

Since exchanging messages is the chief objective of data communications systems, the processing capability of the computer has been applied at both ends of the communication path. Computer-run can offer geographic independence to both sender and receiver; either can transmit messages or have access to the other's files, from any point to any other point on the network.

A sophisticated use of the computer's capability emerged for the network Arpanet, when it was realized that a network could be exploited in more than one way as a medium of intercommunication. Workable software support was needed, and it became available in the form of service programs that supported an exchange of information between host computers. The development of software took advantage of an underlying network file transfer protocol and its associated "server" processes for the distribution of messages to users of the same or other host computers. As we have pointed out in the preceding section, the next step was to view the message as a whole structured object. Besides distinguishing the components of a message, manipulation programs were designed to interpret the contents of those components.

Necessity being the mother of invention, and a message program being needed for carrying out such operations as sorts and searches on "user fields," the data type of each such field had to be made known to the program; consequently, the agreed-upon structure of a message was defined as one rich enough to support the existence of user fields and to allow the inclusion, in each such field, of the data type of its contents. The development and operation of networks dedicated to message-handling underlined a great many requirements. Some basic principles were promoted in answer.

To create a message is to insert a record into a data base.

A message is a field in the data base and as such affects design of the data base, the methods of access, and the choice of communications.

To send a message is to provide a set of recipients with access to the records.

Problems are created by the fact that addresses indicate, not recipients, but mailboxes.

Like the telephone companies, we need a sort of directory and a real-time algorithm for updating it.

Message systems designed on the concept of data bases are especially suited to collaborating groups and teleconferencing.

If technology can be mustered to support this approach, some rather powerful effects may be achieved.

Conventions

A message may be viewed as a device by which an author grants a recipient or recipients access to certain information. A message system must therefore ensure that access—and ensure that it be granted only to designated recipients and denied to all others. Message systems have an additional problem: A recipient may wish to know with some certainty the identity of the author and perhaps also of its sender. Identification facilitates the creation and distribution of information, the reference of one message to another, and the replying to or forwarding of a message. These activities are supported by the presence of appropriate information in specified message fields:

The identification of a message is given in the message-identification field.
The form field indicates the author of the message.
The sender field identifies the actual sender.
The reply field gives the address to be used in replying.

Messages generally are of three formats. The author sends a message in one format, the sender transmits it in another, and the receiver gets it in yet another. The first and last of these formats depend more or less on human preference, as whether the message shall be written or spoken, and consequently cannot be decided on a purely technical basis, but no such choice is allowed for the transmission; communications must perfectly agree on the format of transmission. The transmission format is affected by such pragmatic considerations as the writing code and the need to convert to and from a given format during the act of sending and receiving.

A basic question is whether the movement of data and messages for communication is most important, or whether making any movement apparent to the users is.

One view is to consider the message system in its entirety, including the delivery subsystem and all the manipulation tools, as a data base management system. Another concerns the recipient. If we look closely at addresses, we see that they indicate not recipients, but logical entities to which messages are addressed; we call them "mailboxes." The fact that mailboxes are not the same as recipients causes problems. Some way must be provided for the sender of a message to determine what set of mailbox addresses will reach the intended human recipients. One way is to use each recipient's name as the address associated with his mailbox. This can work reasonably well when the recipients are people, but it may not work as well with programs, because such entities may not have distinctive names associated with them. This suggests a central agency that is responsible for keeping order among addresses, in particular for preventing identical mailboxes and names.

Protection and accountability also must be considered.

Accountability may be handled in either of two ways. One is to build into the systems a means of determining who is accountable for what parts of each message; this information may be placed in a message in a form apparent to the recipient. The other is to give authors and recipients a means of encoding, in the text, keys by which they may recognize one another.

Protection of access to mailing lists also may be handled in either of two ways. One is to control the access to mailing lists wherever they may be kept, whether in private files or in an information service. The other is to replace the mailing list with a program which, upon receipt of a message, sends that message to the recipients named in the mailing list. A difficulty with this is that, when one redistribution program transmits to another, which in turn transmits back to the first, an unending recycling of messages may result.

Performance Criteria

The mechanisms of a message-handling system must be evaluated in regard not only to technical and financial aspects but also to operating performance. Performance criteria may be grouped in three distinct categories:

Delay

Throughput

Error

Delay is a function of the following time intervals:

Call setup

Call clearing

Network transit

The call setup time is the time interval from the correct receipt of the last bit of a "call request" packet at a source node to the completed reception (including all processing) of an internal "accept" at that same node, but excluding all queueing, transmission, propagation, and processing time at the called terminal end.

The call-clearing time is the time interval from the correct receipt of the last bit of a "clear request" packet at a source node to the completed reception (including all processing) of an internal "clear" at that node.

The network transit delay is the time interval from the correct receipt of the last bit of a packet at a source node to its completed reception (including processing) at the destination node.

Throughput is the number of bytes (or bits) per second that can be maintained continuously on a circuit. The objective is that the throughput of, say, a virtual circuit (with full data packets) is limited only by the attainable throughput of the slower of the access lines of the two communicating terminals.

Error, the last of our criteria of performance, involves the following:

Bit error (due to burst or white noise)

Circuit disruptions detected by data link control procedures but recoverable at higher levels

Probability of network reset

Probability of loss of data integrity

The last two are virtual-circuit errors.

Bit errors are generally recovered through error detection and correction by retransmission; such schemes are governed by data link control procedures, some of which are standardized, like the X.25.

Circuit disruptions also are detected by data link control procedures but are usually recovered only at high levels.

Virtual circuits introduce virtual-circuit errors. The probability of network reset is the probability that a virtual circuit will be reset because the network has detected the unrecoverable loss of a packet. The probability of loss of data integrity is the probability that the network is not detecting, and, therefore, not delivering, a packet with a mutilated data field, a duplicate of a packet, an out-of-sequence packet, or a lost packet.

The User's Requirements

By and large, the user's requirements will fall into one of three classes, and users will be well advised to establish into which one their interests fall.

The first class of requirement is high volume, remote deadlines, low-cost operation, and long messages. This class today is implemented through circuit switching. Generally speaking, the users are satisfied with the service but not with the cost. Their needs are best served through remote batch operation. Accumulation can be at the source point, for instance, the branch office, and then the line used for four or five hours per day, *as if* there were one long message being sent.

The second class is small volume, medium deadlines (a "stack" of them can be made, as in the SWIFT system), and medium-sized messages. Money transfers fall in this class. Deadlines are important, but the time intervals are not in fractions of a second. A dedicated DTE with a local memory can best carry out this job.

The third class is interactive service, immediate transactions (access to memory for a small amount of information), small messages, and very near deadlines. Time sharing (inquiry, status, balance, etc.) with its demanding deadline is an example of this class. Cost is a key issue; near deadlines can get very expensive, and therefore they require a network approach. Packet switching is the answer, although intelligent terminals may turn the tide back to message switching. (The virtual circuit may be expensive; a Datagram is probably better adapted to transaction-oriented operations.) The important thing is to design networks so that they are open to cost effectiveness as technology evolves.

Network performance must be studied in detail, along with data integrity. It will focus on three factors: speed of transmission, delay (time between transmission and delivery of the first bit of the message), and throughput (number of bits transmitted, divided by time between transmission of the first bit and delivery of the last bit). These factors are independent of each other, and so trade-offs can be made in good service, queues, error control, leaders and the like (Figure 29.2).

The implementation of choices calls for a pronounced flexibility in design. The next generation of communications technologies will be characterized by a modular and growth-oriented approach, and this is feasible. The whole technology and the basic economics behind it are in full swing. The field of data communications is based on a shift in economics that makes it necessary for us to continue to reevaluate where we are and where we wish to go. To use technological developments to our advantage, we need perspective. A single technological event will help to build the framework, but in itself it is not really important. Telephony, for example, was the first commercial use of electricity; it was a physical discovery that remained latent for nearly half a century. What *is* important is the broad view. Many see it, but few have given it expression.

Figure 29.2

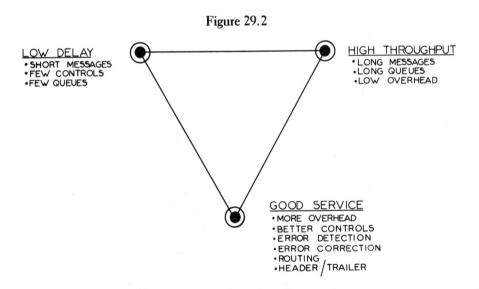

Examples with Message Systems

For an applications example, let's look at the implementation done by Manufacturers Hanover Trust Company.

Seeking to streamline its channels of internal communications, Manufacturers Hanover Trust found of great value the electronic mail system it installed in 1980. A management estimate indicates that about 19 percent of the user base is senior management, 28 percent is professionals, and 53 percent is middle management. Currently, users share over 3,000 terminals on the system. The biggest savings come from the elimination of phone calls, followed by the elimination of paper memos and meetings.

Many users have determined through surveys that the system saves up to 30 to 40 minutes a day per person. Multiplying that by the number of employees and by the average pay, one derives an estimated saving of $7 million per year for a two- to three-thousand-employee company.

Manufacturers Hanover trust has also been involved with networking. In Manhattan, where its headquarters is located, the bank has a metropolitan area network based on CATV technology.

Several locations in New York City have been connected with a channel on the cable network while the bank's corporate headquarters employs a broadband LAN. The solution is expected to save the bank about $1 million a year by replacing costs that would have gone to the telephone company.

Another implementation example is given by the Metropolitan Insurance Company. With the minis, clerks used some functions and not others because they are not user-friendly.

With each PC dedicated to one person, this has radically changed:

1. Data entry done at the local level is significantly simplified.

Specifically designed software and input devices help the clerks enter the application for insurance, subsequently forwarding the file to the mainframe for processing.

2. Sales agents use the PC to do prospecting.

This integrated application involves client handling, report generation, and the evaluation of P/L. The mini does this also, but the PC brought improvements.

3. New managerial functions have been implemented.

They include MIS, inquiry, file verification, commission evaluation, premiums, electronic mail, and a cash quote system.

4. The application base is being refined, advancing with PC installations for the agents.

With minis, it would have been too costly to expand the network of intelligent machines to the agent level. The PC makes this expansion not only feasible, but also mandatory.

Metropolitan Life Insurance is now actively planning for the integration of voice, data, text, and image so that it need not change its network design with the evolution of the applications environment. (Early estimates indicate that by integrating voice, text, and data, the resulting load will most likely be 88 percent voice and 12 percent text/data.) The project calls for handling voice, text/data and image high-speed on the same pipe at 6.2 MBPS. The network will cover all of the United States with voice-given preference.

Economics are also behind this drive. According to projections made by special-ists, the use of high technology in voice handling will save about $75 million over the next 10 years to this organization.

30
From Electronic Mail to Funds Transfer

Five broad areas characterize the range of electronic mail implementations: electronic funds transfer (EFT), merchandizing services, workstations for company mail, commercial and industrial electronic mailboxes, and household applications. These classes have common points, but also distinct differences in terms of requirements.

One common need is complete communications software addressed either by names or electronic mailboxes, through message switching (with store and forward) or packet switching facilities.

Electronic mail is producing a significant change in business practices and is propelled by the widespread use of the telephone. It is replacing a major part of the first class mail load; substituting for many of today's business telephone calls; competing with Telex, TWX, and Mailgrams; and replacing some interoffice memoranda.

Though electronic mail is a generic reference, it is well to keep in mind that several technologies can serve this market: facsimile, timeshared message switching services, packet switching networks with interfaces to BSC and asynchronous units, and standalone word processing equipment.

The facsimile is most versatile since it permits the transmission of a wide range of information formats without substantial data processing requirements, but offers none of the flexibility of computer-based systems with respect to such features as message composition and editing, storage, automatic retrieval, and features relating to the convenience of the recipient.

With electronic message systems, we need to identify the recipient and look most carefully who he is and what he really wants or needs. We also require that messages be properly examined as to context and structure.

A Telemail Application

To follow the practice of an electronic mail system offered in the U.S., the following briefly describes GTE-Telenet's TELEMAIL.

The user's effort to communicate with other users network-wide is minimal. What he needs to do in *signing-on* is to:

1. Switch the terminal to "ON". If he is using an acoustic coupler that is separate from the terminal, switch that ON as well.
2. Make sure that both the terminal and the coupler are in the REMOTE position.
3. Dial the local Telenet telephone number. When he hears a high-pitched tone, fit the telephone receiver into the coupler. Make sure the telephone cord is on the left side.
4. Press the RETURN key twice and wait for the network to respond:
   (RETURN)   (RETURN)

Telenet will ask what kind of information he is using (TERMINAL =). The user must type in the terminal ID code given to him by his TELEMAIL Administrator, or press RETURN. Then, Telenet will send him an @ sign, the signal for, "What do you want to do?" Since he wants to use the TELEMAIL service, he should type in MAIL. TELEMAIL will ask for his user name:

User Name? XXXXXXX (RETURN)

Next it will ask for password:

Password? XXXXXXXX (RETURN).

Notice that the user can't read his password—and neither can anyone else. A password is a security device that prevents unauthorized people from accessing a personal mailbox. But once he has correctly entered his user name and password, TELEMAIL responds with:

Welcome to TELEMAIL: Your last access was: (date) (time).

Hence, when the user has successfully established contact with the TELEMAIL system, the first thing he will see is a "welcome banner" indicating the date and time of his last access. Then, if new messages have been posted at the bulletin boards to which he has access, he will receive a notice to check those boards.

If new messages have been sent to the user since his last access, he will receive a scan table of summary information about those messages.

The first column is the scan number, an incremental numbering of his mailbox messages. He can use the scan number to select particular messages for priority reading.

The second column shows the date and time each message was delivered to his mailbox.

The third column shows the user name of the person who sent each message.

The fourth column shows the subject of the message. As such, this is TELE-MAIL's basic information element to the authorized user of the network.

The fifth column tells him the number of lines contained in each message.

Finally, he will receive a "COMMAND?" prompt. TELEMAIL is asking what he would like to do next. After any "COMMAND?" prompt during his TELE-MAIL session, the user can type "SCAN" to receive this table of information about new messages that he has not yet read. If there are no new messages in his mailbox, TELEMAIL will tell him "NO NEW MAIL".

Stated differently the SCAN command produces a table of information about messages he has not yet read. TELEMAIL will provide an automatic scan table each time he signs onto the system or will tell him there is "NO NEW MAIL" in his mailbox.

The "READ" command is used to display the contents of each message in the user's scan table. The display occurs in order of scan numbers. When a message is displayed, he will first see the envelope information:

The first line has two parts: the date and time the message was posted and a message number.

Every message sent on the TELEMAIL system is automatically assigned a unique message number for tracking within the system.

The second line is the sender's user name.
The third shows the user names of all direct recipients of the message.
The fourth displays the user names of all courtesy copy recipients of the message.

Courtesy copy recipients are optional to the sender of the message, just like a typical memo.

The fifth line is the subject of the message, which also appeared in the scan table.

The second part of the message is the text which appears exactly as the user typed it. After a message is displayed, he will receive an "ACTION?" prompt. TELEMAIL is asking what he would like to do with this particular message.

There are three basic Action commands: FORWARD, ANSWER, and PURGE. If he does not wish to act upon a message as soon as he receives it, the user must press "RETURN" in response to the "ACTION?" prompt. The message he has just received will remain in his catalog until he chooses to take action on it at a later time. Then, the next message in his scan table will appear. TELEMAIL will pause to prompt "ACTION?" between each message.

The "FORWARD" command indicates that he wishes to send a copy of the message he just received to one or more additional recipients. TELEMAIL prompts the user names of his direct recipients, separating the user names with a comma. The next prompt is for the user names of the courtesy copy recipients. If he wishes to leave this line blank, the user should press RETURN after the prompt

Next, he should type in a short subject for his message. This subject will appear in his recipients' scan tables. When he forwards a message, TELEMAIL gives him the opportunity to add his own comments to the message, just as he might annotate a memo before giving it to someone else.

The user should press "RETURN" after each line that he types. When he has finished entering his comments, he should type a period on a line by itself and press "RETURN" once more. When he signals the end of his message with a period and "RETURN", he will receive the "SEND?" signal prompt. TELEMAIL is asking if he is ready to post the message for delivery.

When he types "YES" in response to the "SEND?" prompt, TELEMAIL confirms the posting by displaying the current date and time, and assigns a unique message number to his message. After the "FORWARD" command process is complete, he will receive another "ACTION?" prompt. TELEMAIL is asking if there is any other action he would like to take upon the message he received.

If the user has no further action to take at this time, he must press "RETURN" in response to the "ACTION?" prompt. The message he received will remain in his catalog, and the message of his scan table will be displayed. This way, the "FORWARD" command is a prompt for envelope information and comments, then sends a copy of the message he received to his designated recipients.

Pressing "RETURN" in response to the "ACTION?" prompt causes the next scan table message to be displayed. In consequence, the user will receive an "ACTION?" prompt. TELEMAIL is asking what he would like to do with this message. The "ANSWER" command indicates the recipient's wish to reply directly to the sender of the message.

When he enters the "ANSWER" command, he will receive the prompt for TEXT:. TELEMAIL is asking what he would like to say in his reply. There is no prompt for "TO": or "SUBJECT": because the envelope information for his message is taken automatically from the message he is answering. The user can type in as many lines of text as he wishes, pressing "RETURN" after each line. When he has finished entering his text, he should type a period on a line by itself and press "RETURN" once more.

When he signals the end of his text with a period and "RETURN", he will receive the "SEND?" prompt. TELEMAIL is asking if he is ready to post the message for delivery. When he types "YES" in response to the "SEND?" prompt, TELEMAIL confirms the posting by displaying the current date and time and assigns a unique message number to the message.

After the "ANSWER" process is complete, he will receive another "ACTION?" prompt. The object is to ask if there is any other action he would like to take on the message he received. If he has no further action to take at this time, he should press "RETURN" in response to the "ACTION?" prompt. The message he received will remain in his catalog and the next message of his scan table will be displayed.

The "PURGE" command indicates he has no further use for this message and would prefer to have it erased from his catalog, but the user should be sure that any message he purges is one he never needs to see again.

TELEMAIL confirms the erasure with the message "PURGED". In response to the repeated prompt for "ACTION?" the user should simply press "RETURN". If there are no more messages to display from his scan table, he will receive a new "COMMAND?" prompt. TELEMAIL is asking what he would like to do next.

To file a message just read, at "ACTION?" the user should type:

"FILE IN" (FILENAME)

To get a list of all his files, at "ACTION?" or "COMMAND?" he must type

"DISPLAY FILES"

To get a scan table of all the messages contained in a particular file, at "COMMAND?" he should type:

"SCAN" (FILENAME)

To remove a message from a file but not purge it entirely from his catalog, he must type:

"REMOVE (SCAN NO.) FROM (FILENAME)"

The "COMPOSE" command indicates his wish to create a message of his own. TELEMAIL will first prompt for the envelope information of his message. The "TO:" line is for direct recipients and the "CC:" line is for courtesy copy recipients, just as if he were sending a standard memo. It is a good idea to place his own user name in the "CC:" line to keep a copy of the message he sends. The "SUBJECT:" line should be a short, concise header for the message he is sending, that subject will appear in his recipients' scan tables.

The next prompt is for the "TEXT" of his message. The user can enter as many lines of text as he wishes, pressing "RETURN" after each line. When he has finished entering text, he must type a period on a line by itself and press "RETURN" once more. When he signals the end of his text with a period and "RETURN", he will receive the "SEND?" prompt. TELEMAIL is asking if he is ready to post the message for delivery.

When the user types "YES" in response to the "SEND?" prompt, TELEMAIL confirms the posting by displaying the current date and time and assigns a unique message number to his message. As soon as the "COMPOSE" process is complete, he will receive another "COMMAND" prompt. TELEMAIL is asking what he would like to do next.

The "CHECK" command enables the user to scan and read messages posted to a bulletin board. Just as he might walk down the hall to read news items on a company bulletin board, with TELEMAIL he uses the CHECK command to move from his own catalog to a common catalog, one that contains messages of general interest to a large number of people. When he enters the "CHECK" command followed by the bulletin board name, TELEMAIL confirms that he is looking at a different catalog with the message, "NOW USING BULLETIN BOARD".

Typing "SCAN" in response to the next "COMMAND?" prompt gives the user a typical scan table, showing information on new messages in the bulletin board catalog that he has not read before. He can choose to read a specific message in his scan table by typing the "READ" command followed by the scan number assigned to that message. He can also display all of the new bulletin board messages by typing the "READ" command alone.

After the message is displayed, TELEMAIL will again prompt the user's command. It does not prompt for "ACTION?" as it does when he reads his own mailbox messages because he cannot act upon messages in a bulletin board catalog. When he has finished with the bulletin board and wishes to return to his own catalog, the user must type "CHECK". TELEMAIL will confirm that he is "NOW USING HIS OWN CATALOG AGAIN", and prompt for the next command.

TELEMAIL also assures on-line assistance.

COMMAND?   ? (RETURN)

gives a list of all commands available on the TELEMAIL system.

ACTION?   ? (RETURN)

offers a list of available Action commands.

COMMAND?   ?   COMMAND NAME   (RETURN)

provides a brief summary and list of options for that command. Furthermore, "Control H": deletes characters. The cursor will backspace and "delete" characters as it moves. When you release the Control key, you can resume typing normally, overstriking the deleted characters.

"Control X": deletes a line. The cursor will move to the start of the next line and wait for input, as if he had never input the line before. "Control R" replays a line. The system will redisplay the most recent line he entered. "Control S" stops display. The system will "freeze" output until the user enters "Control Q" to resume. "Control Q": resumes display. The system will continue output normally after "Control S".

There is also available a "BREAK KEY". At any time that TELEMAIL is displaying output, the user can press the "BREAK KEY" on his terminal to interrupt the output and return to the "COMMAND?" prompt. Pressing BREAK will in no way alter or damage the output. When the user is ready to sign out from TELEMAIL, all he need do is press the "BYE" command. The system will confirm the completion of the session.

Throughout this message interchange, TELEMAIL protects the confidentiality and security of the mail by providing two forms of identification passkeys: the user's own password and his personal ID. The password is for security at sign-on. The personal ID is for security with regard to private messages. Quite evidently, to maintain maximum security, the user should periodically change passkeys. The "PASS-KEYS" command enables him to change both his password and personal ID.

When he enters "YES" in response to the "CHANGE PASSWORD?" prompt, TELEMAIL first asks him to enter his current "old" sign-on password and is then prompted twice for the new password. The repeated prompt avoids the problems that might occur if he made a typographical error the first time he entered it. When the process is complete, TELEMAIL confirms that his password has been changed and prompts for a change to the personal ID.

When the user enters "YES" in response to the "CHANGE PERSONAL ID?" prompt, TELEMAIL first asks him to enter the current "old" ID. Then, he is prompted twice for his new ID. When this process is complete, TELEMAIL confirms that his personal ID has been changed and returns to the "COMMAND?" prompt. The user is advised to contact his TELEMAIL administrator if he forgets his passkeys.

The knowledgeable reader easily understands that the TELEMAIL protocol described in these pages is for a "dumb" terminal. The above description demonstrates the most complex set of operations the user will need to go through in implementing electronic mail.

Today, it is very easy to use packages (programmed applications) with a cheap intelligent terminal, such as a personal computer. A package such as Microlink handles all protocol routines by the typing in of a phrase number, like "2.1". Such simple, easily available software for PCs can also be called upon to add a carriage return at the end of the outgoing text line and to respond to host prompts.

Operating Through Workstations

A PC on every desk brings forward the concept of workstations—the computer-based unit able to handle an impressive variety of tasks, including company mail. This development goes beyond the advent of the word processor and reaches into ways and means for controlling the very large share taken by company mail as a percent of all hardcopy typed or printed.

Studies among industrial and financial institutions have indicated that between 70 percent and 90 percent of all hardcopy produced in a firm is internal company mail. Why print it in the first place? Why not to leave it in the memory of the machine, make reference to it when needed, and even have exception reporting (flashes) on a video screen as the exceptions occur?

The latter evidently requires a significant amount of organizational prerequisites, and the keys to this problem are procedural. The prerequisites are the proper hardware and software support. Hardware capabilities must be beyond those of the simple WP—and the personal computer can answer such requirements.

An electronic mail function based on packet or message switching and capable of distributing a letter or document to multiple terminals (whether video or hardcopy) includes features such as:

error detection and correction

store and forward

formatting

journaling

redialing

retransmit.

The variety of message formats is no more an obstacle to software development, and the low cost of terminals is in itself a promotional factor.

Given the high costs of manual handling, users who generate large volumes of message traffic may well find that the price of workstations justify the overall savings both in labor and network costs.

Sophisticated terminals contain word processing, message editing, and addressing capabilities. Operating on/off, they consume no bandwidth during message composition or reading time. In contrast, classical timeshared systems with "dumb" terminals have to rely on system computers for message processing services. These systems consume transmission bandwidth during message composition and reading and are, therefore, quite expensive.

Users will also find that the most demanding requirements are those relating to organizational prerequisites. This has many faces, the most important being an analysis of reasons for the functions being offered, and of the dependability of those functions.

A significant finding is that the large majority of all printed paper in an organization is for internal consumption, and studies among institutions (industrial, insurance, financial) have revealed a very high percent of internal hardcopy consumption.

Finally, about 30 percent of all first class mail involves billing and payments. This can be incorporated in EFT.

Perspectives in Electronic Funds Transfer

The potential for the implementation of electronic funds transfer (EFT) to corporate money management is a subject of interest both to bankers and to corporate treasurers. Bankers are seeking to serve corporate needs in a profitable manner, and they view electronics as a means of increasing both control over and mobility of funds.

Let's look at some EFT statistics. The yearly number of commercial transactions in the U.S. now stands at 100 billion. Of these, 80 percent are made in cash, 10 percent are by check, 8 percent are through credit cards, and 2 percent are through

EFT. However, it is projected that by 1995 the statistics will be 67 percent in cash, 20 percent through EFT, 9 percent by check, and 4 percent through credit cards.

The payments system now works through two main channels: direct mail payments by customers, and retail outlets. For many direct mail payments, the appropriate vehicle seems to be the automated clearing house (ACH), such as for utility payments, mortgage payments, and insurance premiums. Automation of this type of payment has a particular advantage in that it requires no particular level of processing sophistication on the part of the bank from which the payment emanates.

Receipts generated by retail outlets, however, present a different and more complex problem for EFT planners.

At present, the standard method of controlling and expediting receipts from diverse retail outlets is based on deposit reporting systems and depository transfer checks (DTC). Under this approach the store manager deposits his receipts to a local bank and, typically, calls a data capture computer to report the deposit amount. The recording computer provides data to a concentration bank which, in turn, creates and clears a DTC to transfer the funds. With appropriate deadlines and through judicious selection of concentration banks, it is possible to clear funds to a concentration amount in one business day.

The cost of this system is not insignificant, with roughly half the costs being lodged in the functions of creating, processing and clearing the DTC. Thus, retail managers must be instructed to effect a transaction only when funds are sufficient to justify the cost, and this situation frequently leads to excessive balances in the depository bank.

The DTC approach seems to be retrogressive because the data required to effect a transfer are collected in machine-readable and transmittable form and then converted to a paper document. Therefore, it seems both logical and cost effective to convert the DTC to an electronic debit for ACH clearance. However, because of ACH rules for prenotification and operating constraints on both banks and post offices, Postal Service analysis of an ACH application for its funds-mustering function indicates that, on average, a full day of funds availability would be lost.

At this stage, the ACH is not the answer, and this is likely to be the case for other firms with similar situations.

Since the objectives of the system are two-fold—to maximize control over and mobility of funds and to maintain accounting, accountability and audit control over the individual depositing unit—the following proposal was considered.

1. Within each mail processing area of the Postal Service, each individual post office would be assigned a unique depository account, all in a single bank.
2. After posting daily deposits, the depository bank would debit each account and transfer the balance to a single master account.
3. Funds would be transferred from the master account to a concentration bank account for corporate use.
4. The depository bank would transmit transaction data—date, amount, account number—to the Postal Service for accounting and audit purposes.

This approach appears to be a straightforward EFT-type application for corporate cash management. However, unlike ACH, it does require a degree of automation sophistication somewhat above the minimum level required for check processing. Furthermore, since cost/effective automation is a function of volume, pricing is an important consideration.

EFT in the Supermarket

Another interesting area for EFT applications is the retail area.

The ultimate success of retail EFT in the supermarket will depend on how well the concept satisfies the requirements of three groups: financial institutions, supermarkets, and consumers.

What are the major requirements of financial institutions regarding EFT in the supermarket?

Putting aside the need to stay abreast or even ahead of competition, it appears that the key requirement is for a cost/effective way to serve a greater number of customers. It is recognized that the consumer is becoming relatively more important as a source of funds for financial institutions and that access to these funds will be a requirement for the continuing growth and success of many institutions. Supermarkets have a surprisingly similar set of requirements for EFT.

Food retailers also recognize that EFT can provide a competitive advantage which, at least in the near future, will yield increased sales and higher market shares.

There are two other requirements important to supermarkets.

One is the need to reduce or at least not to inadvertently increase operating costs. Most of the discussion of the economic impact of EFT on retailers centers on reducing bad check losses. This cost represents a significant dollar amount but is not a critical controllable cost. Instead, retailer interest is focused primarily on the impact of EFT on labor costs, including costs associated with directly serving the consumer and those involved in bookkeeping and cash control.

The other requirement involves the opportunity to derive revenue from EFT. It has been suggested that the only thing a retailer has to sell is shelf space. To the extent that this is true, it appears that this perspective would apply equally well to card-based services as to groceries. Supermarket executives strive to build traffic in the store and then to sell a profitable mix of merchandise. As EFT becomes implemented, it too will have to pay its way.

Now, how well are the current EFT systems satisfying the requirements of both financial institutions and the retailer? While EFT in the supermarket is a new application still experiencing growth pains, it is possible to learn something from the experiences to date.

Studies indicate problems with consumer acceptance of the system, and that in many situations the requirements of both financial institutions and retailers were not being satisfied. For the financial institutions, for example, the transaction volumes for these terminals were generally lower than anticipated and most institutions did not experience either the expected increase in new accounts or the gain in market share. Certain studies conclude that most merchants were not receiving an adequate return for their investment of time and resources in EFT and that, in fact, many were receiving no payment at all while contributing space and labor to the effort.

While part of the difficulty was related to the problems of introducing and marketing the systems, the question can be raised as to whether these systems were designed to satisfy the requirements of the consumer. Before this question can be answered, however, it will be necessary to develop a more comprehensive statement of the consumer's requirements which can serve as a framework for such evaluations.

Foreign Payments Procedures

Electronic funds transfers have found a welcome ground in foreign exchange operations because of the complexities of effective control in that area. (Experience in the field is the *sine qua non* of developing and implementing control systems responsive to the unique character of the activity.)

As a result of large, well-publicized foreign exchange losses, improvement of control over foreign exchange trading has been given high priority by bank management. Obvious control deficiencies such as permitting traders to deal on their own account can be eliminated if the following controls are installed and strengthened:

1. Removing recordkeeping, recording and trade confirmation functions from foreign exchange traders and placing them under the control of a separate accounting group.
2. Developing position exposure, maturity gap and customer limits, and reporting actual positions against these limits.
3. Introducing end-to-end computer systems able to handle foreign exchange operations.
4. Giving management the necessary expertise to man such systems at a senior-to-senior administration level.

There is no question that establishing well-studied computer control systems such as EFT greatly reduces the risk a bank incurs from conducting a foreign exchange trading operation.

There is danger, however, that the managers responsible for overseeing trading activities will assume that adequate control exists once the controls are in place. This danger is particularly great if, as is often the case, these managers do not have the detailed technical knowledge necessary to understand the ways in which a trader can distort or suppress limit data or engage in undetected speculation, even when segregation of duties is in effect.

Two additional foreign exchange controls—limit discrepancy exception control and nostro balance management—are desirable additions to a limit reporting system. The former can ensure that the data being reported on limit reports channeled through an EFT network accurately reflects actual exposure to risk. The latter provides management with a quantitative measure of the magnitude and profitability of the traders' currency speculation activities. *

The following explains the nature of limit discrepancy and nostro balance controls, why they are desirable, and what problems may be expected in gathering the data necessary to implement them.

To place these controls in the proper perspective, their relationship to basic limit reporting systems must also be discussed.

Limit reporting system: Position exposure, maturity gap and customer limits are specified to limit a bank's vulnerability to the uncertainty caused by fluctuations in exchange rates, errors in contract terms, or default by any of the parties to a foreign exchange trade contract.

Most banks monitor the risk incurred in each currency at least on a daily basis by issuing a Position Exposure by Currency report. Control is maintained by monitoring the "net position," defined as the balance in each currency held in foreign bank accounts, plus total purchase contracts outstanding minus total sales contracts in that currency. The net position is compared to specified currency exposure limits. Methods for translating each currency position into, say, an equivalent U.S. dollar and policies toward temporary "daylight" violations of exposure limits vary from bank to bank.

Maturity gap reports are used to monitor the time interval over which a foreign exchange trader is permitted to generate a currency sales contract that is not offset by a corresponding purchase contract for the same currency, or vice versa. Control is maintained by monitoring the difference between purchases and sales over a specified time period, generally semimonthly, and comparing the difference (gap) to either an individual or cumulative limit. Maturity gap reports thus have a function similar to that of position exposure reports in that they limit the amount of risk faced by the bank as a result of fluctuations in exchange rates.

Their primary function, however, is to prevent the Position Exposure Report from conveying misleading information.

By preventing the total value of trade contracts outstanding with a single customer at any one time from becoming too large, the bank spreads the risk of default and therefore decreases the risk of large losses.

Limit discrepancy exception control: The reporting structure outlined above provides a good level of control if the data inserted on the limit reports can be verified to be accurate. It is on the question of verification that most limit reporting systems are deficient. Even if segregation of duties is in effect, it is possible to manipulate the contents of limit reports either by withholding foreign exchange trade information from control personnel or by deferring notification of a trade until a later date.

---

*Unfortunately, neither of these controls has been implemented within basic limit reporting.

Table 30.1.

Effect of trade discrepancies on limits.

Discrepancy	Limit Report Data Is Affected If:	Limit Effect		
		Position Limits	Maturity Limits	Customer Limits
A confirmation is received which shows a trade date shown on the original copy of the trade contract.	Date shown on original copy of the contract is incorect.	Position exposure for the date the trade occurred will be misstated by the amount of the trade.	1. If forward trade, maturity gap limits may be exceeded. 2. If spot, the spot and total position limits will be misstated.	Liability for the date indicated will be misstated by amount of the trade.
A confirmation is received for which no conrtract exists on file.	Trade was made and not reported.	1. If spot trade, all position reports between trade date and value date are misstated by the amount of the trade. 2. If forward trade, position reports are misstated by the amount of the trade.	Same as above.	Liability during the period the trade was unreported will be misstated.
A confirmation query is received	Trade was made and not not reported.	Same as above.	Same as above.	Same as above.
The confirmation specifies as a "buy" a transaction that is specified on the contract as a "sell" or vice versa.	The type of transaction shown on the bank's trade contract copy is incorrect.	Position exposure for the date that trade occurred will be misstated by twice the amount of the trade.	Same as above.	Liability during the period for which the type of trade was misstated will be incorrect by twice the amount of the trade.

419

Table 30.1 (continued)

	Limit Effect		
Discrepancy	Limit Report Data Is Affected If:	Position Limits	Maturity Limits	Customer Limits
A different currency is specified on the trade confirmation than was shown on the trade contract.	The currency shown on the bank's trade contract copy is incorrect.	The position exposoure for currencies shown on both the trade contract and the trade confirmation will be misstated.	Maturity gap positions for both currencies will be misstated.	Liability during the period for which the type of currency was misstated will be incorrect by the difference between the U.S. dollar equivalent for the correct and incorrect currencies.
Different value dates are specified on the original trade contract and the confirmation.	The contract value date is incorrect.	Position exposure for the period between the actual and erroneous dates will be misstated by the amount of the transaction.	Maturity gap positions may be exceeded.	Liability during the period between the actual and erroneous value dates will be misstated.

Suppression or alteration of trade contract data prior to its leaving the traders can be used to manipulate each of the limit reports prepared for management. A summary of potential alterations in the reports that can originate from various types of contract misspecifications is shown in Table 30.1.

The only solution to this problem is to receive written trade confirmations from all foreign exchange customers and to match the information on each of these confirmations against the original trade contract information furnished by the traders.

This theoretically simple solution, however, has seldom been adequately applied in practice. Electronic mail can help answer this requirement in an efficient manner.

The implementation of an EFT system in foreign exchange operations can stimulate efforts to improve foreign exchange trading, the successful functioning of which is vital to the growth of world trade and investment and to the well-being of the bank. An end-to-end solution between Swift and foreign exchange minicomputers can provide the administrative authorities of the bank with tools never before available for the control of exchange operations. Computers can also give the operators a new and valuable faculty in nostro balance management.

Nostro accounts (nostro meaning "ours") are accounts maintained by a bank in its foreign correspondent banks in the currencies of the foreign country. The accounts have a variety of uses, one of which is to provide clearing accounts for currency transfers in support of foreign exchange operations. Interest is not paid on these accounts, the use of the funds by the foreign bank being considered "payment" for the privilege of maintaining the account. In some cases, average balances maintained in the accounts* are specified by formal means, but many average balances have been fixed by tradition or by "gentlemen's agreement". The average balance to be maintained in each nostro account as compensation for use of the account is known as the "peg balance".

Average balances maintained in interest-free accounts represent an opportunity loss to any bank, although the required average peg balance is a legitimate cost of business.

---

*Analoguous to compensating balances in domestic banking.

31

Videotex in the 1980s

Personal Computers and Videotex

Videotex can be considered as a system of interdependent partners:

politicians and other authorities

telephone companies

information providers (organizations, institutions)

information demanders and users (private households and professionals)

equipment manufacturers (modem, decoders, editing machines, video screens)

equipment merchants (radio and TV dealers, office shops)

equipment installation firms

system deliverers (hardware and software)

service bureaus (agencies, consultants).

Services supported and to be supported by videotex range from access to large databases, to home banking, electronic mail, and home information systems. These will make the electronic newspaper a reality.

Current forecasts indicate that during the 1980s the market for electronic newspaper services will grow to more than $500 million, divided about evenly between consumer-oriented and business. Such news services will be used by those who have viewdata equipment and/or home computers.

The real potential for electronic news products lies in providing information in greater depth than regular newspapers can give. Different electronic news products are likely to evolve, geared to the needs of users who have home computers able to act as videotex terminals.

Services will include *demand updates* in which a user with a videotex terminal probes a news database, either to learn what's going on or to obtain more detailed information than he could find in the paper version of the newspaper.

Another possibility is *broadcast updates* where the terminal user is presented with the news in a category or categories which he previously selected as being of interest to him. A further issue is broadcast updates by FM sideband in which the user without a videotex terminal, but equipped with a specially adapted radio receiver, receives news (verbally, on a display or printer) on topics he previously selected.

Through *in-depth current reviews*, a subscriber is able to request that the newspaper organization search its database and print an in-depth bulletin on a topical news item, including reporters' products and other material not printed in the paper version of the newspaper. By means of in-depth retrospective reviews, a subscriber could request a search of all news on a particular topic, going back three months, six months, one year, and so on. He would be presented with an electronically-generated report on the chosen topic.

Though several services could be provided without PC support, the on-line TV set with a decoded attachment will not reach the sophistication of operations which can be achieved by a personal computer interface. There is room for both systems in the marketplace.

Let's further notice that for viewdata services, the response time on voice-grade lines is acceptable — the screen fills up faster than one can read it. Quality is also adequate.

Access to the growing number of public databases (some 3,300 in the U.S. alone by current estimates) will evidently bring into perspective security issues. Logical keys are a "must". Their implementation depends on the system we start with and the available resources. PCs can be instrumental in the manipulation of keywords. They can also make user-friendly the access to the public database, which can be menu or command driven, or a menu program that accepts direct access to data.

For privacy, users will need a way to associate keywords with files. They can search through the text of each file to find a match, but that is slow on most systems, especially if the library is large. A quicker way is to store all keywords on the PC as if it were an index. When the user enters keywords (or selects them from a menu), the query program locates the matching keyword string in the keyword file. That string associates with a specific file or with several secondary keywords.

Just because each file must be uniquely identified by at least one combination of keywords, the power of a PC is helpful. Though — as we will see in the following discussion — dumb terminals (such as a TV set) have been used since the beginning for videotex access, the future is more promising with intelligent machines.

(See also Chapter 4 for a further discussion of videotex and PCs.)

Developing Videotex Systems

Let's look at the history of videotex development and what followed these first efforts.

The British, French, Germans, Japanese, and Americans were among the first to offer public videotex. In England, the original viewdata service was publically offered March 1979 under the name Prestel.

Prestel's main disadvantage is that it isn't yet a *gateway* network. All information providers must deliver or transmit their databases to Prestel computers. With the videotex systems that support communicating databases, providers keep their databases on their own computers and the systems provide switches to them.

In France, Télétel has been the cornerstone of the country's telematics program, bringing the advantages of computers and communications to everyone who has a telephone. Télétel is based on the Antiope standard. Antiope is a broadcast teletex standard, licensed for use in tests in other parts of the world, including one in Los Angeles.

In Japan, Nippon Telephone and Telegraph (NTT) originated the videotex system Captain (Character and Pattern Telephone Access Information Network). The same organization looks after its commercialization.

In Germany, the videotex initiative was taken by the state-owned Post and Telecommunications Organization (Bundespost). Bildschirmtext has been tested in two public trials since the beginning of June 1980. Their purpose was to determine the user acceptance of this new information and communications medium as well as possible social, cultural and economic effects with regard to the introduction of videotex on a large scale.

The Bildschirmtext trials are sponsored by the Länder North Rhine-Westphalia and Berlin in cooperation with the Bundespost. The Bildschirmtext trials are being conducted in the Düsseldorf/Neuss area (local telephone areas of Düsseldorf, Neuss, Neuss-Dorf, Dormagen, Hilden, Mettmann, Ratingen and Meerbusch-Büderich) and in West Berlin.

The German Bildschirmtext system is based on a Prestel license, but it does offer gateway. (The Germans originally commissioned the communicating database software for Prestel, then gave a contract to IBM for a network of Series 1-based gateways.)

Yet, with or without gateway capability, the importance of videotex systems is that they are very simple, are based on proven technologies, and can be used anywhere.

In England, for example, Prestel now masters some 14,000 on-line terminals (TV sets installed in home and industry). Today, few computer-based systems exceed such an on-line capability. In Switzerland, Zürich and Lausanne have 1,000 connections at each site with a further 1,000 users in other parts of the country. The test market concept has the following goals:

study of the spreading videotex effect

research on marketing and economics—including advertising

evaluation of possible regional competition

a concentration of expertise and financial possibilities.

In America, a significant number of trials have taken place and many have been successfully completed. (See Chapter 4.)

One of the most significant American implementations (where the U.S. and Germany hold the lead) is in home banking. Consumers have been able to make bill payments and ask for their balance over TV lines using keypads and keyboards that plug into a TV set.

An adapter links the home TV set with telephone lines, enabling the user to view bill-paying requests on the TV screen before sending them to the bank, to request loan information, to ask for deposits, to be informed on his account balance, and so on.

As we underlined in the chapter on electronic mail, the spread of TV- and telephone-based automation—of which banking is only a small aspect—is integrally linked to the creation of new on-line systems to replace the postman. A great deal of the success of this effort will depend on standards. (In May 1981, AT&T announced the videotex protocol to which it plans to adhere in its future home information systems activities. AT&T's presentation protocol specifies what information in 7- or 8-bit units will be transmitted between host computers and user terminals, and what types of picture any given string will create when correctly received and interpreted by the user terminal. In short, this is a top-level alphageometric standard which makes Telidon (the Canadian videotex protocol) a subset.)

A presentation level protocol (PLP) defines the method of displaying graphics while retaining compatibility with other systems. (See also Chapter 19). PLP describes some formats, rules and procedures which will be used to encode text, graphics and display control information for videotex applications.

The Mechanics of a Videotex Facility

To judge the acceptance of the videotex service by subscribers in the West German market trial, 20 company-owned computers were connected to the two Bildschirmtext central computers. In the first configuration, the packet switched network was simulated by a network of fixed lines, and the German packet switching network Datex-P was integrated in mid-1981.* Technical details of the market trial include:

1. A communication protocol above the X.25 level.
2. The integration of Datex-P (public packet switching network).

---

*Datex-P is based on a Datapac architecture.

3. On-line data collection capabilities. That is, data input to external computers via data collection pages.
4. Access to the external computers via the two Bildschirmtext central computers.
5. Representation of Bildschirmtext pages in a standard page format.
6. Tree-structured viewdatabases (VDB) in the central computers with access to pages by means of menu selection.
7. No restrictions on applications, for instance, database structure in the external computers.
8. Access to external computers via data collection pages.

Let's discuss the mechanics of this videotex facility. The Bildschirmtext Central System comprises three key elements: terminals, a computer, and a database. The terminals (typically "dumb" TV sets with modem and decoder) are employed by the users, system operators, and information providers for their respective functions. The viewdatabase contains all the information that the user may access. The computer controls all retrieval and entry of data and the accounting of charges for these functions. External databases are stored on the computers operated by information providers.

The facility provided at the network level is a logical channel (virtual circuit). Each permanent virtual circuit (PVC) allows two-way communication of variable-length blocks of data. The Bildschirmtext protocol level is implemented upon the facilities of the PVC and specifies internal structures to the data blocks.

More specifically, the Bildschirmtext protocol blocks provide the handshakes shown in Figure 31.1—

requests for establishing a connection

positive or negative acknowledgement

request for disconnection

acknowledgement of disconnection

Line 24 message request

collected data block

acknowledgement of receipt of data block

transmitted frame data

numbered and unnumbered frame requests.

The physical, data-link, and network levels are based upon CCITT recommendations providing procedures compatible with the Datex-P network.

The system assures the mechanism by which the user can obtain and relinquish access to external computer databases typically supported by information providers. During the course of retrieving data from an external computer, the user may wish

Figure 31.1. Videotex handshake.

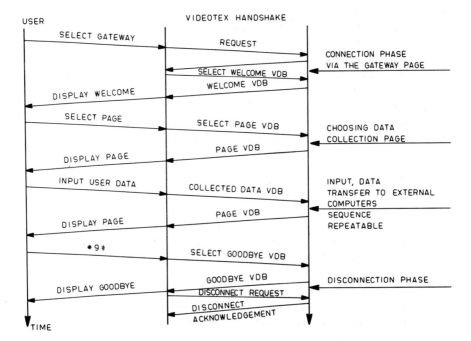

to return to the central Bildschirmtext database. He may achieve this by selecting the goodbye page by keying *9#, or, alternatively, he may be routed to the goodbye page by choices contained in other pages. When the goodbye page is retrieved from the external computer, the user is automatically disconnected from the external computer and the virtual circuit is released. The user may then proceed to retrieve frames from the Bildschirmtext database by direct selection or by choices contained in the goodbye page.

Goodbye frames are owned and maintained by information providers operating external computers, and are held in their external databases. They are similar to information frames except that they carry a different task number.

When a goodbye page is retrieved on behalf of a user, the system sends a *disconnection request block* to the external computer and waits for a *disconnect acknowledgement block* in reply. The user must retrieve the frame either through menu selection or direct access external information retrieval commands. The goodbye frame will then be displayed. The text of the frame makes it clear to the user that his connection to the external computer has been terminated and that any further commands will be interpreted in the context of the Bildschirmtext database.

To assure the gateway function, certain actions are necessary on the interface between the central Bildschirmtext computer and the external computer. Three sequences are primarily invoked by the gateway function:

A *connect sequence* attempts to establish a connection between the user and the external computer.

The result of the attempt, whether successful or unsuccessful, determines the next action open to the user (Figure 31.2).

A *welcome page sequence* requests a welcome page from the external computer and receives the incoming data.

The actions for the central Bildschirmtext computer and the external computer for this sequence are properly elaborated, including all forms of page selection, as in Figure 31.3.

A *disconnect sequence* is used to disconnect a user from the external computer to which a connection has previously been established through the system (Figure 31.4).

The only valid response from the central computer is a *disconnection acknowledgement*. Receipt of any other response or timeout occurence is equivalent to disconnection acknowledgement.

Connection, Transmission, Disconnection

Transitions between the states of the communications system (Bildschirmtext computer, external computers, user terminals) are accompanied by an exchange of protocols. (The connection sequence is shown in Figure 31.2.) It involves a handshake between the central Bildschirmtext computer and the external computer. After the connection has been established, the system is ready to transmit text and data. Figure 31.5 identifies the handshake.

For disconnection, the circuit between Bildschirmtext and the user level is incomplete. To enable the data to flow, a logical connection must be made, and this is only possible if Bildschirmtext sends a request for connection.

An important step is waiting for *access approval*. Upon sending a connection request to the user level, the link interface enters this state to wait while software checks are performed at the external computer on the password entered. The result of the checks can either be a connection acknowledgement resulting in transfer to the *welcome state* or a connection refusal leading to disconnect. Receipt of a bad block results in a wait for disconnect confirmation.

If the checks performed by the external computer indicate that the request for connection comes from an authorized user, the welcome page request setup is entered. The logical connection between the central and external computers is now complete, and Bildschirmtext sets up a welcome page request and sends it to the external machine. This request results in a transfer to the following state.

Waiting for data from external computer retrieval is necessary while the external machine searches for and retrieves the specified frame. Receipt of a bad data

Figure 31.2. Connection sequence.

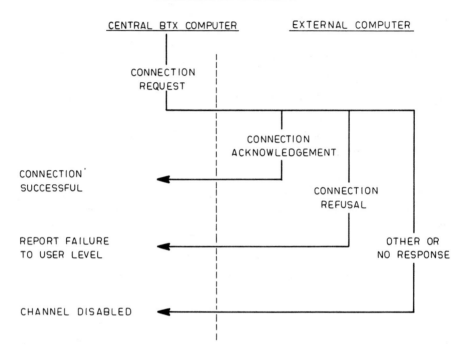

CONNECTION SEQUENCE

block results in a transfer to "state two wait" for disconnect confirmation. A timeout results in immediate disconnect.

If the frame transmitted by the external computer, upon leaving the preceding state, is of the "information" type, a *connection* is accomplished. A specific *goodbye page* request leads to transfer to a waiting state for goodbye page retrieval.

If the welcome page received by the central Bildschirmtext computer is of a *data collection* type, then further exchange of protocol blocks must follow to retrieve the control and prompt frame(s). This state is entered while a frame request is being set up within the central machine. The sending of a frame request to the external computer results in a transfer to the next state.

The interface is in the state of *waiting for a data collection frame retrieval* while the appropriate data collection frame is being searched in the external computer. The arrival of the next frame in the central Bildschirmtext machine results in a transfer to the next frame state.

Frame request set-up is an intermediate handling level entered while a request for a prompt frame is being set up within the central Bildschirmtext computer. Sending out a request results in a transfer to the preceding state. The central ma-

Figure 31.3. Frame selection sequences.

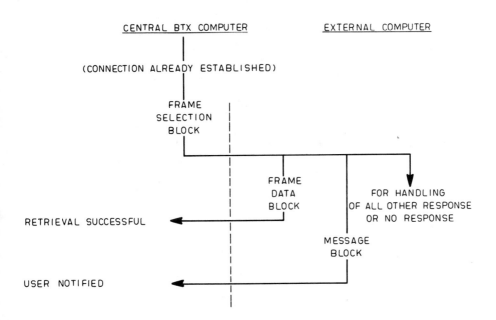

FRAME SELECTION SEQUENCES

CENTRAL BTX COMPUTER

EXTERNAL COMPUTER

(CONNECTION ALREADY ESTABLISHED)

FRAME
SELECTION
BLOCK

FRAME
DATA
BLOCK

FOR HANDLING
OF ALL OTHER RESPONSE
OR NO RESPONSE

RETRIEVAL SUCCESSFUL

MESSAGE
BLOCK

USER NOTIFIED

chine can receive an asynchronous disconnect from the external computer while in this state, resulting in a transfer to waiting for disconnect acknowledgement.

When all data collection frames have arrived at the central computer, the interface is at a connected state while the user is doing data collection. If the user requests disconnection, a *disconnection request* will result in transfer to *waiting for disconnect confirmation.*

Completion of data collection and the sending of a collected data block to the external computer results in a transfer to the next state.

When collected data is sent to the external computer the link interface enters the *awaiting data handling response* state. A timeout results in disconnection.

The link interface enters the state of *waiting for goodbye page retrieval* from the external computer while a goodbye page is being retrieved.

Following a disconnection request from the central Bildschirmtext computer to the external computer, the link interface enters this state. Receipt of a disconnection acknowledgement from the latter machine results in a disconnection.

Error recovery is an important operation. The error handling sequence is shown in Figure 31.6. If any errors are found in the protocol blocks received, this state is

Figure 31.4. Disconnect sequence.

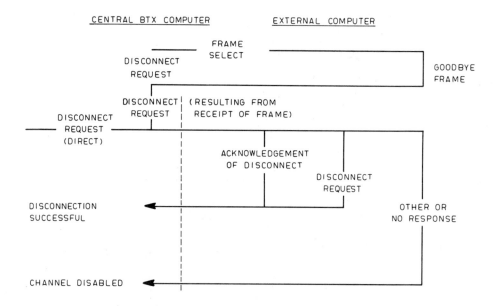

DISCONNECT SEQUENCE

entered. The computer decision is then made to flag the line as failed or to attempt a recovery. For recovery, a disconnection request is sent.

The link interface enters the state of *waiting for disconnection acknowledgement set-up* while the central computer sets up a disconnection acknowledgement.

The link interface has failed if application level recovery is not possible. Action is necessary to rectify the fault and move the link interface to disconnect status.

Videotex services are supported within this general framework. A *password* request sets up a logical parameter indicating whether a password must be inserted by the user before access is allowed via this gateway. This password is input on Line 24 (of the video screen) as part of the input sequence.

Also for identification purposes, the system supports an *external computer identifier* as a numeric parameter which identifies the external computer to which access is provided by the gateway. The system operators allocate this number to information providers. The external database is set up and controlled entirely by the information provider who operates the external computer. External database frames are requested and received by the central Bildschirmtext computer.

Each of the user facilities available in the external data information retrieval function invokes a sequence of actions on the external computer interface. The

Figure 31.5. Transmit collected data sequences.

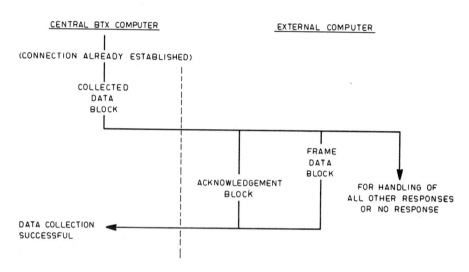

sequences are described in terms of the central machine actions taken and the minimum necessary complementary actions by the external computer.

The information retrieval function invokes a *frame selection* function. Though there are five different forms of frame selection, the exchanges between the central and the external computers are essentially the same as shown in Figure 31.3.

The data collection function being supported provides a mechanism by which users may enter text and data into the Bildschirmtext system, this being transmitted to an information provider. A *transmit data collection* sequence transmits the contents of the protected and nonprotected fields to the external computer.

The response from an external computer which has received a collected data block can be a frame data block or an acknowledgement block. If it is a frame data block then the frame is displayed to the user. If an acknowledgement block is received and NEXTFRAME is equal to the current frame, then all nonprotected fields are cleared. The frame is displayed again; otherwise, a frame select block is sent out for the frame number specified in NEXTFRAME.

The displayed data collection frame contains fields which will subsequently be transmitted to the external computer. All of these fields are initialized to spaces or any other values set up by the information provider. The field may be designated as protected or unprotected.

Unprotected fields (except name and address fields) may be overwritten by the user. When the frame has been displayed to the user the cursor is positioned at the beginning of the first unprotected field and the corresponding prompt message is displayed on Line 23. The user may enter data in the current field, overwriting its

Figure 31.6. Error handling during established connection.

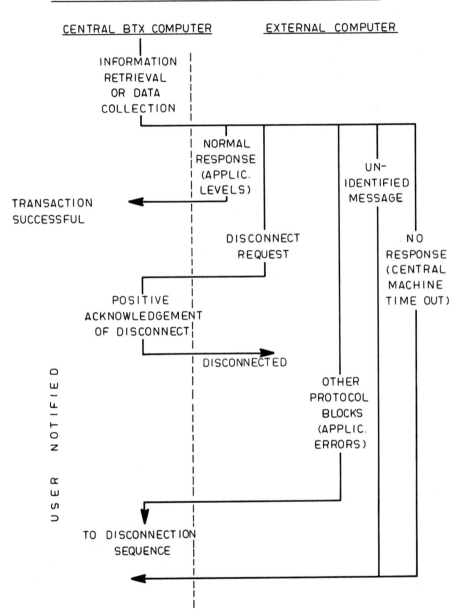

initial value character by character. Input to the field is terminated when the field is full or when the user enters the specified terminating character. The cursor is then moved to the first character position of the next unprotected field and the next prompt message is output on Line 23.

All prompt frames except the last must be completely filled with information. If necessary, a prompt message may be divided between two successive prompt frames. At certain points in the execution of the data collection function, sequences of actions are invoked on the external computer interface. The sequences are described in terms of central computer steps taken and the minimum necessary complementary actions by the external machine.

Lessons from the Market Trial

The participants in the German videotex implementation, for technical and market evaluation purposes, represented different groups of the total population. As in the Berlin test, the choice was fairly free, left to the individual consumer. The following characteristics have been noted:

> Persons with higher education tend to join videotex, while those of lower education tend to abstain.

> The same is true of persons in qualified professional and managerial positions, while workers and employees of lower professional levels are underrepresented.

> In comparison with the total population in the trial area, participants in the Bildschirmtext test have a higher household income and have a better-defined interest in information handling of all sorts.

For instance, more than 50 percent of the households receive professional magazines. Also, households joining Bildschirmtext on their own initiative are well-equipped with entertainment electronics. Some 61 percent of the participating households have two or more TV sets, and 29 percent have a videorecorder. Such households will most likely be the first to join the general implementation of videotex.

Let's now look at the structure of the information providers (IP) population.

Roughly one-third of IP in the sample are publishing houses and advertising agencies. Half of all pages in the viewdatabase are occupied by this economic group. Among the other economic sectors are trade firms with about 12 percent of all IPs and banks and insurance companies with 10 percent.

Typical media structures have been "Closed User Group," "General Information Service," and "Open Videotex Service".

A Closed User Group typically characterizes internal company information exchanges, such as headquarters with factories and sales offices. General information services have been provided by publishers and advertising firms. An open videotex service is offered by an IP to its clientele (an example is home banking).

Usage statistics are quite important. On average, for households in the Düsseldorf/Neuss area, the length of the Bildschirmtext connection is about 35 minutes per week. This is average, but the spread is great. In research done in this area, nearly a third of the participants admitted that they did not use Bildschirmtext during a four-week period, but there have been participants who used it for about 7 hours per week.

Participants commented that, as far as household usage is concerned, videotex is to them an additional information source, complementing existing media which could be substituted by Bildschirmtext. News, special advice, plays, entertainment, and jokes are among the favored choices in this class.

Since the general implementation of Bildschirmtext is best received by persons with high knowledge and a good information absorption level, such persons will use the service more than persons with a lower information capability. Thus, Bildschirmtext may increase the knowledge gap between the "information elite" and the rather disadvantaged sectors of the population.

In conclusion, videotex is part and parcel of developments in information technology. Though, in principle, everybody, every organization, and every public institution can participate as an IP or end user, only the better-qualified will be able to derive benefits and put to practical use the obtained results.

32
Retail Banking Through Videotex

Retail banking through videotex has been implemented both in the United States and in Germany. In developing retail products for consumers, the First Bank System of Minneapolis built its own network. To the contrary, the Bank of America chose the strategy of a joint development with *Times-Mirror* of Los Angeles. The latter example is that of a third-party system currently tested by the world's largest financial institution for banking purposes that is also able to provide stock market quotations and electronic shopping.

One drawback of such a system is that banks cannot always tailor the service for a specific audience, as did the First Bank System for farmers. Management also worries about relinquishing control to the third party, fearing that customers will eventually identify the service with the information or computer network instead of the bank. This is one of the reasons why, in its test marketing in Palos Verdes and Pasadena, the Bank of America takes every care to uniquely identify its home banking service with the bank's logo.

Generally, the marketplace is divided between public and private. The public market sells as a utility, whether this concerns:

central computer hardware,

PC and terminals,

basic videotex software,

gateways into different operating environments, or

networking and its implementation.

437

Whether a private or public offering, videotex will employ many personal computers. A microprocessor-based system is the best and easiest way to handle videotex, though this has not yet been implemented in the two case studies we will be considering.

Subscriber Agreement at the First Bank System

In May 1982, the First Bank System of Minneapolis initiated videotex services to 200 farmers and 20 small businesses. The bank has found farmers willing to pay for home banking (HB) but reluctant to pay for such items as electronic shopping and news, which are free on television or in store catalogues. Yet, management believes that in the longer run home banking will be supplemented by other services.

The videotex service, called FirstHand, was developed by the bank to suit farmers. It offers typical (HB) services as well as commodities prices, production information, and weather and agriculture news. There is no signature recognition capability associated to it and no PC implementation at the customer site. A dedicated video terminal is being employed but is not microprocessor-supported.

First Bank acts as systems operator of the entire offering—not just banking. A contract is signed with information providers and customers (subscribers) outlining services being supported as well as the liability of the bank and other parties.

First Bank has a written subscriber agreement to guarantee both the financial institution and the consumer of services to be provided. It also constitutes a reference point in case of litigation. It is therefore quite important to follow the highlights of such accord at First Bank as it may be repeated in a similar form by other HB institutions.

The subscriber is first informed that his name will be held confidentially and not given to any IP. The bank will, however, make subscriber names available for promotional mailings by FirstHand information providers only, to be coordinated by an independent direct mail firm.

The subscriber is also told that, as a totally new service, this is a test and is slated to end at a predetermined date (in this case, October 31, 1982). Should the project continue beyond the stated deadline, a new agreement will be issued. The consumer is given the right to discontinue the service at any time. Because of the uniqueness of the trial, he may receive inquiries from the press as to his opinion of the service. He is under no obligation to give out information or answer questions, but it is informally understood he will be welcome to do so.

Since FirstHand operated in a test environment, the bank reserved the right of adding to and/or modifying what appears on the system during the course of the experiment. The financial institution also reserved the right to remove the terminal from a customer's home at any time for any reason, the terminal being property of the bank. The consumer was further cautioned that, as a participant, he is responsible for any goods or services purchased through the use of FirstHand videotex and for payment of said products or services. However, during the initial phase of the project (May through July 1982) the system was offered without a monthly charge in exchange for comments and usage of the service.

Beginning July 1982, a user fee was established to access the system. The consumer was notified a minimum of 30 days in advance of this charge, but he was under no obligation to continue with the service beyond the installation of the user fee.

Quite importantly, the user was notified that the service was provided on an *as is, as available* basis. Information appearing on the screen was to be up-to-date and accurate to the best of the bank's ability and that of the IPs; however, the consumer was held responsible for implementing sufficient procedures and checkpoints to satisfy his requirements for accuracy of the information input and output.

In exchange for such a written agreement, the bank and its information providers assured the consumer of the following on-line access to vital data:

1. *Weather*: Current weather conditions, mid-range forecasts, 30-to-60-day outlooks, and historical weather patterns over local, regional, national and international areas; also an analysis of what the weather trends means for his area.
2. *Markets*: Information was projected to include cash and future prices (updated every 15 minutes); market trends and analysis, outlooks for particular crops, a guide to hedging.
3. *Banking and financial data*: Videotex assured home access to the consumer's First Bank accounts. He could transfer funds, make balance inquiries, pay bills. FirstHand also gave him current statistics and trends; bank prime rates; savings rates; T-bill rates; accounting and recordkeeping; tax tips; loan amortization and lease/purchase models; depreciation schedules; and financial planning advice.
4. *Classified ads and auction information*. This included the latest local classified ads and information on nearby equipment auctions.
5. *Crops*: Soil conditions, production tips, information from the latest scientific reports and publications, and yield estimations.
6. *Agricultural news highlights*: Up-to-the-minute worldwide agricultural news and headlines and Department of Agriculture briefings.

The rationale for such offerings has, of course, been that modern agribusiness is a highly competitive industry. To keep pace, farmers need current information. From First Bank's standpoint, the object was to make FirstHand an integral part of the consumer's life in terms of:

Family and personal finances, providing on-line information on deposits and loans, and trust planning. As with all HB systems, the user can transfer funds between accounts or inquire about his current checking and savings balances.

Shopping: The consumer can get information from major retailers on sales and specials using his FirstHand terminal to make purchases and other transactions with local and regional stores, restaurant or concert reservations, orders from catalogues. He can also read restaurant reviews.

Community information: Getting a complete list of community and entertainment events, phone numbers and hours of operation on his FirstHand screen.

News, weather, and sports: The latest local, regional, national and international news and weather, as well as sports scores, standings and schedules.

Contributors to the system were the bank itself but also a number of information providers, among them:

1. Agridata Resources, a firm contributing marketing and business advice to farmers in America for over 16 years, publishing *Farm Futures* magazine, *Top Farmer Intelligence Newsletter*, and *Top Farmer Market Insight*.
2. B. Dalton Bookseller. Its contribution included the weekly Top Ten Bestsellers, book reviews, special requests, new arrivals or books of local interest, with ordering made easy through the Videotex terminal.
3. Dayton's. This IP's contribution permitted browsing through weekly sales items, new arrivals, and advertised specials from the Dayton's department store in Fargo.
4. *Forum of Fargo-Moorhead, Valley City Times Record, Wahpeton-Breckenridge Daily News*, with international, national, regional and local news, weather and sports provided by the hometown newspaper.
5. North Dakota State University. The University particularly contributed farm production tips and techniques.

The IP's included local retailers providing merchandise and advertised sale items. In this, as in all preceding references, if the consumer found something he wanted he could order it right from his terminal.

Among the criteria used for the selected population, age was not the most important (typically, users are 20 to 55 years old). However, the selection of the 200 users preferred men rather than women, stressed higher income brackets, promoted potential users with university education, but did not take into consideration the type of crop the farmer grew.

Quite importantly, the experiment kept careful statistics by terminal: hours of usage, time on, number of sessions, types of questions. This is valuable data for tuning the videotex service and in keeping it flexible for future growth.

Placing Emphasis on Marketing

The First Bank System did not move from brick and mortar branch offices directly into videotex. It already had a fairly large network of 180 automated teller machines (ATM) scattered over four states. In a fifth State, Wisconsin, it participated in the TYME network, a shared ATM utility. Most of its ATM were on-line.

(When ATM came along in the early 1970s, it was thought they would revolutionize the payment and settlement systems. ATM looked like one of the new technologies from which we would benefit dramatically, but results were rather disappointing. While the break-even point stood between 2,500 and 3,000 transactions per month, the effective number of transactions per machine ran around 300 per month or less. The ATM could hardly be considered significant until banks revised the way they "sold" the service. Only after imaginative new approaches were adopted in marketing the ATM service did the volume of activity in these machines increase, reaching 3,000 or 4,000 transactions per month per machine. When one realizes that a human teller can do about 3,500 per month, the ATM begins to take on some meaning.)

The more the planners studied the more they began to see emerging patterns. It became apparent that the bank was not going to deal with the marketplace in one total mass. Different market segments have different needs, and a bank's ability to deal with the individual characteristics of these different segments becomes most important.

FBS targeted its research specifically toward the agricultural community, and the market research which followed helped establish these criteria:

1. *The type of service.* It was established that videotex should include more than just on-line banking.
2. *Low cost.* Low cost became absolutely essential, and management spent a fair amount of time defining what low cost meant.
3. *User-friendly.* The challenges were underlined by the nonspecialist user, the topology (spread out over thousands of miles), and the need to keep it easy for all concerned.
4. *Information enrichment.* Just supplying information into the home was not enough, doing something with the information was important. So, a two-way transactional capability was implemented.
5. *An integrated system approach.* The bank did not want to buy one piece of equipment from this manufacturer, another piece of equipment from that manufacturer, a third one from still another. It had to be a compatible, integrated system.

Once management defined the criteria, it searched for a technology—and also looked into another vital component: markets. This defined the information to be provided.

Farmers want spot and future prices, trends, forecasts, and analyses by type of commodity. They also want farm management with recordkeeping capabilities. The farmer/rancher wants to put information into the computer and store it until he needs it again. Travel information, health information, and personal data can all be put on the screen very simply. The same is true of HB and financial services.

First Bank's experience unearthed interesting findings, such as that a national newspaper had no appeal to local videotex users. The most important data videotex can provide is *local* data.

Another interesting finding concerned pricing. When the service is built up, there may be no need to charge the subscriber. If the system is structured correctly, it will pay for itself. The information providers pay for: page creation, storage, and transaction costs, and gain in exchange direct customer contact. As for the bank, a senior executive said, "We are in a position now to practically define any market we want to."

Project management was not costly. In the critical planning months— November 1980 to March 1982—two to three people worked on the project. This number increased to 10 from March to November 1982, plus some outside programming effort.

In the broader sense, the following lessons were learned from the First Bank experience:

1. The customer is not afraid of technology.

The 200 participants displayed a willingness to use the product.

2. Once the service is established, there will be several revenue streams.

Typically, there are split among the IP, the bank, and the subscriber.

3. The product offered to the consumer is really the content—not the technology.

The technology is the carrier of the content, but not the end goal. The end product must be market-oriented—based on customer reactions. So, research should first be done to ascertain customer desires, and *then* the database can be effectively designed.

4. From the start, provide the understructure necessary to train the customer.

Remember, the end user is no computer expert and the system is made for him. The average consumer is, in a way, afraid of the computer when the station is complicated, and complication leads to fear.

In terms of planning the service, one of the original queries was how much to train the customer. The experience has shown that a 15-minute talk in a demo center makes him able to open the terminal, install it and *go*. The customer also gets a little folder which shows how to plug in the machine and turn it on. The bank's central staff does not interfere with the end user.

The Database and the Network

Figure 32.1 presents the basic components of the First Bank System's videotex network. The central processor is installed at the bank's premises in Minneapolis. Two machines are available: one for development, the other for production. The consumer communicates with the latter.

During the experiment, the production machine supported 40 ports serving the 200 consumers and 20 firms. No fixed ratio was established between the needed

Figure 32.1. First bank system's videotex network.

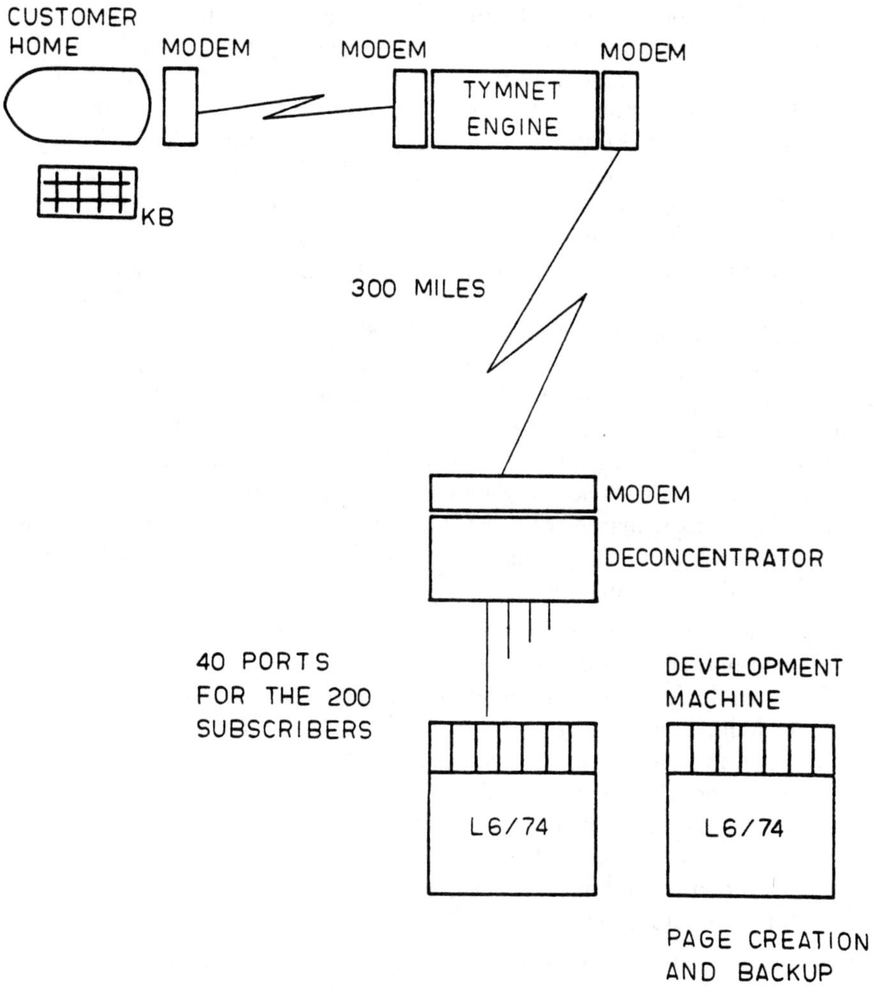

CUSTOMER
HOME   MODEM   MODEM   MODEM

TYMNET
ENGINE

KB

300 MILES

MODEM

DECONCENTRATOR

40 PORTS
FOR THE 200
SUBSCRIBERS

DEVELOPMENT
MACHINE

L6/74

L6/74

PAGE CREATION
AND BACKUP

ports for a given number of users, though one source suggested 1:30. (It is, however, true that users forgetting their connection is open can close the others.)

The development machine is necessary for page creation and backup to assure the end user with fresh and detailed information. The consumer's interests—markets, weather, local news—are the first choice, and *then* comes banking and merchandising.

The information developers pick up data by area of interest and provide it interactively as steady show, catalogue entries. The database is accessed in two modes: menu and keyword. Database design and update has particularly underlined the need for people who are creative and also have technical knowledge. The same

First Bank development group works with the IP and helps them with their applications.

The work is done on-line. The three newspapers, for instance, located at remote sites in an equal number of municipalities participate as IPs through word processing terminals. The WP are their means for controlling the content of the pages offered to the consumer. However, contrary to other Videotex systems, there are no closed user groups (CUG), with the exception of the Bank itself and Penney's.

The system supports other types of protection levels. Every terminal has an ID chip in it, a unique number; this must match the terminal file. A PIN (personal identification number) number is provided (the account number is not necessary). There is no magnetic stripe usage at the terminal level, but First Bank is testing a "smart" card.

Some headquarter stations have a chip card reader on an experimental basis. Interestingly enough, the chip in card usage came into play when market research demonstrated that some of the farmers had a fear regarding security: "You mean I'm going to open a telephone line from my home to a computer in Minneapolis, 300 miles away, and then I'm going to pull that information back into my home again? Anyone can tap into the line and get all of my information."

So, First Bank management decided to see if the smart card solves this problem, starting with those subscribers who identified themselves as having this problem. This card will do three things:

1. It has the PIN number which provides better security for entering the system than normal PIN authorization procedures.
2. When the farmer uses his smart card, the communication line is scrambled, including any message that runs from the terminal to the computer 300 miles away and back. Only the card chip can unscramble it.
3. Every monetary transaction that occurs on the system will be reported on the smart card. The farmer has a record of each transaction by date, type of transaction, and amount. If he wants to look at what he has done, he can put the smart card in the terminal and the information will be displayed on the screen from the chip.

Interestingly enough, the card being used is the regular First Bank Card, the normal proprietary card with the magnetic stripe on the back, but with a chip imbedded in it, programmed to perform the above three functions.

First Bank's original database offered 700 pages for agrimarkets, 700 pages for newspaper items, and some 30 pages for order entry by Penney's. The menu is now organized around the information provider, the way the information element is selected. This facilitates communication, but there is no automatic debit for marketing/selling. Hence, there is yet no checking on balance and debiting of the bank account. (Other HB networks provide that service.) However, the retail banking mechanism offers current account (DDA), savings, and loan operations, all of which represent more than 25 percent of the total videotex activity. Other financial services include discount brokers and insurance services.

Videotex Payments by the Bank of America

The Bank of America chose to work on a videotex experiment with the Los Angeles *Times-Mirror*, and both looked to AT&T to come up with a black box attachment which could incorporate modem/input/decoder for less than $500, including total message encryption. The current solution adopted for the test was expensive. The dedicated video, keyboard, and black box cost $2,300, and by this token the expense was higher than a home PC solution.

The explicit goal is to enlarge the rate of services without augmenting the risk. A senior executive phrased it this way: "The biggest exposure is not in the payment of bills, since there are limits to amounts, but in 'kiting'—the transfer of payments."

With the dual objective of enlarging services while controlling risks, Bank of America's plans range from HB to the Convenience Banking Center in Silicon Valley. It also includes POS, check verification, new advanced ATM concepts, and video communications. The magnetic stripe card rather than the chip card is being used.

The *Times-Mirror* experiment supports 80,000 pages, 2,000 of them run by the Bank of America. Among other information providers are newspapers, restaurants, theaters, and grocery stores.

The gateway is an X.25 protocol to an IBM mainframe. In 1983, an integration with home TV was made possible by changing the adapter. A keen emphasis is being placed on videographics for the consumer. In the future, the bank projects freeze frame implementation and the integration of full-motion video.

Alphageometric graphics have been selected as being superior to alphamosaic. The current system supports 6 colors and 6 gray scales, but this is transient. The Bank of America will adopt the new AT&T standard (PLP) with 64 colors.

The customer working with Versatel (Bank of America's HB tradename) can:

make payments from his bill-paying checking account to payees: merchants, financial institutions, utilities and so on

stop payment on a bill he has requested to be paid on a future date

transfer funds between certain of his Bank of America accounts

view a daily summary of his checking account activity

add to or update the information the bank has relating to his HB service, such as the name of the companies he wants to make payments to.

To join the service, the consumer needs to sign the Versatel Home Banking Agreement and the *Times-Mirror* Trial Participant Agreement as well. Thereafter, he receives a personal Passcode which he will use in combination with the number on his Versatel card each time he uses the HB service.

As long as he keeps his Passcode secret, no one else will be able to use his home banking service. To keep it safe, the customer is invited to keep his Passcode separate from the material he uses with his videotex services. If he believes someone has discovered his Passcode and may use it without his permission, he should contact the bank immediately.

Beyond the stated HB services, the Bank of America offers the following to Videotex participants: personal finance information and advice; income tax questions and answers; a guide to checking and savings plans; maps and lists of Bank of America branch locations; maps and lists of Versateller Automated Teller Machine locations; information about using and sending money abroad; travel tips; and currency exchange rates. The consumer can review on-line daily balances of his Bank of America checking, savings, MasterCard, and BankAmericard VISA accounts.

There are no special fees for using Versatel during the trial. The participating client will pay the same for HB transactions as he used to pay for checking, savings, and credit card transactions. The minimum balance requirements on his checking account also remains the same.

For each on-line transaction, Versatel confirms and gives the transaction number. Many customers review electronic payments (utilities and so on) over the 30-day period the records are kept.

Bank of America is also designing a new system for foreign exchange trading. It is based on the IBM PC and the Nestar local area network. Gateways will integrate everything into packet assembly—personal files, information exchanges, telexes, and Reuters reports.

PART SIX

Software Prerogatives

33

Communications Software

Computer and data communications systems are combinations of subsystems made to work together by software, which allows users to control the components of the system. Control must necessarily be appropriate to a particular environment. The requirements follow the environmental and operational perspectives. For instance, a priority structure calls for a provision relative to resource allocation.

Usually a data communications system encompasses many tasks. Task-to-task switching *must* be accomplished, calling forth a rational approach to server programs.

Routines handle the characteristics of each individual service component. Figure 33.1 identifies five classes of prerequisites: overall performance, communications control, terminal control, network control, and network operations. The last two are the object of the network architecture; the first two, of the system architecture. Terminal control concerns both types.

The software-implemented communication functions include the following:

Storage and forwarding of data

Routing

Switch monitoring

Flow control

Congestion control

Error detection and correction

Response handling

Security control

Interrupt

449

Figure 33.1
Software functions for data communications

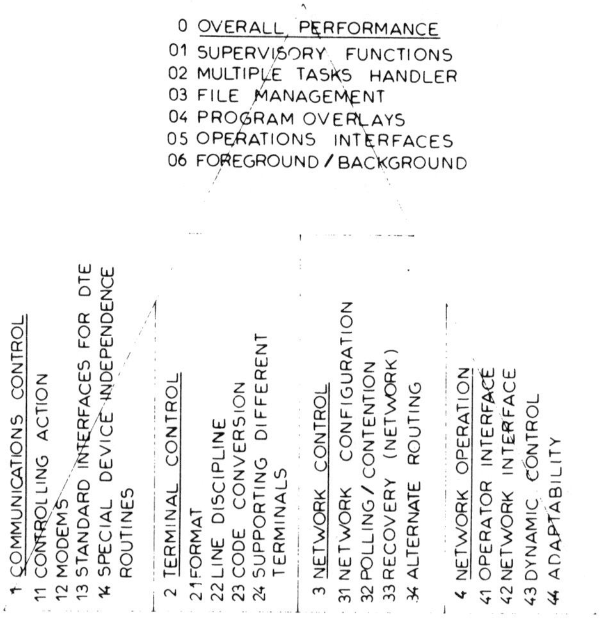

0 OVERALL PERFORMANCE
01 SUPERVISORY FUNCTIONS
02 MULTIPLE TASKS HANDLER
03 FILE MANAGEMENT
04 PROGRAM OVERLAYS
05 OPERATIONS INTERFACES
06 FOREGROUND / BACKGROUND

1 COMMUNICATIONS CONTROL
11 CONTROLLING ACTION
12 MODEMS
13 STANDARD INTERFACES FOR DTE
14 SPECIAL DEVICE INDEPENDENCE ROUTINES

2 TERMINAL CONTROL
21 FORMAT
22 LINE DISCIPLINE
23 CODE CONVERSION
24 SUPPORTING DIFFERENT TERMINALS

3 NETWORK CONTROL
31 NETWORK CONFIGURATION
32 POLLING / CONTENTION
33 RECOVERY (NETWORK)
34 ALTERNATE ROUTING

4 NETWORK OPERATION
41 OPERATOR INTERFACE
42 NETWORK INTERFACE
43 DYNAMIC CONTROL
44 ADAPTABILITY

Terminal handling

Information display

Line concentrating

Statistical calculations

Customer billing

The network functions must be first defined and then documented (Figure 33.2). The structure of the network, its topology, the projected usage, the operating environment, all influence to a considerable extent the goal and mechanics of software implementation.

Like any other logical support, communications software must be thoroughly tested. Not having proper program and system tests and the tracing of hardware, software, and data errors can be disastrous. A good rule is this: test the software often for "bugs" and establish a maintenance and stand-by policy. We shall examine the details in this chapter.

Figure 33.2
Network functions

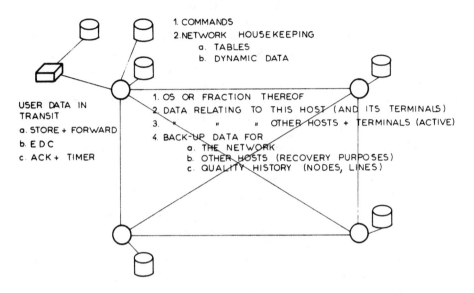

1. COMMANDS
2. NETWORK   HOUSEKEEPING
   a. TABLES
   b. DYNAMIC DATA

1. OS OR FRACTION   THEREOF
2. DATA RELATING TO THIS HOST (AND ITS TERMINALS)
3.   "   "   "   OTHER HOSTS + TERMINALS (ACTIVE)
4. BACK-UP DATA FOR
   a. THE NETWORK
   b. OTHER HOSTS (RECOVERY PURPOSES)
   c. QUALITY HISTORY (NODES, LINES)

USER DATA IN
TRANSIT
a. STORE + FORWARD
b. E D C
c. ACK + TIMER

Developing the Software

The software for a data communications system aims at an efficient management of the hardware resources. In an interactive environment this means a service responsive simultaneously to many users. The prerequisites of the service are security for each user's resources, systematic job rotation, program-loading and storage, and interfaces with a variety of peripherals.

The user's tasks must be protected against alteration and destruction. The size of the memory must be decided upon (sometimes during the initialization dialogue); it varies according to the user's need. Every effort should be directed toward security.

A network's resources may be shared among multiple users by means of an interrupt-driven, time-slice facility. Interrupt packets may be transmitted by the network before all the other packets awaiting transmission and delivered to a DTE even when it is not accepting data packets. Interrupt packets contain neither send nor receive sequence numbers. They handle interrupt conditions, which are signaled between DTEs without being subject to the flow control imposed on data packets. The acceptance of an interrupt, however, must be confirmed before a second interrupt is allowed to cross the DTE. Algorithmic solutions will control the status of a process awaiting input or output.

When interrupts occur, an interrupt handler mechanism, activated by a clock, gains control, and then a procedure is followed that is peculiar to a given communications system—that is specially designed for it, in fact. The handling of interrupts is an example of how the software of a data communications system serves to structure that system. Software controls the interrelationships among hardware components, for example, by ensuring the potential communication path between two terminal devices or between a terminal and a host.

The software itself may be regarded as a system and its structure discussed in terms of the programming language used to construct it. The hardware may be regarded as having a static structure; programmed activity would have a dynamic structure. The static structure discloses the kind of faults that might exist in a system and the provisions that have been made for dealing with them. The dynamic structure, which is equally important, deals with the effects of these faults and how, or whether, the system will tolerate them and continue to function. The activity of a data communications system may be visualized in terms of many different structures, depending on one's point of view.

One basic, well-established concept of the dynamic structure of a system's activity is the process. Of vital concern is sequence or flow control in process structuring, namely, the creation, existence, and deletion of a process.

In choosing to regard a system (or its activity) as a collection of components, and to concentrate on their interrelationships while ignoring their inner details, we deliberately consider a particular abstraction of the total system. We usually identify a set of levels of abstraction, each of which might relate to the whole system or just a part. The importance of levels of abstraction is that they enable us to cope with the combinational complexity that would otherwise be involved in a data communications system constructed from a very large number of very basic components. When we define interrelationships among subsystems, we impose a structure on a system and describe how components are constructed, related to one another, and functioning.

Figure 33.3 illustrates the complexity of topology. Other things being equal, the number of connections increases exponentially as a function of the number of components, and although the physical links in a network will not be $n(n - 1)/2$ for n nodes (chiefly for reasons of economics), they will surely be greater than n to take advantage of the possibility of alternate paths. The effect on the routing algorithm is evident.

Software Functions

Special software is needed for the user of a computer and data communications system, and it may be divided broadly into two parts, communications and data bases. The functions relative to communications are the following:

1. Convert high-level statements (of the user programs) into packets to be handled by the transmission subsystem.
2. Divide messages into packets when they are too long for the transmission subsystems and reassemble them after transmission.

Figure 33.3

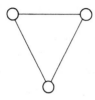

$$\frac{n(n-1)}{2}$$ NUMBER OF CONNECTIONS

n = NUMBER OF COMPONENTS

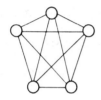

3. Make sure that the network protocols are observed.
4. Use numbers for maintaining correct sequences.
5. Perform local flow control.
6. Queue the messages and handle priority.
7. Correlate requests and responses to the requests.
8. Determine where a requested function is performed, or where requested data reside.
9. Establish communications with the node that owns or controls the requested functions or data.
10. Obtain that node's agreement to establish a session.
11. Exchange information about protocols to be used in the communication.
12. Check that the communicating nodes have the resources, such as buffering, necessary for the communication.

The primary components of the communications software necessary at the level of the local host or intelligent DTE are driver and handler routines for computer communications, line control and task-scheduling routines, and a message-handling and routing package. Other necessary software are programs for logging message traffic, routines for operator communications, a switchover and switchback capability of the communications lines in case of processor failure, applications support and interface routines, link-handling routines, and a switchover–switchback capability for disc storage in case of processor failure.

Some of the software will be oriented to the data base, as we shall see; still other software will concern transaction-processing support routines and a significant amount of system support and utility programs. Such software would supplement the subsystems for communications support and for particular applications. The following are necessary for network control and monitoring: program and data file transfer, data file display, and peripheral status display. Further software functions are gathering of system statistics, display of system statistics, system resource enabling and disabling operations, remote resource enabling and disabling, system maintenance support, system access control, system initialization. All of these are the *components of data communications systems.* To recapitulate:

The *operating system* controls the overall functions of the processor.

The *applications system* consists of the programs that act on the messages received and transmitted.

The *communications control system* assembles the message received and passes it to the applications system; it also prepares messages for transmission and passes them to the line handler.

The *line handler* provides the primary control of messages to and from the communication line.

The *supporting services* are for maintenance, reliability, and supervision, such as loopback testing and downline loading.

We shall speak of these fairly sophisticated functions shortly, but let us first look at two issues that condition the degree of complexity one may be willing to adopt.

The first issue is the state of the art (Figure 33.4). The ability to utilize more and more complex systems grows with experience, both our own and that of others. Another factor is our goal, which may be expressed according to whether or not to use human intervention at the local site and how large a network to use. Ideally, one would not wish human intervention, because it costs money and produces errors, but the software then becomes that much more complex. That is why most software developments in data communications started with the prerequisite of a pushbutton approach. Moreover, they are slowly moving away from it through other methods (downline loading, upline dumping, and loopback programs), as we shall see.

The second issue, relating to what we can do in the way of automatic pushbutton functions, is the capacity of the memory of the machine (Figure 33.5). Memory is not as expensive as it was in the early 1970s, but is is not yet as inexpensive as it will be in the early 1980s. A microcomputer typically has a capacity of 64, 128, 256, or 512 KB. Three things share the memory: operating systems, applications programs, and terminals. An on-line terminal generally needs 1 kilobyte or more of central memory which helps determine how many terminals a minicomputer can manage. Usually, at the minicomputer level, an operating system consumes between 35 and 50 percent of central memory—an efficient one at that. Another 25 to 30 percent is taken by the applications programming (often squeezed in with overlays). The balance is taken by the terminals. The limits of communications software are set.

Figure 33.4

Levels of complexity: one machine, two machines (automatic modem), *n* machines, and *m* persons, where *m* > *n*.

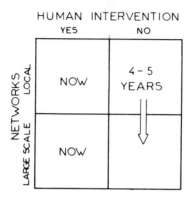

Figure 33.5

Capacity of memory machine. (**KB**, kilobytes; **MB**, megabytes; **T**, terminal)

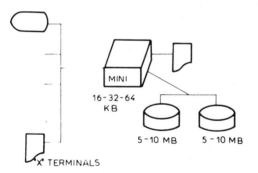

OS	8	12	24 KB
AP	4	8	24 KB
TERMINALS (1 KB/T)	4	10	16 KB
	16	32	64 KB

Downline Loading, Upline Dumping, and Loopback

Downline loading, or memory deposit, is an integral part of a distributed operating system. It is the process by which a host or a DTE sends to other DTEs. It makes no difference whether it handles applications programs, data, other operating systems sections, or a maintenance discipline. At the user level, we speak of three types of configuration: one with no disc, one with no people, and one with no disc and no people (Figure 33.6).

Downline loading has no disc. It is the typical job of a concentrator and requires a minimal memory at the periphery. (The term comes from the practice of hierarchical systems.) Downline loading helps the communications linkage to test for failures and actuate other devices from remote locations.

Figure 33.6

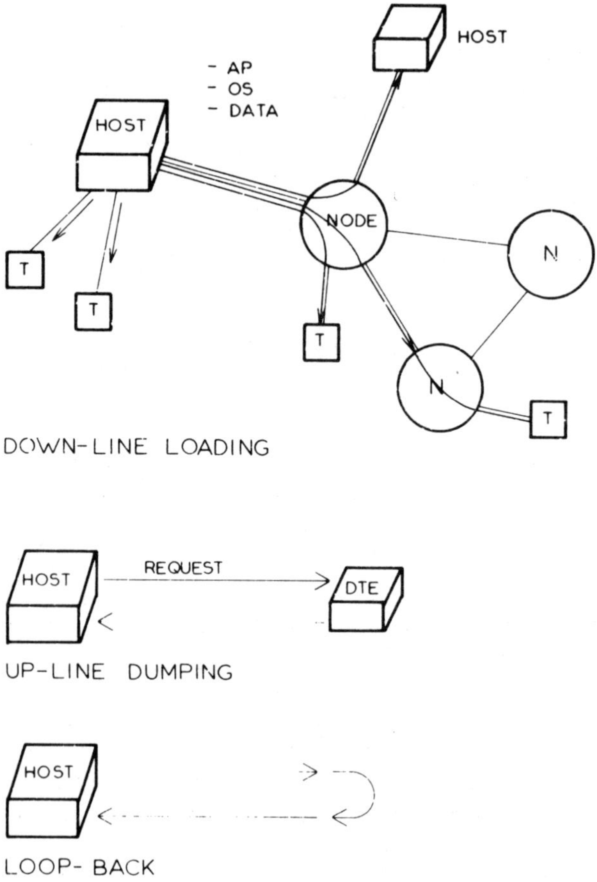

DOWN-LINE LOADING

UP-LINE DUMPING

LOOP- BACK

Upline dumping, or memory examination, involves no people. It is a means by which the host checks the operations and errors of other DTEs. A host may request from a DTE a particular file, or send information, ask to have it treated by a terminal, and then examine whether or not it has been altered.

Loop testing, or loopback, involves neither people nor discs. It tests the data link. It allows one to send a pattern down the loop, turn it around, and examine the results

Software should make it possible to push a button at one terminal and reload a program at another terminal or host computer (where what is stored is available). At the on-line maintenance level such facilities allow network element-testing, data communications tests, and connection-tracing. To test network elements one must decide whether to work from the *host outward* (toward the front end, concentrators, terminals) or from the *terminal inward* (toward the concentrators, front ends, hosts). The decision has evidently an effect on the design and development of the software.

Database Support

A key software feature is the file management system that supports large data bases and runs them. This may involve automatic record-packing, efficient record-level directories, and the security and integrity of the file.

System software should make it easy to add new applications to the system. It must support maintenance of the data base and handle it separately from the applications, easing the job of the applications programs and making access to the data base applications independent. Figure 33.7 diagrams the general flow of events. Ten steps are indicated, starting with the request posed by the user program and ending with the provision of called-for data elements. (A full description is beyond the scope of this book.)

The following are twenty functions of the software for a data base. Inevitably, most of them are also the functions of communications systems.

1. Insert and interpret end-of-record and end-of-file indicators.
2. Transfer whole files, portions of files, records, or fields, as instructed.
3. Perform end-to-end acknowledgments and checking of sequence numbers.
4. Operate batch controls.
5. Perform checkpoint restart.
6. Recover from a reset or restart condition in the transmission subsystem (if possible, without breaking the session).
7. Proceed with code conversion, as necessary, if several codes are used in the system.
8. Insert and delete files.
9. Search a file or dispersed files to find information according to keys.
10. Determine where needed data are located.

Figure 33.7

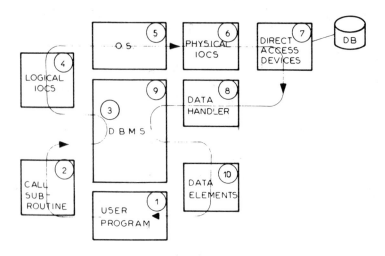

11. Put the data in a format for output (to fill a screen, print tables, and so on).
12. Add appendages to data, such as page headers, dates, page numbers, and repeated information.
13. Provide for information enrichment on the basis of applications (e.g., substitute coded identification numbers for repetitively used screens, formats, messages, or segments of text).
14. Operate menu selection of other dialogues in which only the results of the dialogue are transmitted.
15. Conduct data base interrogation dialogue that assists an operator of a terminal in formulating queries.
16. Permit users to refer to virtual terminals and also to use other virtual machines.
17. Permit programmers to use *logical* input–output capabilities and to map them to the characteristics of specific machines.
18. Provide users with access to more than one transmission subsystem.
19. Perform routines for reducing the number of bits transmitted (compaction, zero, blank suppression).
20. Make the operation of the transmission subsystem transparent to the user.

System Design Requirements

Let us put the foregoing into some perspective. Communications software must exercise extensive supervision over the controlling and monitoring of the message-handling functions of the system. Controlling and monitoring include such items as command, response, alarms, reporting, repair of message, and retrieval of data. In any and every computer and communications network the programs manage all supervisory functions (reports, retrievals, table change). In general, one or more DTEs may be designated for the system's supervisory position.

The communications software must provide for:

Routing control

Skip poll, resume poll

Hold and release

Test

Message repair

Inquiry and response

Commands may be classified as of five major types: line control, message queues, routing, privileged control, and alarm monitoring, which are described below.

Line control controls the flow of traffic for a line. It may give the command to skip polling or resume polling for a terminal, a line, or all lines, or it may control output by commanding a hold or reset for a terminal, a line, or all lines, or it may monitor the commands for the purpose of acquiring statistics.

Message queues control the queues of messages handled by the network.

Routing monitors the routing facilities. The routing-control commands can establish alternate routing, duplicate delivery, and routing report requests.

Privileged control is for such tasks as direct retrieval, fault isolation, and configuration control. Configuration control involves host-interface configuration, processor or disc file configuration, and system thresholds and reporting intervals.

Alarm monitoring handles messages that alert the system to some abnormality or status change. The following are the conditions usually subject to alarm monitoring:

Line failure and line restoration

Front-end failure and restoration

Terminal failure (polling or addressing) and restoration

Excessive number of messages in queue

Buffer availability

Secondary storage failure

Switchover and recovery execution or failure

Abnormalities in host processor

Alarms generated by the system may apply to a center or to the network. The first type of alarm concerns the computer-center hardware and software, such as disc files, magnetic tape units, system control, monitoring functions, overlay failures, and so on. The second type concerns the lines, terminals, line termination units, and so forth.

Alarm messages usually include the time of occurrence and some text identifying the terminal or line affected and describing the abnormal condition.

The reports give information about traffic and equipment relating to lines, terminals, and processors. They may be displayed so as to alert personnel of the conditions. They are of three kinds:

Generated and delivered to the reports position when requested by the supervisor.

Generated periodically, at predetermined time intervals, and delivered automatically to the reports position.

Generated periodically, at predetermined time intervals, and delivered automatically to terminals.

The Implementation Schedule

Finally, by way of conclusion, Table 33.1 presents an implementation schedule for data communications. Two words of caution are necessary.

First, this schedule, largely derived from data communications experience, does not reflect anything nearly as complex as the computer and data communications systems described in this book. Rather, the table is drawn from a condition of transition, from an on-line environment operating for a number of years but under stress because of rapidly multiplying requirements (number of terminals and applications) to a structure much expanded and more sophisticated. An example is the change from a mainframe (and primitive front end) to a specialized communications hardware and software able to handle, say, over a thousand terminals and a network control center. Typically, such a conversion would leave intact the original centralized nature of the network.

Second, the schedule in Table 33.1 presupposes a project team with able specialists under a competent leader. Skill and knowledge are the basic ingredients of a good data communications system. It is not enough, though; just as vital is to put in charge a person who knows how to get work done, respect timetables, and draw out of everyone the best each can contribute. Projects do not conform to timetables of their own. They must be managed with an iron hand and with persistence, against odds, and through the labyrinths of company politics.

Table 33.1
Implementation Schedule for Data Communications

		Weeks*	
Function	*Men*	*Unit*	*Sum*
1. Functional description (preliminary proposal)	4	4	4
2. Complete specifications	4	8 to 12	16
3. System design (startup)		1	17

4. Hardware list
    Order hardware
    Programmer training
    Installation site
		4 to 7	24

5. Interface specifications (if data communications must interface to other systems)		1	25

6. Software development
    Modules
    Design reviews
		16 to 20
		(in parallel)
			45

7. Acceptance test procedure		1	46

8. Acceptance test
    Hardware
    Software
    Communications
    Personnel
		10 to 12	58

9. Installation check-out
    On-site tests
    Functional acceptance
    Test transactions
    Total transactions
		2 to 3	61

10. Editorial documentation (review)		2	63
11. Complete acceptance test		3 to 4	67
12. Pilot branch sites		8 (1½ years)	75

*Time scales are not linear. If 2 to 3 men work on this project, it may take roughly 8 calendar months.

34

A Network
Operating System

In a computer and data communications network, the architecture provides the logical design, the engineering the physical design, and the software the dynamics of the situation.

How is the network going to work? The logical design includes three groups of commands. The first is the basic commands, which create communications paths and use them to pass data. The second is file-sharing, which permits a DTE to transfer or request data from a file or input–output in another DTE. The third is program control, which allows a DTE to start and stop the execution of programs on another DTE of the network.

The preparation of a processor for on-line operation involves some primary tasks, such as initialization (loading with no record of prior activity), checkpoint (the process of recording dynamic status), and recovery (reinitializing, using the last recorded status).

Recovery is the fundamental activity allowing the system to resume operations. Initialization consists of loading the resident software in the central memory and then extending control to the applications initialization process. This includes the functions of (1) establishing the disc configuration and setting up the disc addresses, (2) initializing the data–channel interfaces and the disc-file control parameters, (3) reading the overlays (for instance, from tape to disc) and building the overlay index, (4) loading the tables resident in high-speed memory, (5) modifying the tables for initial conditions, and (6) handling the queue tables and building the checkpoint directory.

During operation the status of the system will be checkpointed periodically for use by the recovery functions in restoring the system after outage of a processor. Included in this operation is the handling of queue pointers for all store-and-forward status traffic, status indicators for circuits and terminals, circuit, line, and terminal tables as an alternate routing requirement and, generally, system-configuration data.

The preparatory work pinpoints the need of a description of the data to be checkpointed. The same is true in defining checkpoint frequencies and identifying the calls to be issued for checkpoint functions.

Finally, as in checkpointing, the basic recovery procedures must be part of the network's operating system, such as reading checkpoint data and setting up operating parameters.

The application recovery routines are dumping other functions, ceasing polling of procedures, transmitting notice of canceled messages, retransmitting all messages in process at time of failure, sending go-ahead messages to nonpolled DTEs, and restoring status, message queue, and log locations.

An organization such as that described is, to a considerable degree, influenced by the structure and the functions of computer-oriented operating systems. Today network operating systems are added into maxicomputer operating systems (particularly transaction-oriented routines and front-end applications), and not vice versa. This is an unfortunate result of past practice and of present technology.

Architectural extensions are built on the primitives of the operating system. The reasons are historical. New developments might make networking functions the primitives for the operating system, and then the operating system will be less dependent on location; the scheduler will reside in one computer, the "swapper" in another, while the device drivers will be scattered. But even today the aim is to have no human intervention and no pushbuttons, the host doing all the work down line, as we have stated.

Designing a Basic Operating System

The design of an operating system to serve a given architecture must above all consider and reflect the goals of the network. A network for data communications may be used in three different ways: for remote communications, the primary aim being to move information from one place to another, for the sharing of resources (resources in one system shared by other systems), and for distributed information, involving autonomous computers designated for problem handling by a division of labor or immediate access or specialization.

Remote communication, the first above, involves a large number of terminals geographically distributed but connected in an arbitrary topology. The network would have relatively few large host computers. Other things being equal, this is the least complex operating system of the three network types.

Because the major computer-run resource today is the data base, resource-sharing networks will be using data base systems to make their contents locally available, but fundamentally such networks will be centralized storage systems, transferring files or information elements to remote line printers or plotters.

Distributed information systems will incorporate the foregoing characteristics but use advanced technology to reduce cost by distributing the storage of the user locations and sharing low-usage devices among many systems, providing for both local and remote access to files in a widely distributed data base system.

The software of a communications network will not only see that the right things happen at the right time but also effect "reconciliation." Since the different elements are not homogeneous, the codes and speeds, the terminal classifications, the data bases, their sizes, and their use must be made to work together very precisely by means of logical functions.

The location and availability of terminal and host, the support of data input (rates, codes), the loading projections, and the protocol requirements are factors in the design of software. Others relate to growth: percentage utilization, future throughput projections, and physical limitations of sites or hosts

Figure 34.1 presents a comprehensive view of the requirements, outlining the component parts and their interrelationships.

At the level of the host, the low or high speeds of the circuits, the hardware or software front-ending, and the line discipline should determine the operating system's software. The requirements of terminals will revolve around low or high speed, hardware or software implementation, and interactive or batch operation.

Figure 34.1

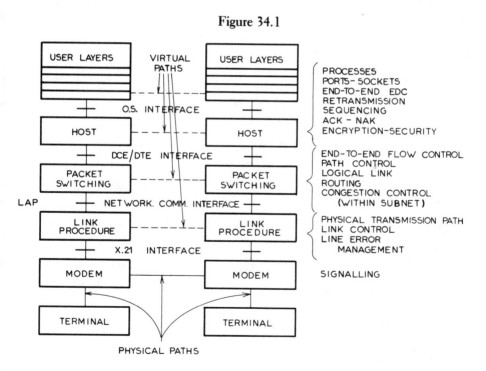

These have an impact on what is necessary in terms of buffering, switching and routing, line discipline, turnaround, and delay.

Switching and routing must be studied, not only in regard to the function involved, but also in regard to destination control overhead, monitoring needs, and methods of error control. This leads to diagnostic services, namely the signals required, the procedures used, and the control overhead.

The throughput requirements call for an examination of turnaround, of delay in forwarding, of multiplexing, and of buffering. The network startup has its prerequisites, many of which are related to software; such is the case of testing and of the procedures needed for access.

Operations must steadily be upgraded, expanded, and maintained. Distributed systems versus centralized ones, diagnostic services, and reconfiguration are other examples of needed support. It is, therefore, no wonder that the development of a comprehensive software able to cover these services entails a large investment. Table 34.1 outlines the investments made by one leading computer manufacturer in developing his network architecture.

The Software "Constant"

The sources of heterogeneity within a computer network and among communicating networks are the hardware components, the operating systems, and the applications software. In the typical case heterogeneity of components results both from the use of hardware devices and software routines and from the variety of functions the network is expected to perform.

Table 34.1
Investment in Network Architecture by a Manufacturer

	Completion (%)	Design (man-years)	Observations
Data link	95	10	X.25 capability in process of development
Routing	80 ⎫	30	Design follows layered solutions
Virtual circuit	90 ⎭		
File access	70 to 80	15	Intermediate step to data base management system
Data base management system	0		
Information enrichment	0		

Signal carriers (wires and microwave links) work with different transmission techniques, and the irresponsible switching by telephone companies among differing media throws the user's network out of synchronization. At the local site processors and terminals of different architecture and word sizes work differently, and within the same processor some devices, such as line printers, may be variously controlled. Interfaces at devices and signal carriers with different operating modes call for extraordinary ingenuity from designers of software. We should not forget that operating systems themselves may be multiprogrammed, real time, batch, or time sharing. The users' applications also are various. Programs employ networks in various ways, and file systems and data bases have different access modes and formats.

All this underlines the need to have, somewhere, a sort of constant, a base of reference. The constant would be to software what the "bus" is to hardware (Figure 34.2). With this concept, within a network the software might be treated as if it were a hardware component, without undergoing revamping (portability).

A careful study of what should be included in the operating system and how it should be distributed is the only way to give the software modules the advantages of interfacing. Functions should be defined a priori, among them network control, routing of message traffic, system protection, logging and journaling, queueing, tag build, and output services. Each would be divided into subfunctions. For example, system protection would include control of memory and disc overwriting, monitoring of failures, and management of traffic flow, and network control would include configuration management, communication line monitoring, message queueing, assignments of centralized privileges, isolation testing, and table changes.

The exact divisions and subdivisions are a matter of choice; no two systems are alike, but a functional orientation would permit a subdivision of the elements such that they might be organized in the concentric manner shown in Figure 34.3. Here use is made of the fact that complex problems may be divided into specialized parts, the latter organized in a modular fashion; then together the modules constitute the components of the network operating system. This organization is a valid framework within which portions of a complex problem may be defined and solved. The solutions may be tested independently and later integrated into the total system.

Let us always remember that the problem with software is testing: we must spend at least half of our time and effort in testing the product. The task is simplified if we deal in small lots. Let us not forget, either, that a new, "announced" architecture fundamentally represents a software adjunct to existing processors and operating systems, extending the systems by offering new network capabilities. The modular aspect is, therefore, once again underlined.

Properly designed, software makes networks and users share resources, communicate between distributed components, and move data to and from terminals, at the same time and fairly efficiently Properly designed, the operating system is

Figure 34.2
The information-passing mechanism inside the computer.

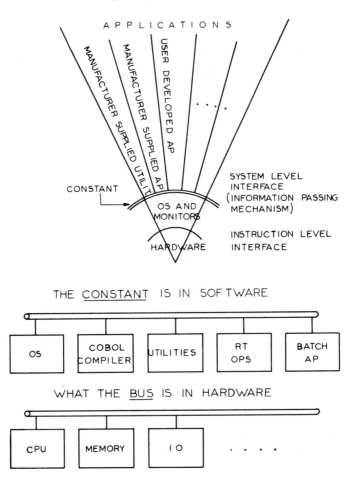

optimized with respect to the three network types we have outlined. All-inclusive designs will not work; they are cumbersome, ineffective, and resource-consuming.

Operating Systems Background

Regarding the fundamentals, the basic purpose of any operating system is to get a group of people to share a complex computer installation in so efficient a manner as to maximize the throughput of their jobs.

In the early days of computing the entire installation was, practically speaking, allocated to one user at a time; most of the operations were manual, and operating

Figure 34.3

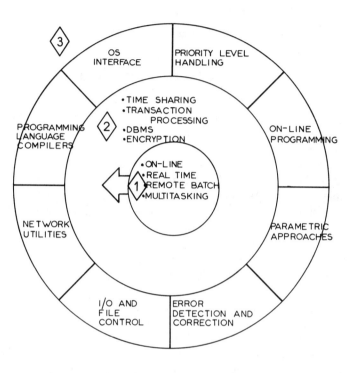

system software was almost nonexistent. Standard software was therefore introduced to facilitate the complicated task of operating the different units of a modern
computer.

For example, input–output control systems (IOCS) were devised, the backbone
of which is (usually) a parametric processor program that drives the input–output
system or, more precisely, the input–output control routines. It manages the
device drivers, to which are connected the peripheral's controllers, each controller
running one or more devices. Supervisors (monitors) interrupt processing, job
scheduling, and resource allocation. This software constitutes the basis of any
modern operating system, and the user communicates with it by means of an
appropriate command language.

At this point we might note the historical development of operating systems,
because we can detect a cycle repeating itself:

> 1953, Computers and maxicomputers
>
> 1957, Input–output control systems
>
> 1964, Disc and other operating systems
>
> 1971, Minicomputers
>
> 1978, Microcomputers and microminicomputers

That is, we started with computers, then added something, and now are back to computers again. Of course, the minicomputer of the 1970s is much more powerful than the maxicomputer of the 1950s and the micros of the 1980s are equally more powerful than those minis.

Now let us see what was slowly added a quarter of a century ago to put some muscle onto the bare bones of computer systems.

First there was a single processor operating system. Then this started to become a fairly complex software system incorporating many different components. Components performing supervisory functions were frequently used. Prompt execution was essential. It was therefore expedient that some of them reside in the memory at all times. Less critical components were stored on discs so as not to overload the memory and were reloaded into the memory only when needed. Reloading was, and still is, done by erasing other programs no longer needed for current operations; this is known as "swapping." With this background we can return to Figure 34.3 and look at the process inside the first circle, the core of the procedure, which includes on-line, real time, remote batch, and multitasking.

A rational organization in successive layers is shown in Figure 34.4. Seven layers are identified, beginning with the most basic, the selector. The selector scans the stack of waiting tasks to find a process to start; then it transfers control to the starter. If there is a priority condition, a given task is pushed to the background and later moved to the foreground. The starter also will reestablish the process in its previous state.

Device availability routines, as the term implies, signal the availability of a device, or a data base element, to the next process awaiting access to that resource. Some associated routines are needed, such as an input–output interrupt handler, which converts interrupts from the various devices into device availability routines. Device drivers contain the supervisor and input–output programs. The supervisor is composed of subroutines, such as terminal control, including enabling or disabling, echoing, changing terminal priorities, and switching, as the need arises. The so-called DB locks in an operation associated with the data base. A file or information element in the data base might be locked by a previous user, in which case routines must see to it that a new request is added to the queue of jobs awaiting access to the data base. Conversely, as a user exits a data base, the file or information element must be unlocked.

Depending on system configuration, the input–output drivers may include storage media, line printers, and terminals. The handling of buffers is important, one solution being circular buffers filled from one end and emptied from the other; this permits the input–output handler a greater flexibility.

Figure 34.4

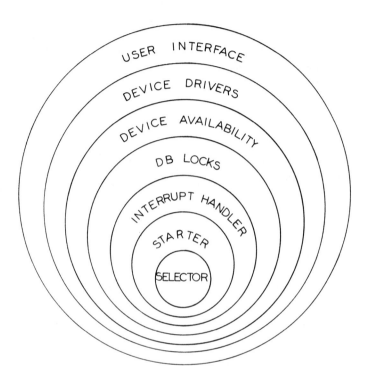

Within the user interface the generation of reports is another vital consideration, since a great number of reports is necessary (soft copy rather than hard copy)
to provide information on traffic and equipment status, relating to line, terminal,
and processor activities. Reports that alert personnel to abnormal conditions or
exceptions may be generated and delivered to the reports position when requested
by the supervisor, or they may be generated periodically at predetermined intervals
of time. A still better option is to generate reports periodically at predetermined
time intervals and deliver them automatically to terminals; even information identifying no abnormal conditions is vital information.

The main parts of a typical communications-oriented operating system are the
subject of the following sections.

Executive Functions

Executive functions are responsible for maintaining real-time supervision of the
system environment. This assignment basically involves input–output control,

including input–output scheduling, data transfers and device manipulation, job and task scheduling and the necessary resource allocation and event-monitoring, system communication along with input–output queue maintenance and console support.

Other functions under executive control are hardware error detection, recovery from errors, program error control, support for timing services, and the needed accounting procedures.

System Management

System management is primarily concerned with the nonreal-time parts of the operating system. These support both system and applications programs by means of such services as system generation, program maintenance, including that of libraries and catalogues, compiler interfaces, support utilities.

Within system management linkage must pass information between subroutines and furnish a common entry point. For instance, when a user task requests a service provided by the supervisor, a command must be issued containing an identification code designating the function to be performed. The handler should save the state of the task at the time of the call, examine the code, and select the proper system routine to be called. Returning the system routine to the handler restores the user to the precall state, adding the returned values. These are the basic parts of a multiuser time-sharing system.

Data Maintenance

Data maintenance allows the user to access and process data in general. It involves file management facilities, including directories, and user control of the access. Under data management are also the input–output support for different access modes (sequential, index sequential, random, and so on) and for file record, the facilities for file display and copy, and peripheral-device support, including format conversion and data editing.

Terminal Handling

Terminal subsystems typically offer a particular service to the user and support a restricted class of terminals. The diversity of terminal subsystems is illustrated if we consider at least three different solutions for an equal number of requirements. The first is time-sharing programs which usually are general-purpose, primarily supporting low-speed typewriter terminals in a line-at-a-time mode. The second is job entry programs, which can be conversational approaches that support high-speed locally buffered cathode ray tube terminals in a full-face interaction mode.

The third is remote job entry subsystems, which support binary synchronous communication to remote batch terminals.

A ring of special software thus interfaces between the basic operating system and the functional programs, which are goal oriented (Figure 34.5). The latter are the link between the operating system's special software and the applications programming. A special software functional interface may, for instance, submit job streams to either of two batch-processing subsystems and return the printer or display streams to the user terminal.

Evidently, the design of future operating systems would be influenced by the requirements of networking, but today the design of entirely new operating systems for widely used central processing units is rather uncommon.

The system design problem faced by computer centers is to provide network service on a machine running an immense and amorphous collection of system software. This makes it necessary to add a network interface to an existing operating system by superimposing rather than by integrating, which would be more rational (Figure 34.6). Consequently, software development can be a major undertaking, particularly for operating systems on large-scale central processing units. That is why it is useful to examine the requirements of interfacing to existing systems.

Figure 34.5

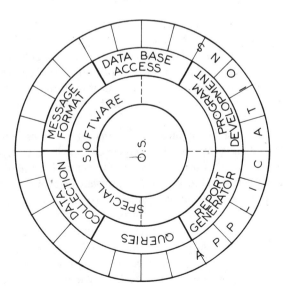

Figure 34.6

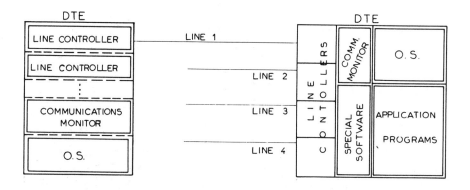

The Server System

Classic operating system functions, device routines (for instance, input–output operations), and channel interfaces (to pheripherals) constitute the traditional architecture of an on-line-oriented operating system (Figure 34.7). Now, they must be modified to achieve a high degree of true parallelism.

The object of server systems is service to the user. Terminal subsystems are of particular interest; they serve users communicating with terminals as input–output devices.

Present-day input–output devices controlled by a particular subsystem are logically and exclusively allocated to it by the operating system. The nondynamic nature of this so-called device binding, however, is a reflection of the batch-processing orientation of the past, and this approach is now changing. The problem now is to provide for interprocess communication through a standard, robust, and flexible mechanism that affords the explicit definition of interfaces and protocols.

New approaches must be applied to the management of terminals, input–output units, central memory, and the "processes" in the central memory.

The server, or terminal support software, must match symbolic port names, provide multichannel and bidirectional data transfer, disconnect signaling when a process dies, and queue and handle requests. To do so, it must run local resources, reach into remote resources, and provide what is necessary in terms of data communications facilities (Figure 34.8). Running local resources means to supervise control, file access, input–output with the network and, eventually, ensure encryption. Many facilities are needed. In the last chapter we spoke of two operating requirements, which are practically unknown with batch operations,

Figure 34.7

THE TRADITIONAL ARCHITECTURE IS :

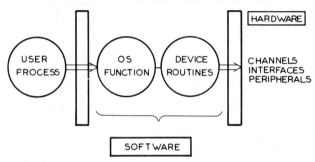

NOW NETWORK REQUIREMENTS CALL FOR
A "SERVER" SOLUTION TO THE "OS" FUNCTION

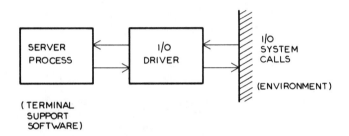

even with the classic star or hierarchical real time: downline loading, needed for unattended operations, and upline dumping (and loopback), necessary for network-testing and maintenance. Further faculties may be required. Debugging cross-net software is difficult; conventional "static" debugging techniques are totally inadequate. The ability to plant break-points and probe interactively is absolutely essential.

Users of Arpanet have pointed out the difficulty of trouble-shooting the cause of failure in a production system. Many subsystems and at least two host central processing units are involved in the simplest Arpanet operations.

To be able to ask the user–server system to report its status, we must implement not only novel but also intelligent solutions. Figure 34.9 shows three steps in the evolution of a local software solution to meet this end.

From the unintelligent and basically hardware terminal we progressed to an intelligent solution with a network interface, but it has not been enough. Hence the new server systems with the facilities of data base and message-handling, with a number of network interfaces, specialized by function, and with encryption.

Figure 34.8
(QL = query language)

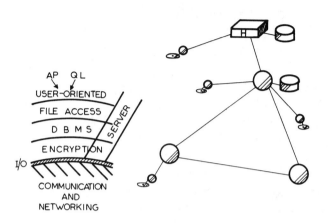

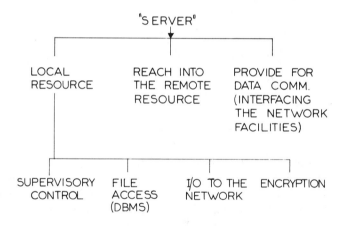

Figure 34.9

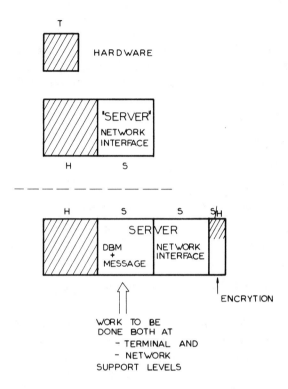

Distributed Operating Systems

It is not uncommon to see resident operating system routines occupy more than a quarter of the main memory, in this way reducing the amount available to users. In small systems the percentage can be even greater as, for instance, 8 kilobytes out of 16. Moreover, because of the numerous supervisory functions they have to perform, a substantial portion of the total execution time is spent by those routines doing administrative work, while the user tasks wait for the connection point to become available. Lastly, no matter how carefully programmed such systems are, they inevitably will be error-prone because of their size alone.

A number of changes and innovations in hardware as well as operating system structure and design have therefore been suggested, with the objective of improving overall performance by solving some of the problems outlined above. With respect to software we have, most notably, the development of synchronization primitives at low levels (semaphores) as well as at higher ones (mailboxes and monitors). Whether centralized or distributed, the operating system must ensure that the flow of information through the system is flexible and efficient.

Within the local site the distributed operating system contrasts with a traditional one, in which all input–output transfer involves the central memory. It makes feasible the exchange of data directly between any two peripheral units.

Furthermore, distributed operating system functions, or at least a good many of them, can be converted to firmware. Among the reasons for converting to software-plus-hardware solutions are:

Legal (patents, investment protection)

Marketing competition

New developments in products

Faster operations (e.g., compiler capability)

Standardization (normalization of certain operations)

Making feasible the breakup of the operating system and its distribution throughout the network

Reducing error probability

Providing efficient interfaces for device independence

The system must also make it easier to connect peripheral units from different manufacturers to a given computer (equipment independence).

Once a microcomputer can be programmed to handle a particular device, the actual interfacing problems are greatly reduced, as long as information transfers between system components are governed by a standard communications protocol.

35

Error Detection and Correction

To perform failure recovery correctly and achieve a good data communications environment, we must deal very precisely with the control of errors. Several methods exist for error control over a communications facility. A practical and effective approach incorporates into the design an error-detection mechanism and provides for retransmission by the sender.

Retransmission can be initiated by a negative acknowledgment (NAK) from the destination when it does not receive the intended message, or a positive acknowledgment (ACK) from the destination when it does receive the message and a time-out device in the origin. This way, the origin will retransmit the message when it fails to receive a positive acknowledgment and the time has run out. The second solution is preferred with the newer protocols such as the bit-oriented XDLC.

The designer must decide how much error control the system should offer. A little? Error detection by means of check bits? A complete error control service? The last sounds preferable, but is costly.

As a general rule, if an error is detected, the message is erroneous. However, not detecting an error does not necessarily mean that the message is correct.

Communications errors within an XDLC operation may be classified into three categories.

Network detectable, but not recoverable. These result in virtual circuit resets.

Network detectable, and recoverable. There is no reason to disconnect or repeat.

Network undetectable (and unrecoverable) due to a deficiency of the error-control algorithm.

To ensure that the receiver did indeed receive the information sent by the transmitter, a cyclical redundancy check is performed. The transmitter calculates the frame check sequence (FCS) upon the address, control, and information fields as they are about to be transmitted. The resulting FCS is included in the transmitted frame. The destination, using the same polynominal controls, compares the result with the FCS sent from the origin. If these results are equal, the frame is accepted. If not, it is rejected.

The error control procedure must strike a balance between cost and security. Retransmission also means cost, delay, lower throughput, and greater possibility of error. With packet switching, error control costs on the average ± 1 percent of the budget.

Errors and the System View

Errors will never be really corrected—much less eliminated—until a systems view is taken of the data communications problem. A system is a set of components with their interrelationships designed to provide a specified service. The components of the system can themselves be systems. Their interrelationships comprise the algorithm of the system. To complicate matters a little, there is no requirement that a component provides service to a single system; it may be a component of several distinct systems.

The algorithm is specific to each system individually. The error-free behavior of a system is a measure of the success by which it conforms to predefined specifications. Without such specifications nothing may be said about errors, their causes, and the way to control them. Deviation of a system from its specified behavior is called a failure. Various formal measures related to an error-free performance may be based on the actual or predicted incidence of errors and their consequences.

Systems are never completely error free; they meet their specifications for a fraction of time. Errors may be permanent or transient, and the extent of the damage which they produce may be localized or distributed. Since errors are items of information, error detection and error recovery are issues that help ensure dependability. Errors are not extraneous and misdirected events, but an integral part of the process. Their importance is comparable to the other intended critical factors of a system.

A fault is not an error. It is something generic to the mechanical or algorithmic construction characterizing the system. Under some circumstances faults will cause the systems to assume an erroneous state. Furthermore, because the service provided by a system is related to one or more environments, fault-tolerant systems differ with respect to their behavior in the presence of a fault. If the aim is to continue to provide a fraction of the full performance and capabilities until the fault is removed, we speak of "fail-soft" solutions.

Error Reduction

No matter which DTE a user chooses, he wants to be sure that it can support a data control faculty. Errors may come from a simple, keying activity (e.g., errors made by the operator working on the keyboard), from the equipment itself (machine errors), from the transmission line (usually, noise*), or from other equipment communicating with this DTE.

A DTE must provide, through hardware or software, the needed controls to check and correct errors. Error detection had been performed by a variety of means, the two most popular being parity check and hash total.

Parity check is where an extra bit or byte, called a check digit, is added at the end of the message-carrying digits, and controlled against a pre-established algorithm. If to the number 12345 is added a check digit—say, odd/even type: $1 + 3 + 5 = 8$; $-2 + 4 = 6$, and $8 - 6 = 2$—then the number will be written 123452. The last digit, "2," is for control purposes. If the operator inputs by mistake 132452, the machine will do the above calculation, establish that 13245 does not correspond to the check digit "2," and signal an error.

Hash Total is simply a summation of the fields used for checking purposes which has no other meaning than to permit the receiver to check the numbers in a lot against it and accept or reject the lot as a whole. The hash total, or squaring control, is applicable to data entered in the numerical fields. Its object is to check if a list (block of data) has been input correctly by the operator, if an error in keying has been made, or if a figure has been lost in transmission. (The ability of a terminal to respond is generally known as visual input check. The possibility for checking the input data, as it is keyed, must be complemented by that of a feedback to the operator. This is usually carried out through the printing of the text itself or through its visualization.)

But these classic approaches, parity check and hash total, are obsolete for today's large-scale communications requirements. They imply high cost, significant redundancy, and low dependability because of compensating errors, while the noise in the transmission does not always last the length of one single bit. For these reasons, error control through polynomial error checks is much more efficient.

Unbuffered terminals, however, still need old parity checks. In fact, the best error control an unbuffered terminal can achieve is the detection of an error through some parity check. Buffered terminals can detect errors and call for retransmissions, but only if they know how to notify each other about errors and recognize the requests for retransmission. A protocol is required. Fault isolation becomes easier, too, since the protocol provides a means of identifying the source of errors.

Error control must involve control of field† length, detection of the omission of fields, and assurance of the total introduction of a field. These are applicable to data input, data transmission and the reception of messages. The utilization of terminals, which allows control of data in transmission, is of great importance in a data communications environment.

Key issues relate to format, that is, the way the data is organized and presented on hard copy or through visualization. Format controls may be obtained by means of software. Other cases are the following:

*Noise is any unwanted input.
†A set of one or more characters, not necessarily lying in the same word, which is treated as a whole; a unit of information.

Preventing an alphabetical field from invading a numerical zone (the assurance that in a numerical zone there are no alphabetical characters)

Determining whether a numerical zone should be subject to parity checks or hash totals

Verifying a functional sequence

Normalizing a zone (the word "normalizing" should be interpreted with reference to the operations which follow and their requirements, for instance, data transmission, handling by another computer)

Carrying out functions such as perforating, printing, read–write on cassette, and the like

Insertion or deletion of specific fields of data into the records stored in memory.

Control possibilities may exist at different levels of sophistication. Their presences make the terminals very different from one another, therefore constituting a parameter* which must be considered most carefully in a comparative analysis.

We must also consider the management of the output data, generally known as editing.† Editing is done mostly through software: for intelligent terminals it is done by their own programs and for other terminals it is done through commands transmitted on-line from a computer, minicomputer, or microcomputer. In either case, the aim is to formalize and direct the handling of data by editing the fields; injecting (or, alternatively, suppressing) blanks, zeros, punctuation signs; using service characters to structure the printed (or visualized) output; returning the carriage to the origin; controlling the paper feed (for instance, skipping or jumping lines); printing on different modules depending on the nature of the data; and varying the position of the printer on the printing lines.

A terminal that allows the aforementioned kinds of data management will be that much more useful to the person or organization faced with specific editing problems. On the other hand, such terminals are expensive.

An Integrated Approach to EDC

Error detection and correction, EDC, protocols are very important with transaction-oriented interactive environments and heavy data loads. Error messages must be generated for all machines, programs, operator errors, and operational information.

Error status and statistical data must be recorded in a dedicated storage device (for instance, a diskette), printed upon operator command via an "error retrieve" routine, or made available on video. Error recording and subsequent printed error history should be provided for the central processing unit, timers, input–output channels, and devices, storage devices, and operator stations.

---

*A quantity to which arbitrary values may be assigned; used in subroutines and generators to specify item size, decimal point, block arrangement, field length, sign position, etc.

†The arrangement of information; it may involve the deletion of unwanted data, the selection of pertinent data, the insertion of information prior to printing, zero suppression, etc.

Programmed diagnostic tools must be available to help in problem isolation. Users should be given extensive training, documentation, and hands-on experience in the application of diagnostics.

Error reduction presupposes concrete policies (and policing) to ensure that they are put into action. Error detection and retransmission techniques require automatic request for repetition, ARQ. This has become a standard error-recovery technique utilized for both half-duplex and full-duplex protocols.

To sum up, error recovery techniques should cover all information, not just the data part of a message. Messages may contain information pertaining to file organization, data type, format, record attributes, record length, size, device characteristics, or other data relevant to protection and characterization of the file systems involved. If a piece of data is important enough to communicate it, it is also important to protect it from errors.

The Cyclic Redundancy Check

The cyclic redundancy check (CRC) polynominal is a 16-bit check providing an undetected error rate less than $1 \times 10 - 12$ per bit. This is the basic error protection algorithm in packet switching.

The frame check sequence (FCS) field is a 16-bit cyclic redundancy check of all data in the XDLC frame except the opening and closing flag fields and any zero insertion. The transmitter performs the computation and sends the FCS field. The receiver performs the identical computation, discarding the frame if it is in error and does not advance its count. More precisely, the transmitter indicates its 16-bit trailer. The binary value of the trailer is calculated on the basis of a multiplication by x^{16}, then division by the generating polynominal, $x^{16} + x^{12} + x^5 + 1$. The integer content digits are ignored. The transmitter sends the complement of the resulting remainder value; high-order bits are transmitted first. The expected error performance is the detection of all odd numbers of errors in the frame and any error burst less than 16 bits in length. This is done in hardware because time for software handling is 16 milliseconds.

Other error-detection mechanisms are longitudinal redundancy check (LRC), a parity check applied to certain bit positions in every character in a block; vertical redundancy check (VRC), a parity check applied to all bit positions in one character; and data complement, a data verification technique employing one complement (inverted) check bit for every information bit.

Bit Error Rate

The most important performance criterion of a data transmission link is the measure of the quantity of errors the system introduces on the average, that is to say, how large the bit error rate, BER, or the probability of error, $P(e)$, is.

BER is the number of erroneous bits verified in a bit string. This defines the quality of transmission. Experimentally, the BER is measured and defined by the equation

$$\text{BER} \;=\; \frac{N}{N_t} \;=\; \frac{N_c}{B_{t_o}}$$

Where N_e = number of bit errors in a time interval t_o

 N_t = total number of transmitted bits in t_o

 B = bit error rate of the binary source

 t_o = measuring time interval, i.e., error counting time

BER is used to indicate the number of errors in the handling of bits given by a piece of equipment or transmission line. As a unit of measurement, it reflects the dependability of a communications link. For instance, in a given network 300 baud lines commit 1 bit error on 10,000 bits transmitted—hence, 10^{-4}BER; 1,200 baud lines commit 1 bit error on 1,000 bits transmitted—hence, 10^{-3}BER. For a random, stationary error-generation process and sufficiently long measurement interval t_o, the measured BER gives an estimate of the true $P(e)$.

As an example of the influence of environmental factors, for a given piece of equipment there is BER degradation due to temperature variations.* Temperature acts as an agent and affects degradation of circuits and the life cycle of the terminals.

The evaluation of probability of error, $P(e)$, of nonoperational (out of service) channels is a well-known measurement technique. Performance evaluation of such systems is done with a pseudo-random test signal sequence transmitted through the measured channel. The receiver computes the $P(e)$ by comparing the received bits with a stored replica of the transmitted bit pattern. The main problem associated with simple nonoperational BER measurements is that it is not feasible to evaluate the performance of an operating system carrying the unknown digital data stream of the customer.

Operation of an automatic phase-tracking system requires three main elements: a fast error monitor to detect the better channel (the pseudo-error monitor); an error-free data switch to select the better channel; and a means of maintaining the two paths in phase with each other to eliminate switching errors.

Let us see the features built for a data above voice, DAV, system used for multiplexing of voice and data. The pseudo-error detector provides an accurate estimate of the data system error rate at all times, and by operating on 1.5 megabits per second without adding or using any more bits is highly efficient and very rapid. Since it uses an error-multiplication technique, a predicted error rate of, say, 10^{-8} can be read out of the pseudo-error detector before errors have actually occurred in the main data path.

Apart from the normal built-in fault monitors, a means is necessary to determine if real data continuity is maintained throughout the system. This is

---

*The amount of level drift is about 1.5 decibels over the 0°C–50°C range, and is almost totally dependent on the performance degradation of the modulator/demodulator (data set).

achieved by monitoring the multiplex framing bits in the 1.5 megabits per second data stream. By employing techniques to avoid ambiguities in the reporting of loss of framing bits, a subtle failure may be rapidly pinpointed to a particular piece of equipment and the transmission of random, but totally false, data can be avoided.

Four methods exist for generating pseudo-error characteristics: shifted detection threshold, intersymbol interference enhancement, noise addition, and sampling phase offset. Practical conditions generally govern the choice of method.

Error Rate and the Dependability of Carriers

In-service and on-line monitoring may be achieved with test sequence interleaving, parity check coding, code violation detection, and pseudo-error detection.

Pseudo-error detection techniques remove both the shortcomings of long evaluation time and the requirements to interrupt data traffic of nonoperating systems. For pseudo-error detection a "secondary" decision device is connected in parallel with the main data path. This secondary path has intentionally degraded performance and its output sequence has an error rate much greater than the unknown error rate of the main receiver. This amplified error rate is obtained by taking the main receiver output data as a reference and counting the number of disagreements with respect to the secondary output data stream. Every disagreement is called pseudo-error.

The two most important elements in the performance of a pseudo-error detector are the ability to achieve a sufficient error multiplication factor and the capacity to reach a stable multiplication factor in the presence of nongaussian perturbations. A pseudo-error device must be tested to determine its ability to detect burst perturbation in the input signal to the phase shift key (PSK) modulator and demodulator. Such bursts (clusters of errors) may arise in certain nonideal transmission systems and include signal interruptions noise bursts, tone bursts, and a combination of these.

Since some of the possible solutions to one problem result in a degradation of capabilities available to solve the other problems, efficiency compensation, and error control must be studied to yield a useful compromise between performance and cost of the communication terminal (modem).

Current technology permits the following solutions: Noise found in telephone and, generally, communication channels tends to bring about clusters of errors. These bursts may be handled by an interleaving technique, which has the effect of splitting the bursts into isolated errors with many correct bits in between. The isolated errors are then easily handled, for example, by a simple current code.

Recurrent codes, also called convolutional codes, do not have a readily definable block structure. Check bits are periodically inserted and always depend on the same pattern as preceding information bits. With this scheme, mean time between errors is improved by two or three orders of magnitude with only modestly complex equipment.

We must stress the fact that current knowledge of the dependability of common carrier systems and facilities and of the techniques for modeling this reliability is far from satisfactory. Possible causes of system failure reside in switching systems, long- and short-haul carriers, along with probable causes of short-term and long-term outages.

The impact of common carrier reliability on computer communications systems depends on the type of system being contemplated. This impact is most critical on systems that rely heavily on stringent response times where occasional failures to obtain a response in a brief time period cannot be tolerated.

In data communications practice, private-line characteristics are relatively stable, impluse noise can be reduced, and line conditioning provides more nearly ideal frequency response. However, inexplicable anomalies can occur, for example, a private line exhibiting a variation in bit error rate of 2×10^{-5} to 3×10^{-7}. Probability distribution functions for line availability and duration of failures result in rule-of-thumb summaries. They indicate a wide variation in line availability from 99.9 to 10 percent. Many line failures are repaired in a few minutes, but some persist for hours. A guide for a line selected at random to transmit data at 2,400 bits per second indicates that bit errors will occur about every 40 seconds, failures lasting 1 minute will occur every day, and a 1-hour failure will occur each month.

Control of Errors on Voice-Grade Lines

In designing data systems for use on voiceband channels, the communication engineer faces the challenge of approaching maximum channel capacity as closely as possible, within reasonable economic bounds. The problem may be organized into three distinct tasks: devise an efficient signal design to match the channel characteristics, provide automatic "equalization" or compensation for signal distortion caused by the channel, and design error-control—a means for automatically correcting data errors caused by unavoidable bursts of noise.

There are two classes of errors, each handled with a different approach. The first group is relative to the communications discipline as a whole and the one to which protocols are particularly suited. Although error control has been the subject of many protocol solutions in the last decade, it is still handled by the computer and communications industry almost uniformly in a most simple, pragmatic way. The data stream is subdivided into blocks which are augmented with enough redundant bits to afford reliable error detection. Whether it finds an error or not, the receiving terminal automatically stops after every block and briefly becomes the transmitter, sending back a message either to acknowledge receipt (ACK) or to ask for a repeat for the block (NAK). Regardless of whether the line is four-wire or two-wire, transmission is always in one direction at a time.

There is, however, an alternative to this approach. High-speed transmission proceeds in one direction while the low-speed reverse channel conveys information about the accuracy of the received data, telling the transmitting terminal to stop and repeat one or more blocks of data when an error was detected. Such uses of reverse channels have turned out to be far fewer than envisioned, and half-duplex operation still is the more common mode.

With wideband possibilities now available, the simplicity of the half-duplex operation comes at the cost of efficiency—the continual interruption of data transmission. Efficiency will especially decline in cases of long propagation delays, for example, with earth satellite channels. In such cases, it is preferable to transmit data continuously, interrupting and retransmitting only when an error has actually been detected.

The second class of errors includes those which particularly concern the transmission facility and the technology behind it. In the case of analogue signals, one of the earliest methods for combating noise was the substitution of wide-swing frequency modulation (FM) for simple amplitude modulation (AM), but, generally speaking, there are two methods of correcting errors regarding the link facility itself: the reverse-acting method and the forward-acting method.

In the reverse-acting method, the receiver only detects the presence of errors and notifies the transmitter that certain data must be repeated. This method has two disadvantages: a reverse-direction channel is required, and the data flow must be interrupted while data are transmitted.

The reverse approach is commonly used with data processing systems in which virtually all errors must be corrected. Various coding structures have been found useful. In block code, check bits are usually inserted at the end of a block of data and are determined entirely by the data bits within that block; both encoding and decoding proceeds on a block-by-block basis. In recurrent code, check bits are inserted periodically, being determined by a certain grouping of preceding information bits stretched over the so-called constraint length. There are four check bits per constraint length, producing a four-field overlap among the information-bit groupings which determine the check bits.

Interleaving techniques applicable to either type of code, use crossword puzzle arrays to rearrange data for the purpose of coding and decoding. The data flows columnwise but is encoded and decoded rowwise. Although a cluster of errors may occupy an entire column, it would affect only one bit per row. Thus, use of a single error-correcting code is sufficient.

The forward-acting method inserts enough redundant bits in the data stream before it is transmitted to allow the receiver to detect and correct most transmission errors without any interruptions. Forward-acting error correction with sophisticated codes would be practiced only if reverse communication were not feasible, but cannot give as much protection as detection-retransmission, especially during extreme channel disturbances.

With either correcting method it is essential to have a continuous knowledge of the data system error rate. Without this knowledge, the condition of the system is unknown and performance degradations in a long-haul system become very difficult to locate. Techniques have been used where known bits are added to the data stream or where some of the bits in the data stream are fixed and monitored.

Testing the Network

It is appropriate to end this chapter with a few words on testing the network. Network tests are an integral part of error-free performance and must be designed in to the system at the start of the project. The failure modes must be pre-established, and failures studied as to their aftermaths.

To support reasonably error-free environments, the network housekeeping functions must include accumulation of error statistics, automatic trouble shooting, accumulation of test statistics and test results, bit error rate testing (including bit pattern generators), link testing, accumulation of recovery statistics, automatic alternative routing, and switching alternatives.

It should be possible for each node in the network to accumulate error statistics and participate in alternative routing. Furthermore, as terminals become increasingly intelligent and equipped with microcomputers, it should also be possible to participate in network diagnostics.

36

Journaling

Many particularly important questions in distributed information systems relate to the broad and vital area of data assurance. Elaborate procedures for guaranteeing data integrity can consume a large part of a system's time and resources.

Some questions about data assurance are the following:

What is the maximum load of transactions the system can support in the presence of a given rate of failure?

How will the response time vary as a function of the failure rate?

What proportion of system time will be taken up by recovering from failures or preparing checkpoints as opposed to useful transaction processing?

How should the journal be kept to ensure recovery security and protection and still be a cost-efficient proposition?

Control responsibility, logging procedures, tests, and performance control and balancing are among the activities necessary for a sound policy of recovery procedures.

The failure of a system occurs when that system does not meet its specifications. Recovery is the restoration of the data base after a failure to a state that is acceptable to the user. A failure may be due to a deficiency in the hardware or the software, which leads to erroneous systems operation and to the pollution of the data. Failure may occur in transmission lines, or may be the intentional or unintentional introduction of erroneous information which destroys the integrity of the information stored in the computers and communications network.

To minimize lost time, a system should operate in checkpoint, rollback-recovery, CRR, mode. A consistent and complete journal should also be kept for recovery and statistical purposes; Table 36.1 presents a basic form. The logging must include the last transaction in order to know "where" to restart, and the operations

Table 36.1 Sample Journal for Distributed Recovery and Restart

Control	Logging	Audit Trail per Transaction	Shadow Updates	Image Copying	Roll-backs	Check Points	OP Backout (local)	Systems Backout
Authentication								
Sequence								
Encryption								
Timing								
Quantity								

involved at time out which might have been incomplete, interrupted, or have affected other operations. These two elements regard the quality of the recovery process. There is also the element of speed of recovery, which influences the mean time of system interrupt, MTOSI.

The Journal Is the Means

Journaling retains in one or more storage media (tape, disc) copies of information that passed through the network, and/or was delivered to intended destinations. Networks must include journaling in one or more locations because of the ability to retransmit copies of information previously delivered and the need for restart and recovery. But the maintenance of journals presents logical and physical problems as well as security.

Distributed data assurance issues involve access rights, retrieval, additions, deletions, modifications, batch perspectives, on-line responsibilities, recovery mechanism, and protocol dependencies, plus a number of data base considerations, including questions relating to the data dictionary.

Each one of these issues may be divided into a number of concrete points; for instance, retrieval involves process access, process limits, authorization, isolation by distribution and destination point, query validation, and completion testing, as well as other issues relating to the retrieval mechanism per se, such as protocol sensitivity. Additions, deletions, and modifications call for such activities as logging, audit trail, effective performance in operations, and synchronization.

It is not enough simply to maintain a journal. Information elements (IE) in the journal, such as input statistics, sequence number within the input statistics, output station, send time, receipt time, etc., must be defined a priori. Care should be taken in the collection of every item intended to help identification and retrieval.

Figures 36.1 through 36.4 detail one approach to the establishment of good journaling procedures within a data communications environment. The journaling is divided into three functions: network, data base, and overall control. Each is broken down into component parts. Among themselves they outline the functions journaling should accomplish. (Operational statistics, a part of the control function, is further exemplified by exploding it into its component parts.)

We should guarantee efficient, automatic on-line application recovery from system crashes, power failures, resource interlock between transaction, and system transaction aborts. Application recovery means transactions are not lost or entered a second time for no reason. Other requirements are imposed by the on-line environment. Journaling must provide the data needed for recovery from media failure without reentry of transactions and without errors. But a whole precedural mechanism must be set up besides the journal.

Staging delays record updates until transactions are complete so they can always be aborted with records left intact.

Figure 36.1

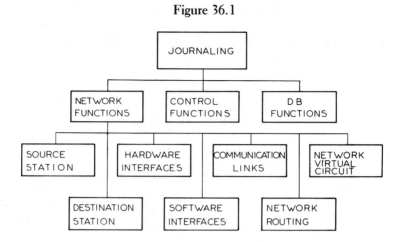

Record looking prevents simultaneous updates of records.

Security guards against unauthorized activity with user sign-ons, passwords, and identity codes.

We may also have user and terminal work classes that define what transactions are available to the user or the terminal. With distributed information systems, such grouping will usually be done at the minicomputer or work station level. But networks accept terminals of all kinds and must therefore provide the needed communications software at the user level and work class, without the prerequisite of a local intelligence.

Procedural Prerequisites

Network elements consider all information to be volatile. After a failure the software is reloaded with initial conditions, and hardware errors are cleared. Preparation of a processor for such operation involves three primary tasks: initialization—loading with no record of prior activity, checkpoint—recording dynamic status, and recovery—reinitialization using the last recorded status to resume operations. The loading of the basic software resident in the high-speed (central) memory is a responsibility of the operating system. Application-dependent functions are loaded by special software.

The requirements posed by these operations must be reflected in procedural steps to be followed in keeping the journal. Journaling is no random event, no dumping of transaction data irregardless of their importance. It is a concrete, deliberate policy followed to enhance recovery, security, and operating statistics. The journal entry must contain the (1) overhead data, which includes identification of source device (code), input sequence code, input time, message type code, output

Figure 36.2

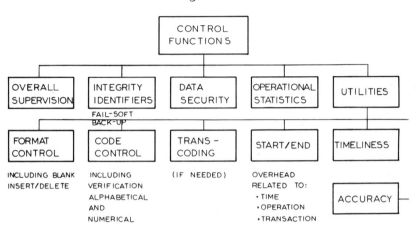

station code (destination), output sequence code, and output time, (some items, like time, may be inserted by the host processor), and (2) the message proper.

Whether centralized or decentralized, journaling has three basic purposes: storage of copies of information for reference and control, storage of intermediate data—when necessary—and retransmission, and the means of effecting restart–recovery following a failure. The journal may also be used for statistics and billing purposes.

With centralized processing, keep the journal on disc for the first and second day. Dump on tape the n-2 journals every two days, and store the tapes in a safe place for subsequent retrieval as needed.

Distributed recovery and restart are more demanding in terms of journaling requirements. They imply the use of a systems mechanism able to perform in an efficient and uninterrupted manner logging, audit trail, shadow updates, image copying, backups, checkpoints, and backouts. They also require precise management of activities such as synchronization of maintainability, protocol choices, procedural characteristics, data base organization, studied transaction sequence, user knowledge of system behavior, and timing and precision.

The existence of a network helps substantially in automating these activities since it is impractical to mount and dismount tapes, discs, cassettes, and floppy discs all the time. One of the first and most valuable applications Citibank put on the Citinet was the automatic handling of the logging and back-up copies.

Distributed Recovery and Restart

There are five levels of recovery and restart to be studied within the overall perspective of a distributed environment:

Figure 36.3

Much valuable data can be compiled from the data base journal, e.g., frequency by type of request, receiver, files addressed, stop action, author/ sender/stations, amounts handled, time in/out, recovery, etc.

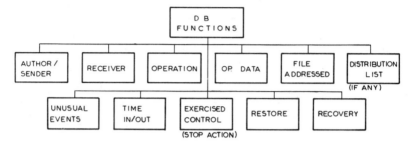

1. System recovery
2. Node recovery
3. Local process
4. Per transaction
5. Per data element (information element)

Recovery is a complex operation involving at least five procedural steps: system restart, reconfiguration (when needed), stabilization (restore), reload, and rerun. Recovery is also an expensive undertaking. Measured against the total system down time (TSDT), recovery represents, on the average, 36 percent of the TSDT.

Recovery is involved closely with the data base. The data base consists of a number of files. A file is a logical unit in the data base used to group data; an information element is the smallest logical component of a file. Recovery must reach all the way to this IE level. A recovery technique maintains data—at the IE or higher levels—to make restoration possible. It provides recovery assurance from any failure which does not affect the recovery data, the mechanisms used to maintain these data, and the techniques to restore the data in the data base.

Failures fall into two broad categories, depending on how they react to the recovery technique under examination: (1) failures with which a recovery technique can cope; these lead to a "crash" to be restored by that specific technique; (2) failures with which a recovery technique cannot cope. Such failures are called a "catastrophe," with respect to the recovery approach in question.

Every recovery mechanism is based on an understructure. This must ensure that the processes are not interfering with each other, that it is possible at any time to return a process to some previous and more acceptable state, and that it is feasible to prevent the use of created or updated information until it is known that the process will not have to be backed out. With DIS requirements are extended to controlling the process in the same or different nodes, preserving order while maintaining the structure of a distributed data base (DDB), saving results for subsequent audit to

Figure 36.4

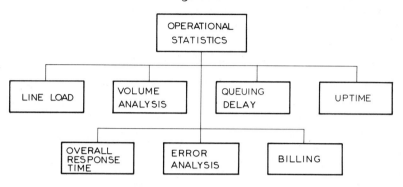

reduce the probability and significance of errors, providing repeatability of process results as required by most auditable applications.

Different types of recovery are possible for a data base:

Recovery to the correct state

Recovery to a checkpoint

Recovery to a predefined valid state (per se)

Recovery to a consistent state (within the environment)

Crash resistance

Crash resistance is provided if the normal algorithms of the system operate on the data in a manner that causes the system to always be in a correct state after certain failures. This obviates the need for the recovery techniques to cope with that class of failures by manipulating and maintaining crucial data during normal processes. Crash resistance restores states implicitly: (a) the recovery operation is "in-process" if the action was taken prior to a point of commitment, or is "post-process" if the action has been committed already. Both the in-process and the post-process recovery approaches are applications related. But if the results of processing are not yet committed, and allowance has been made only for machine errors correctable by a rerun from a checkpoint, then the operation is a systems recovery and not applications related.

The DIS environment also implies another dimension—that of ensuring restart and recovery with segmented files. But before we take on the task of segmenting files and decide what data to put on which DTE, we must study how the system will handle recovery and restart. Without a clear definition of recovery and restart, it is impossible to tackle segmentation.

Recoverability expresses the speed with which system facilities can be restored after correction of a component failure. Restoring should include the necessary correction of any data damaged as a result of the failure. The full recovery process demands effort, analysis, resources, and full knowledge of the application, since the

Figure 36.5

A transaction enters the front end with the intention to modify records A, B, and C. If Record C is write protected, records A and B have been modified prior to stopping at C. For the operation to be reversible, we must store the "before and after" image. This is a security mechanism.

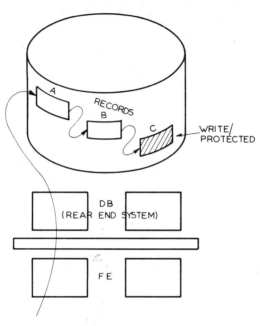

most serious effects of equipment failure are those associated with data damage. Recoverability must be designed into the system—it cannot be added on adequately after the failure. We must acknowledge from the beginning that any system component can and will fail.

Failure Isolation

For each system component—whether hardware or software—the designer must consider two basic concepts: failure isolation and provisions of aids for recovery. After assurance that the system is again operational, we must test the status of applications programs, incoming and outgoing messages, and affected data base elements, and attempt to restore them to normal operation. On recovery, checks must be made to guarantee the resumption of normal operations. Furthermore, failures are more likely to occur when the system is busy—hence, more important to the user's needs—than when it is idle.

Let us assume a front-end/rear-end organization with a transaction-oriented

Figure 36.6
Another possibility is rerouting of the transaction because of component failure.
Log tape helps implement a checkpoint philosophy.

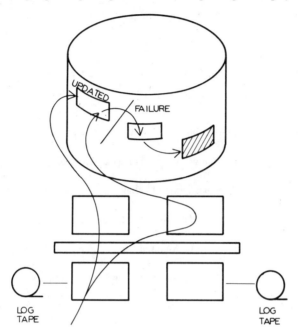

system. All activities must be journaled for recovery and auditing. A feasible strategy might be composed of the following steps:

Bring up the system, loading programs and data.

Begin execution of a program.

As work is performed, the various units of the system should monitor their own operations. Specifically, this means looking for detectable errors.

If an error occurs, a procedure must be invoked, involving retry, refreshment, and recovery.

If the error is "soft," the system is capable of recovering without any specific service activity being performed. The appropriate recovery must be accomplished and processing resumed.

If the error is "hard," no recovery is possible other than initiating a service action, which consists of identifying and diagnosing the failure, repairing the defect, verifying the repair, and returning the system to use.

Availability is increased if we identify in advance all possible failures, classify them into homogeneous groups, look out for them constantly, and work on the basis of exception reporting. Good availability strategies aim at minimizing the amount of

Table 36.2 Security Issues with DIS

Reference	Issue
Processing Unit	Frequency of recordings/check-ups
Storage Devices	Access; authorization
Distributed Entry	Dial-in, CPU, network
Network	Nodes, linkages, data bases
Protocol	Choice, control, compatibility, change
Users	How many? Where? For what purpose?
System Level	Who has access? Of what sort? How is it implemented? Where?
Journaling	Coverage, data procedural, design
Recovery	Policies to be followed, delays, dependability
Security	Higher-up authority, authentication, keys, dynamic change

A protocol for data security helps ensure that access to certain ports on the network are denied unauthorized users.

time and expense incurred to identify and diagnose the failure, repair the defect, and verify the correction and return the system to use.

A statistical function must also be performed which calls for the collection of a variety of statistics concerning the operation of the network. Such statistics may be compiled in reports hourly, daily, or in other time periods for establishing performance and information flow of the network. The statistics must include operating errors, unauthorized access attempts by priority, and authorized access or security.

Paralleling this, a utility function is needed. It involves the collection of activities not directly related to main routing, integrity, and journaling, but acts in a supporting role, for instance code translations, basic format checking such as mandatory fields, sequence numbers, etc., and destination code validation.

Security, Privacy, and Auditability

Security and privacy considerations must retain priority in the design of a distributed information system. They involve application system access, transaction access, user

Figure 36.7
Auditing functions

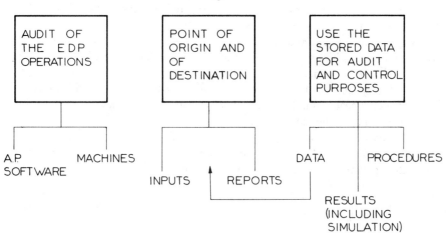

perspectives, and a distributed origin of events. The handling of such requirements presupposes both local and physical mechanisms, involving an a priori definition of access extent, system checkpoints, and application responsibilities.

Three levels of access authorization must be given in a data base system: read only (write protected), read/write, and delete. Let us look at the examples in Figures 36.5 and 36.6. A transaction entering the front end has the objective to modify records A, B, C. But record C is write protected. If operations A and B have already been performed, to reserve them we must have the "before and after" image. This procedure complements the requirements posed by the rerouting of transactions because of failure.

Both for failure and for security purposes, the distributed levels of data assurance include system, application, process unit, and data object. External and internal guarantees must be provided. These include transaction or process mapping (physical, logical), value control (fixed value, variable driven), user accessibility (transaction, passwords), and data orientation (data dictionary, data base organization, and passwords).

Passwords are defined by the data base designer (or administrator) when specifying the read, write, and delete access to the data base. But it is possible to gain access to some data without a password if the data base is designed to allow this. The distribution points (topology of hosts and terminals) must be examined, and a checklist prepared as outlined in Table 36.2.

The audit techniques which can be used for distributed auditability are static, variable, and dynamic. The way auditability is applied differs, but the functions to be performed are the same; see Figure 36.7. They include audit of EDP operations and, eventually, of the network functions, audit at point of data origin and of destination, and use of stored data for audit and control purposes.

Static approaches involve predefined controls, established processes, sampling inspections, and spot checks. Static audits must account for erroneous transactions. Generally, they do not alter the processes being audited; they are not done on-line, and they produce predefined outputs.

Variable distributed auditability also calls for predefined controls and established processes. Although it is not on-line, it does alter processes and the inputs and outputs are defined.

Finally, dynamic auditability is done on-line, deals with changeable processes, has hardly changeable inputs and outputs, involves alterable techniques, and alters the processes being audited.

All three types of auditing must create an audit trail, ensure that there is no error propagation, and last a specified time frame, being repeated in line with an established pattern within the time frame in question.

PART SEVEN

Network Maintenance

37

Life Cycle Maintainability

One of the prime concerns of the network designer is enhancement of system maintainability. What are the goals of maintainability within an on-line environment?

They are:

1. Hardware (its topology and serviceability)
2. Basic software (new releases, support of past releases)
3. Data communications (equipment installed), lines, modems, environment
4. Maintenance for applications programs packages
5. Data base management, file management, operating system for data bases
6. On-line (remote) maintenance capability

For each of these, and for the total system, contractual uptime guarantees must be provided. Systems reliability must be maintained throughout the life of the on-line system.

The total system performance entails operational, hardware, software, and communications functions. Two basic standards may be used to evaluate uptime in an objective, factual, and documented manner.

The first is system scheduled hours (uptime and downtime). The second is the system downtime resulting from different reasons. A simple algorithm reflecting this is:

$$\frac{\text{System usage time}}{\Sigma \text{ of interruptions}}$$

Unscheduled interruptions may be due to hardware failures or to other reasons as listed in Table 37.1. We measure hardware failures according to the mean time

Table 37.1
Performance Parameters

				Operational	Hardware	Software	Communications
		System Uptime Hours		+	+	+	+
CALENDAR TIME	System Scheduled Hours	Hardware	Maintenance	+	+	−	−
			Dump	+	+	−	−
			Recovery	+	+	−	−
			Logistic	+	+	−	−
		Software	Patches	+	+	+	−
			Dump	+	+	+	−
			Recovery	+	+	+	−
	System Downtime	Unknown	Test	+	+	−	−
			Dump	+	+	−	−
			Recovery	+	+	−	−
		Operator	Dump	+	−	−	−
			Recovery	+	−	−	−
		Power Outage	Lost time	+	−	−	−
		Environment	Lost time	+	−	−	−
		Basic software	Lost time	+	+	+	−
		Maintenance error	Dump	+	+	−	−
			Recovery	+	+	−	−

Performance Parameters (continued)

CALENDAR TIME

				Operational	Hardware	Software	Communications
System	System Uptime Hours			+	+	+	+
Scheduled Hours	System Downtime	Line error	Lost hours	+	+	+	+
		Modem error	Lost hours	+	+	−	−
		Supports	Lost hours	+	+	−	−
Neutral Hours	Preventive maintenance			+	+	−	−
	Power-off hours			+	−	−	−
	Idle hours			−	−	−	−

505

between failures, MTBF, and the mean time to repair, MTTR. But the existence of other reasons and the recovery procedures (as we shall see in the following sections) make this measure inadequate. Therefore, over the last few years, we have come to measure in terms of mean time between system interruptions, MTBSI, and mean time of system interrupt, MTOSI. All are measured in hours.

Requirements for Life Cycle Performance

MTBSI and MTOSI are much better means of evaluating the service obtained from computers and data communications systems because they reflect the combined negative effect of interruptions due to a variety of causes.

In general, it is well to remember that all types of interruptions create a prejudice. Short interruptions are software oriented, and long ones are hardware oriented. While it is easy to shut down a system, the problem is to start it up again. For performance and for stabilization computer systems should work round the clock. (But this poses a variety of other problems.)

The stress put on the computer system with every start-up has an impact on life-long performance and maintainability. With life-long maintainability are associated life cycle costs, which are the sum of acquisition, installation, operating, maintenance, logistics, and support costs. The mean time between failures and the mean time of system interrupt have a dramatic effect on life cycle costs.

The selling price of equipment at standard reliability levels is a relatively small portion of total system costs. This total system cost, related to the service to be derived from the system, decreases as the reliability increases. However, it increases very quickly as the reliability level drops. Thus, substantial savings accrue from procuring highly reliable equipment and even greater benefit from designing reliable, easy-to-maintain systems. In a certain military application, for example, switching to highly reliable equipment increased the initial cost by a factor of 2.5. But, over a ten-year period of operations, the total cost dropped from $90 million, for comparable, less reliable systems, to $30 million.

This example emphasizes the need for a long, hard look. With on-line computers and data communications systems, reliability must be studied at four levels: hosts, terminals and concentrators, city lines, and long-distance trunks.

Communications facilities are the single, most important environmental problem in today's systems and will be even more critical in the future. If terminals and line interfaces are designed properly, it should be possible to pinpoint the exact error source and switch to alternative facilities automatically, etc.

A leading European carrier noted the following four percentages of failures reported to its services:

City Lines	3%
Terminals and modems	20%
Long-distance lines	57%
Due to customer (approximate)	20%
	100%

(Host failures were of no interest to the carrier and are, therefore, not included in these statistics.)

Because system reliability is the product of the reliability of its components, $R = R_1 \times R_2 \times , \ldots , \times R_n$. This means that the weakest component (long lines) limits the overall reliability of the system. This is exactly the sore point with starlike networks and the reason for which horizontal networks with backup facilities can offer much better service.

Table 37.2 reflects a German company's experience with two terminals working on-line in a branch office. As shown, the failures occur at the same time for both terminals. Hence, it cannot be stated that the terminal itself fails—it is either the line or the central processing unit (software, hardware, or hardware/software). Whatever the cause may be—and no chain is ever more reliable than its weakest component—only a careful logging of all failures as to origin and reason can guide the designer, the user, and the organization responsible for system maintenance in improving the reliability of the on-line system.

Table 37.2 A German
Company's Experience with
Two On-line Terminals in a
Branch Office

Date of Failure	Terminal I	Terminal II
10/12	2	2
10/13	-	-
10/16	-	-
10/17	1	1
10/18	1	1
10/19	-	-
10/20	1	1
10/23	2	2
10/24	-	-
10/25	-	-
10/26	2	2
11 days	9	9

Availability and Reliability

Within each area of system interest specific attributes must be listed and associated with functional categories. Each of these functional categories will probably have different availability requirements. It is obvious, for example, that the availability of a CPU is more important than that of a terminal, a system control program is more vital than a language component, and a language specification is more important than a primer.

The total system facilities viewed as an integral source of given capabilities may be categorized both according to the responsibility of the user and to the job to be done. Hardware, software, communications, and operational reasons have an impact on systems availability.

Availability is the probability that a system is running at any point during scheduled time. It is calculated as follows:

$$\text{Percent availability} = 100 \times \frac{\text{System usage time (uptime)}}{\text{Scheduled time}}$$

$$\text{Uptime} = \text{Scheduled time} - \text{system downtime}$$

Reliability is the probability that a system will give satisfactory performance—for a pre-established period of time—under operational and environmental conditions defined in advance. It is calculated as follows:

$$R = e^{\,t/T}$$

Here, $\overline{T}$ is the mean time between failures, and t the time over which a system is expected to operate. However, many computer centers prefer to use the following calculation:

$$R = \frac{\text{System usage time}}{\Sigma \text{ of interruptions}}$$

Reliability may also be defined as the extent to which a system or component performs its specified functions without any failures visible to the user.

Availability and reliability regard the system running at any point during scheduled time, and must be examined and ensured within a life cycle perspective. As such, they also define the extent to which the system (all components of hardware, software, and documentation provided by the supplier) may be depended upon to supply complete, correct results when required, given any combination of inputs. Any combination of inputs includes the certainty that the system will be presented and inputs are defined as invalid. Complete, correct results require detection, rejection, and error publication.

Availability and reliability require the timely and accurate provision of services and rest on system and design characteristics incorporated at the drafting stage.

Maintainability is the extend to which preventive maintenance can be performed without degrading availability.

Repairability is the speed with which a component failure can be detected and fully corrected.

After correction of a component failure, recoverability is the speed with which system facilities can be restored, including necessary correction of data damaged as a result of the failure.

Life cycle reliability has practical, easily defined service aspects. A system or component performs its specified functions without any failure visible to the user. The most important thing that can be said about hardware reliability (as, indeed, all other kinds of reliability) is that the basic design must be aimed initially at reliability, otherwise little reliability will be achieved. The question must be asked, Do we know that this can be done and be reliable? If not, such a product should either not be produced or labeled frankly as experimental.

The most obvious place to look for increased reliability in hardware is in the type of components employed in the design. Component and circuit reliability for some parts of the computer has increased through the years as computers have progressed from vacuum tubes to transistors to solid-state logic technology and beyond. Each of these advances has resulted in circuitry with a longer life between failures, which gives more consistent results throughout the life of the system. As dependence on on-line systems grows and the penalties for unavailability become more severe, it is evident that new approaches must be used relative to the reliability of hardware components.

Failing components must generally be self-repairing or self-replacing if they impact critical applications. If we are expected to entrust data to a computerized data base, we must be assured that the data will be available easily to authorized users, secure from unauthorized users, and secure from accidental or malicious destruction. This implies larger, faster, and more inexpensive direct access for on-line storage of the data base as well as higher reliability to avoid the problem of "lost" data, bad tracks, head crashes, and so on.

Reliability standards must be established for each machine, based on the expected failure rate of its components, and for each function, based on its criticality to the application of the user. Any specific on-line system can be designed with a predictable rate once the failure rate of its components is known. It is possible to build a computer system that will never fail completely, that is, it will always be usable even though some parts of it may be undergoing repair at any given time.

It is necessary, then, to analyze the use of each specific machine and establish a particular standard of reliability for that single piece of equipment. Means for the measurement of performance are essential to support the expected fail-soft techniques. It should be possible to tell at a glance which machines are functioning at full capacity, which at partial, and which are down. On those machines working at only a partial capacity, it should be possible to tell from the measurement which functions are impaired and what must be done to correct them. Simulators should also be designed to measure the effect on availability when a particular machine is removed from the system, either partially or wholly.

Availability of statistics regarding reliability experience is essential to users for the configuartion of reliable on-line systems to meet application requirements. The modeling and evaluation of reliability requires detailed quantitative data regarding failure experience and design objectives, coupled with detailed knowledge of impact on the applications of each failure condition. The data should include the mean failure and repair times and distribution characteristics by individual component, with categorization by secondary damage characteristic (e.g., data damaged or not damaged).

The detection of failures is critical and must take place as soon as possible after the failure occurs. The detection system may consist of hardware, software, or some combination, but it must be designed before the system is built so that it can take into account all of the design decisions which are made. Failure detection must be immediate and complete.

The detection mechanism should include a means for diagnosing the failure and isolating it to a specific machine, functional block, or component. It should attempt to pinpoint the failure as precisely as possible to make future maintenance simpler. The detection mechanism should immediately store the failure in the data base and external media. The data base storage is for future reference by the maintenance specialist and should note the time of the failure, the type of failure, the hardware location, the application being processed through the failing area, and any remedial action which was taken by the system or the system support. At the same time the error is logged, an alarm must be given to the operator to inform him that a failure has occurred. The combination of this alarm and the log will enable appropriate external action to be taken.

The system should then initiate internal correction, if at all possible. This may consist of switching in a redundant component in place of the failing component, bypassing the failing component while continuing to process with the remaining parts of the machine, dynamic reconfiguration of all the machines, or any other action made possible by the system's architecture. In general, this action should allow maximum use of the total system while the damaged components are repaired and replaced by external means.

Statistics should be kept on all failures for later analysis to determine if particular components are more susceptible to failure than others. A log of intermittent failures might also be used to determine the progressive weakening of a given component and thus permit its replacement before a failure occurs.

Particular consideration should be given to protective design which will make the system more independent of the environment, particularly in the areas of power, temperature, humidity, static electricity, impact, damage, and cleanliness. The same is true for the capability of implementing on-line maintenance; see Figure 37.1.

Let us summarize what has just been said. Improving service and enhancing actual system performance are worthwhile goals to be followed actively by keeping

Figure 37.1
On-line maintenance. The test is performed on the line, modem, DTE,
environment

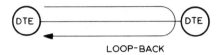

LOOP-BACK

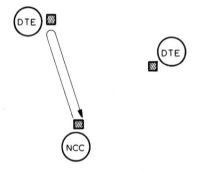

failure statistics and providing special units for telediagnostics and telecontrol. In brief, this means providing an on-line maintenance capability to assist the user. With downline loading and upline dumping facilities, the user can send messages and test the different modems by comparing the answer received to the signal. Further, diagnostics at the user's level allow screening for failures, localizing them, and calling for maintenance on a documented basis.

A data base must be organized so that it is able to give MTBI, MTBSI, MTTR, and MTOSI for each piece of equipment, with classification by type of failure. To ease corrective action interactive approaches should be used, plus a printing exception routine for a given connection, for instance, a connection which had more than five failures in a month.

Software Reliability

For over a quarter of a century computer software has been an adventure rather than serious, planned, and thoroughly controlled work. Many large system programming projects emerged as running propositions, but few have met goals, schedules, budgets, or prerequisites.

The objective should be to make software at least as reliable as hardware, especially in view of typical software repair times. Much more emphasis should be

Figure 37.2
(a) Manufacturer's learning curve with a new software release;
(b) Installation takes place at client's site x months after the announcement

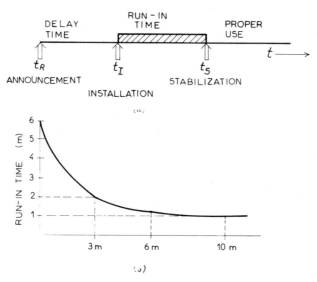

placed on designing for prevention of failure, rather than repair, because of long repair times and the possible severe impact on the user's business operation. Certain applications will be so critical that no software failure can be tolerated, whereas others would be able to withstand some failure. One solution would be two sets of software: one that is very reliable, seldom changing, and with sufficient features to do a job but with no complexities, and the other a more complex, generalized type commonly used today.

Good initial system design, implementation, and testing are of paramount importance. The goal should be that software features will not be approved unless the designer can describe exactly how they may be tested out 100 percent. The specific limits must be tested and made known to the users.

Systems analysis and design must be done defensively, that is, the designer must assume that the worst will happen, invalid data will be presented to the system, unplanned use will occur, and modifications will need to be made. These factors, if accounted for in the initial design, will increase the overall reliability of the software.

Programs must be designed and implemented in a modular fashion—modular by end use, as seen by the user. In the future, when the software becomes a part of the hardware, this concept will be essential. In addition, the modules should be further broken down into small, relatively independent packets. When a failure occurs in software residing in the hardware, it must be possible to remove and replace only the failing portion, with other work continuing to run if it does not require the failing section.

When components are kept at the simplest possible level, changes may be isolated to a few specific components, and, by use of a standard software interface, these components may be replaced easily. Software simplicity helps not only the user but also the manufacturer and his representatives.

Figure 37.2 identifies three milestones: delay time, between announcement and installation, run-in time, between installation and stabilization, and proper use of the manufacturer's new software release. The learning curve of the manufacturer himself is significant and, along with him, that of the client. The run-in time varies from 1 to 6 months, depending on which point in the manufacturer's learning curve the installation at the client's site takes place.

Software design is another important factor affecting overall performance. Each software module should begin with a routine which validates all data input to it. All data entering the system should be checked; errors capable of stopping the software should be trapped. Processing of that data should be discontinued and an appropriate error message written. The emphasis here is on the prevention of software failures. Errors must be detected, isolated, diagnosed, published, and corrected. The design philosophy must be to catch errors early enough in processing logic to prevent or localize the damage caused by them.

When an error has been detected, it should be logged immediately. The user should have the ability to route a notification to the appropriate person, who is almost never the computer operator. With a good message and a log of the failure, this person can diagnose the problem and take corrective action. The criterion for a message to be "good" is if the user can know from this message the exact cause of the failure. Conversely, a message listing three possible causes is not a "good" message.

Other problems with software are operational. Considerable setup time is lost with some routines. In addition, it is sometimes necessary to consume further setup time if a scheduled interruption or failure has occurred and the operators must restart from a checkpoint. Lengthy setup time is certainly inconsistent with the concept of having an on-line system. Only by considering the total system requirements can ways be found to reduce total system setup time to a reasonable amount. Techniques such as overlapping the setup functions instead of having them end-to-end and eliminating others by storing results of previous setups offer some solutions.

Generally, one of the more serious losses of availability is the time required to set up and tear down computing facilities before and after production uses and time out. While the nature of the problem is such that this factor can probably never be reduced to zero, attention should be paid to lowering this major loss of available time.

Operator experience affects significantly both setup and the overall time needed to study the system. Figure 37.3 makes the distinction between experienced and inexperienced operators. Either case is subject to equipment variants, but the

Figure 37.3

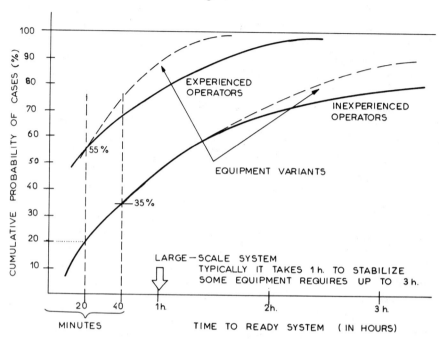

cumulative distribution of cases indicates that the probability is 55 percent for experienced operators versus 20 percent for inexperienced ones to prepare the system within 20 minutes. Further still, experienced operators will, in nearly all cases, prepare the system in less than 2 hours. This happens only in 70 percent of the cases for the less experienced. Evidently, such variations have a great impact on the downtime due to all causes.

A part is also played by how well the programs have been written and how many checkpoints are included to avoid total rerun of programs in the case of timeout. Figure 37.4 illustrates this by distinguishing dump time, recovery time, and total downtime due to all causes.

If we include in total recovery system restart, reconfiguration (if any), restore, reload, and rerun, then on the average

$$\frac{\text{Recovery}}{\text{Total system downtime (TSDT)}} = 36\%$$

$$\frac{\text{Dump time}}{\text{TSDT}} = 7\%$$

The dump time precedes recovery. If the system hangs up, we must dump it. And

$$\frac{\text{DT + R}}{\text{TSDT}} = 43\%$$

Figure 37.4
System downtime

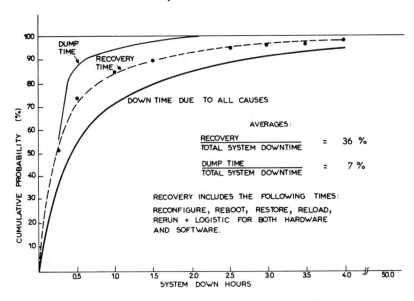

However, some dump may go on simultaneously with recovery, so there is altogether a 40 percent increase over the loss of production time over the MTTR and MSDT factors we will be considering. Figure 37.5 further exemplifies the total system downtime.

The difference between total system interruption versus time of repair is demonstrated clearly. Short hardware interruptions are overwhelmed by the impact of the "other" factors affecting timeout. Indeed, software reasons, system stabilization, operator reasons, dumps, recovery, and the like all represent in this case a high multiple of the hardware downtime. Proportionally speaking, the impact of these factors is felt less in the case of long hardware interruptions. The average in a sample of installations of hardware interruptions over total system downtime was found to be 56 percent. Other significant findings indicated that in nearly 50 percent of the interruptions, the system was down for 0.5 hours or less. This 50 percent of all causes includes only 12 percent of hardware causes. Hence, in the lower end of the interruptions spectrum, 1/8 of the time-out reasons are due to hardware, while the other 7/8 are other causes. This is a significant finding in regard to system reliability.

Portability

The ease of being able to move a given product is becoming increasingly important as computer systems become larger and larger, either as central resources or as networks. Change and increasing movement are typical of today's needs, and this

Figure 37.5

System downtime: time of system interruption versus time of repair

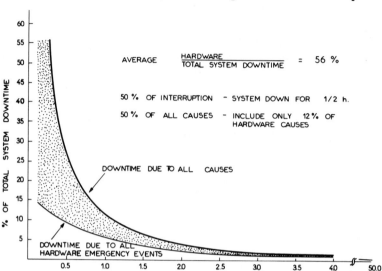

trend is expected to continue in the future. As computer systems become more interwoven into every phase of a company's business, hardware and software portability will affect every operation of the firm. The goal should be to make all hardware components easy to move from one place to another (similar to the way disc drives can be moved today) so that the maximum possible flexibility is attained.

Although this is just as true of software, one of the major problems with software is that it is not readily movable. Most appears to be designed on the assumption that only one machine will ever be utilized in any given company. It is very difficult to move libraries from one machine to another, and maintaining duplicate libraries is extremely difficult to do in a multimachine shop.

Software design, then, should permit one machine to adequately, fully, and easily back up another machine in the sense that any program normally run on machine A can be run on machine B without stopping machine B, without performing special setup, and without spending a fortune developing procedures and supplementary software. This need for smooth movement also includes possible movement between machines with differing configuration parameters, such as memory size, mass devices, and so on.

If the designer solves the problem of being able to move each component, it is fairly obvious that total system mobility has also been solved. An additional problem which may result from moving the total system, however, is the related environmental factors such as air conditioning, water supplies, and power supplies. Figure 37.6 illustrates the impact of power outages due to snowstorms, ice, and electrical storms. Similar graphs may be plotted for interruptions due to temperature variations and other environmental issues.

Figure 37.6

Impact of power outage on a system (Sample size: 200. Average system
downtime due to power outage = 2.3 hours)

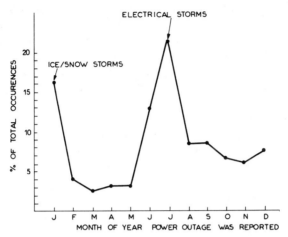

A crucial factor affecting portability is the need for conversions, both software
and hardware. Conversions have been almost a way of life in the computer industry.
Because of the typically small number of programs one had years ago and the fact
that a number of the conversions were limited to hardware items, such as tape drives
at a different density, the problems of conversion and the loss of available time due
to conversions were fairly modest (or obscured). However, conversions now result in
major losses of availability, and the trend appears to be getting even worse.

By way of illustration, consider a fair-sized company approaching 100,000
source modules (programs) during the late 1970s and early '80s: A simple conversion
is needed; in fact, it is so simple that it takes only ten minutes of machine time and
four hours of programmer time per source module. In total, it requires approximately 1,600 hours of computer time and 200 man-years of programming effort.
Such numbers do not appear at all unreasonable to expect. Even fairly small
installations will undoubtedly number source modules in the thousands. Clearly,
there is a need for a system which will permit the industry to go forward at a
reasonable pace of technological advance, and this system must therefore permit
conversion to the advanced technology quickly and easily.

Conversion to new hardware is becoming increasingly complex as the number
of data files and programs grows. Converting from one hardware to another becomes
almost a traumatic experience with the hardware and software systems as currently
designed. Users with libraries of thousands of tapes find that a tape conversion can
cost thousands of hours of computer time. Disc conversions are unnecessarily
cumbersome and timeconsuming. Conversion to take full advantage of increased
memory size can cost a small fortune.

The concept of conversion is applicable, in varying degrees, as one changes the
configuration of the computing facilities complex in any way—adding or subtract-

ing, memory, hardware devices, new or revised software components, and so on. The impact of such changes on the availability of uninvolved system facilities should be minimal.

We are all familiar with possible partial solutions, such as data independence and correctly designed and applied high level languages. Special hardware conversion devices also appear to have considerable merit, for instance, a hardware device capable of transferring all data from one disc methodology to another in a matter of seconds. Conversion over time—a common approach using emulators and dual-density devices—does not appear to be adequate to meet today's real needs, let alone those of the 1980s.

The goal of conversion to new hardware should be to provide a smooth and economical conversion method for each class of hardware, including terminals, memory, tapes, discs, and printers. Furthermore, full advantage should be taken of the new components, instead of merely running just as one would under the old methodology.

Conversion of software is particularly troublesome. Relatively simple changes, such as a new version of a compiler or the installation of a new release of an operating system, are decisions of major proportion to a company performing many different types of computing covering thousands of programs, many of which are operating in real time. Figure 37.7 illustrates this by presenting the mean time of system interrupt as a function of hardware, software, and operational reasons. The reader will appreciate that the low points in MTOSI are due to new software releases and new hardware features. The high points, good availability, identify improvements in MTOSI as the system matures. However, because of new software releases and hardware features, such improvements do not last long. This definition considers the system either up or down. In addition there is "downgrading."

Statistics show that for 90 percent of the occurrences when a peripheral unit (new or old) interrupts the system, the system as a whole, or parts thereof, will be out of service for several hours. This is very important for on-line systems. Statistics document that even if the repair of a given terminal or other peripheral takes one hour, on the average a peripheral will be *out* for 6½ hours more because the maintenance service is not informed on time, the software people do not know how to handle a new problem, and the common carrier is overloaded or subject to failures of aging equipment. Essentially, this means that for remote peripherals, we should add the risk of line interrupt.

A great deal more can be done to build longevity and flexibility into better software and hardware. The central computer resources may be buffered through front ends. Software may be designed with storage parameters which can be varied to take advantage of additional main storage when it is available.

Particular attention is also necessary in the area of data conversion. Technological advances, or simply changes in operating systems are accompanied by changes in format, access methods, etc., so that files created on the old system cannot be read on the new system. A simple conversion tool, capable of transforming the old files with minimum overhead, should be part of the new system facilities.

Figure 37.7

Impact of software conversion on a large-scale system (average MTBSI = 80 hours)

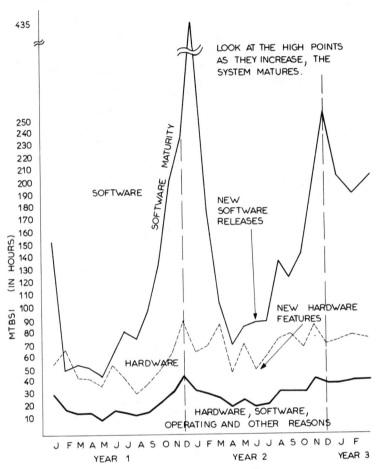

Further, the conversion of documentation still needs a simple solution. This applies to both hardware and software, but primarily to the impact on application documentation. The documentation for an application program must often be changed substantially when a new compiler is utilized or new discs are installed. Ideally, some automatic system should be offered which would produce operating and programming documentation. This automatic system would operate on computer documentation files to convert their data to the new methodology, and a subsequent printout run would automatically produce the desired new documentation. Operating and programming documentation should describe tapes and discs to be mounted, estimated running time, the sort to be used, flowcharts, record structure layouts, and so on. Computer-assisted automatic methodology should be developed so that documentation conversion can be done readily to support all hardware and software changes.

It is appropriate to add that total system conversion is simply not considered to be possible. Any replacement model should simply be an improved system which permits prior systems to coexist and run existing work, producing results identical to the previous system, with well thought out partial conversions as the only practical method of keeping technology advancing.

38

Systems Maintenance

Maintainability was one of the earliest preoccupations for the purpose of ensuring reliability. This issue is once again coming under scrutiny in regard to the life cycle considerations which we have presented. But many factors have changed. Maintainability has broadened, become more complex, and now demands a higher degree of expertise. With the multiplication of the terminals, new parameters enter the reliability equation.

Figure 38.1 gives an example of the growth of on-line systems in the 1970s. Two curves are plotted in terms of terminals installed over the years. They belong to two different industrial organizations, yet they exhibit the same trend.

Maintainability has to be looked at much more carefully now; crucial points where something could go wrong have multiplied. Computers must be used to assist in this task, otherwise the job will escape control. Furthermore, the reliability standards we need to establish should reflect fully the coming on-line requirements, such as electronic mail. The current standards have existed for twenty-five years. Twenty-five years hence it will be the twenty-first century.

Complex data communications networks will bring forward reliability and maintainability requirements beyond the current state of the art. Based on experience, we can only project what may be necessary in terms of availability and on-line maintenance capability through the establishment of a network control center. These subjects are treated here to help establish standards for the work done at the various data communications centers of computer manufacturers and user organizations.

Time of Systems Interrupt

The first phase of system maintainability concerns the extent to which preventive maintenance can be performed without degrading availability.

521

Figure 38.1
Growth of on-line systems

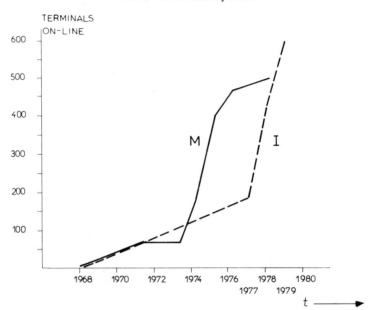

The second, called repairability, is the speed with which a component failure can be detected and fully corrected. The measurement used is mean time to repair, but this as stated, is not sufficient. Reference has been made already to recoverability and to mean time of system interrupt as the objective means for measuring system interrupt. Figure 38.2 presents the distinctions between these factors. Each element of MTTR and of MTOSI is indicated clearly.

Delays due to MTTR are presented in Table 38.1. Within a twenty-day period, such delays accounted for 2.421 minutes. Sixty telephone calls had to be placed over that period (an average of three per day) to pressure the field maintenance into minimizing the timeout. This is characteristic of sites with repeated failure records—hence, the wisdom of a well-organized preventive maintenance program. Although preventive maintenance has been associated with hardware since the first generation of computers, most users would agree that it has a much more drastic effect on availability today than in previous times.

The preventive maintenance required for the numerous kinds of components varies widely, depending upon the component. A unit without moving mechanical parts, such as today's typical semiconductor memories, needs preventive maintenance far less than a mechanical unit with moving parts, such as a disc drive.

But the first requirement for proper maintenance of hardware is that the component be designed for preventive maintenance. There must be such simple provisions as accessibility of the units, handles on removable units, doors that swing

Figure 38.2

Mean time of system interruption and mean time to repair

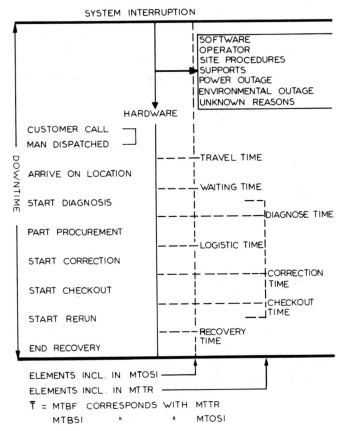

wide enough to allow access to all components, limited exposure to electrical shock, and so on. If an engineer has to assume some impossible position in order to check or remove a component, the chance of preventive maintenance being performed well is reduced.

Another basic requirement is that the entire computer system not be stopped. The concept of varying components off-line for preventive maintenance must be carried further than it is today. Standard interfaces for all components are a must for quick changing of failing parts or the immediate isolation of problems. Such standardization will eliminate many current practices detracting from availability, such as requiring an hour to replace a console typewriter. This capability will also facilitate the addition of new components without stopping the whole machine.

With on-line systems, there is also the problem of interfacing with the telephone company's equipment.

Table 38.1
Delays in Repair of Terminal Failures

Date	Elapsed time in minutes (MTTR)	Telephone Calls Made to Center that Same day to Signal the Failure
10/23	250	1
10/24	260	1
10/25	10	1
10/26	75	1
10/27	81	4
10/30	150	3
10/31	123	4
11/2	30	1
11/3	69	1
11/6	60	3
11/7	118	4
11/8	342	3
11/9	86	6
11/10	36	2
11/13	108	3
11/14	233	11
11/15	150	6
11/16	35	2
11/17	175	3
20 days	2.421 minutes	60

Getting cooperation between engineers on such simple items as coordinating preventive maintenance can be beneficial to the user. But it is handicapped by the lack of standards in the area of preventive maintenance in terms of the amount of time and frequency with which it should be performed on each component. Another crucial issue is the production of a feedback reporting system.

The information systems manager should know what preventive maintenance is being performed on each computer component, and measure this against the degree of reliability. The system should maintain a log of component malfunctions that would pinpoint units needing additional preventive maintenance. An example of this is the type of log that is now maintained for input–output errors. By examining such a log on each component, the engineers could identify those units that were malfunctioning more frequently than designed to. Diagnostic routines must be able to run in the normal job stream without disrupting the entire system. This permits testing to see if a component is failing and to check a newly installed component. The diagnostic routine used in preventive maintenance should also specify which component in a series is failing; an example is when there is a problem in a terminal modem or communication line and the failing component needs to be isolated.

Preventive maintenance of software, for all practical purposes, does not exist. This situation must be corrected. Basic to this is the requirement that software maintenance personnel install changes to correct problems before they are manifested in a catastrophic way. This is not being done, since these people are trained not to install a change until a bad experience occurs with the problem.

Other crucial problems are the slow response to reported problems and the poor condition of the system delivered. Since software does not deteriorate through use as does hardware, if it were delivered in reliable working condition there would not be any need for preventive maintenance.

Preventive Maintenance

To facilitate preventive maintenance software must be constructed in a logical building block process with audit trails left by each component. (Many problems in software are difficult to find because as modules pass data between them, such simple rules as checking condition codes are not followed.)

Further, preventive maintenance of software implies continued testing of the product at the supplier's site, since all copies delivered to users are exact replicas of the end item produced, not similar copies to be continually tested in the field for conformance with the master copy as is the case with hardware. Today's concepts of product testing and integration testing must be extended indefinitely beyond the initial release date. Test scenarios must be expanded continually with more rigorous tests, both devised by the producer's test designers and derived from faults exposed in user installations. Fixes to software problems should become available to user personnel so that decisions can be made to apply a fix to the system prior to the error actually occurring. Fixes should also be tied more closely to logical modules and documentation more clearly describe the problem they fix. Test routines should be available to test whether the fix is operating properly. This is just as essential with software as it is with hardware, yet it is almost totally unavailable. Stated differently, more emphasis is needed in software design and development on principles similar to those used in providing maintainability in hardware.

It is not unusual to find that a failure in a new function added to a software package causes failures in functions that worked satisfactorily on earlier versions. Increased modularity of design would help insulate proven components from changes in other components. An insistence upon standard interfaces would allow substitution of components with similar functions when a new component fails. However, this is not the case, as Figure 38.3 points out. Statistics reported by a major airline clearly demonstrate how, every time a new application is introduced into the real-time system, there is a sharp drop in mean time of system interrupt. Notice that recovery of the earlier MTOSI level is not linear. This seesaw curve identifies the trial and error approach often used to fix software failures.

Measurement of software failures must be done in the same careful way as for hardware failures. On the average, the number of failures due to software exceeds those due to hardware in most installations. It is essential that one is aware of the

Figure 38.3
Introduction of a new application causes a drop in MTOSI

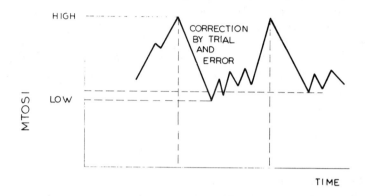

number of system failures that may be expected and the amount of time to recover or return the system to full operation when a failure occurs.

Finally, the application of preventive maintenance to documentation is more akin to software than to hardware. There is also a need for continued testing of the documentation at the supplier's site aimed at better satisfying the requirements for usability, accuracy, completeness, and currency.

Since documentation is not an independent end item but must at all times reflect an exact correspondence with, or representation of, an end product (hardware or software), it must be changed whenever the corresponding facility is changed. Thus, even if documentation were issued in the best condition and there were no need (which there is) to test for outright errors, omissions, and, ambiguous and misleading statements, there would still be a need to make changes in documentation in order to keep it current.

Above all, documentation should be organized to facilitate the diagnosing of problems. Options should be available for transmission of documentation in machine-sensible form for hard-copy or soft-copy replication by the user, as desired, and for access from a central store via remote terminals.

In conclusion, maintenance of the total system depends on the maintenance of software, hardware, and documentation. Total system dependability is not possible without each of these components, and they must all have preventive maintenance at a level that meets the requirements of the total system.

For every basic component we mentioned, maintainability may be expressed in mean time per maintenance action, MTMA. The critical variables to be included— troubleshooting, testing, locating—all relate directly to preventive maintenance.

The effectiveness of the maintenance effort is a direct function of the training of the field engineers in doing their job the best way possible; often this is a long and tedious process. As Figure 38.4 documents, there is a big difference between MTBF and MTTR as functions of maintenance know-how. Reliability never really reaches

Figure 38.4
A big difference in MTBF and MTTR is in maintenance know-how

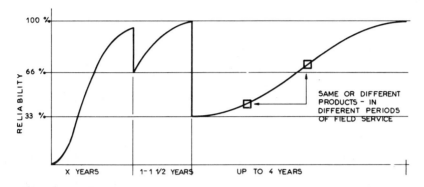

100 percent; it takes years in research and development to get an acceptable level. The product is transferred to manufacturing—and there is a major reliability drop. It takes 1 to 1.5 years to stretch matters out at the production floor. But it takes up to 4 years to fine-tune the field maintenance. The drop in reliability right after a product is marketed can be of appreciable proportion.

Repairability

The cost of maintenance, whether for systematic (preventive) or repair operations, is steadily on the increase. Such cost is very much influenced by two factors—personnel and spares—roughly in a 2:1 ratio.

Traditionally, there has been a certain ratio between the yearly cost of maintenance and the total equipment cost for computers. Figure 38.5 identifies the findings of a research project. Equipment from different manufacturers ranges from $100,000 to $1 million. The percent of sales price varies from 4.50 to 6.8 within this bracket. For minicomputers below the $100,000 level, it can go to 8 percent and beyond. This money is paid to the computer manufacturer (or specialized maintenance firm) for system maintenance and for handling efficiently the problems of equipment repair.

We defined repairability as the speed with which a component failure is detected and fully corrected. To any computer user, repairability obviously is one of the more important factors affecting the total system availability concept. The sooner the malfunctioning component—hardware, software, or documentation—can be detected and fully corrected, the sooner recovery of system facilities can take place to meet the user's requirements. Hardware repair is the most clear-cut concept with respect to computer system availability. However, without valid statistics it becomes an inefficient task.

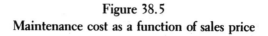

Figure 38.5
Maintenance cost as a function of sales price

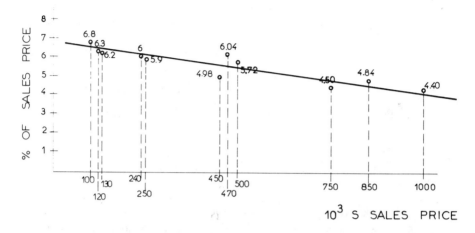

Depending upon the application, the effects of a malfunctioning system range from a simple temporary delay to the creation of catastrophic conditions. Many on-line real-time applications are provided with a backup because of an urgent need to have the system in operation at all times. It is anticipated that future computers will be built with componnents designed for greatly increased reliability. A component failure will be detected easily through the use of improved diagnostic equipment and software facilities.

Diagnostic Centers

Repairability can be enhanced through steady, well-done preventive maintenance. Some computer manufacturers stipulate that they will inspect equipment to see that it works correctly before agreeing to put the equipment on a maintenance contract. The policies of other manufacturers provide for maintenance, but an overhaul, if needed, will be charged to the customer. Policies may stipulate payments on an hourly service rate or a flat rate, or still others may contain general statements to the effect that the manufacturer's first obligation is to support its direct customers before extending such efforts to others.

But the best solution for users is not to be as dependent as they are today upon the availability of the supplier's service personnel to diagnose and repair hardware malfunctions. With improved and simplified diagnostic facilities, plus basic training in the use of these tools, the user's personnel should be able to determine whether or not the malfunction may be repaired without the assistance of the supplier. In those cases where only a simple replacement is necessary, the user should be able to perform the repair. This self-service concept may be accomplished through improved design of components and better diagnostic tools.

A diagnostic plan is most important. Statistics, error messages, oscilloscopes, and so on, are expensive adornments unless there is a rational way to synthesize symptoms and employ the techniques to discover the problem. Once the error has been localized to a component, it should be repairable off-line or it should be possible to connect the device remotely to a diagnostic center.

Diagnostic centers allow centralization of specialized diagnostic expertise (on-line maintenance capability). The techniques required are not novel, since the problem is similar to data flow from tape drives to controllers to channels to switching buses to memory. The distinction with teleprocessing is that other suppliers are involved and integrated test procedures are required.

Measurements are important and so is the steady and comprehensive recording of measurements. Operating statistics enable both suppliers and users to evaluate the personnel involved in repair, the repair procedures that are provided, and the efficiency of the diagnostic facilities.

Software repairability must be viewed from two perspectives: supplier-developed programs and user-developed application programs.

With supplier-developed programs the user finds frequently that the programs do not meet the claims made for them, that they give meaningless error responses that bugs and fixes have not been disseminated to them soon enough to preclude the waste of precious hours or days trying to solve problems for which others have discovered solutions earlier. Software is rarely designed for quick repair. Substantial research effort is needed to develop methodologies which ensure repair quickly.

In user-developed application programs, much available time is lost because the user simply is not sure whether the basic software or the program is at fault. To help correct this, it is important that the software both protect itself and publish clear messages in the event of malfunction or improper use.

Improved design of diagnostics is an important factor in software repairability. Currently, programmers may use only software debugging facilities, and a special software process must be employed to implement the facilities. Some simple means must be found to switch to diagnostic mode, perhaps by hardware.

As in hardware, the measurement used in software repairability is the mean time to repair. It addition, there should be measures showing the nature of the failures in order to improve training of personnel, maintain tighter control over program development and debugging processes, and reduce the requirement for software repairs. In determining the cost of a failure, the time required to make a repair is as important as the frequency of failure.

Repairability of the total system reflects all the problems and solutions discussed above under hardware and software. Often, the point of total system repairability is to isolate the cause of the malfunction.

The mean downtime (or time of system interrupt, MTOSI) includes fault finding, removal, repair, supply actions, reinstallation checking, checking of software, program reruns, recovery, dumps, and restart. The operational availability can be calculated by the following algorithm:

$$\text{Operational availability} = \frac{\text{MTBF}}{\text{MTBF} + \text{MTOSI}}$$

Do-It-Yourself Maintenance

We said that the best solution for users is not to depend—at least not exclusively—on the manufacturer or outside maintenance service. To accomplish the self-service concept in hardware repairability the supplier and the users must predetermine the standards and criteria under which the users may perform self-maintenance. Furthermore, as is advisable in all cases, detailed records of occurrences must be kept for the manufacturer, who should contstantly review this program and improve upon it.

Preventive self-maintenance and repair can be best implemented through an on-line connection to the manufacturer. The remote site operator (user's own field engineer) must be able to do both on-line inquiry and batch data entry. In one application for on-line inquiry, the operator uses an IBM 3275 under CICS software. For batch data, such as transactions to update the master file, the operator keys in the transaction to the central system where it is accumulated on the disc. For support purposes to the user, the manufacturer's maintenance service—and other authorized remote stations—can do inquiries against the maintenance data base through terminals.

Here is how one organization related its experience to the manufacturer-provided maintenance, and the solution its followed afterward. During the first six months the system was used to create new system software, modify existing system software, and work on internal projects. We learned that the response time of the repairman of the company with which we were dealing was between one-half to two working days. We felt that the maintenance contract was not being taken seriously; effective trouble-shooting was not started before 10 A.M. and rarely extended beyond 3 P.M.. In addition, if we were unfortunate enough to tell the field service representative that a repair was not immediately required (such as a magnetic tape giving parity errors), then it was never fixed.

Observing that we could not change the spirit of the field service, our next step was to try to find an alternative. First we asked that regular checks be made on the system. We discovered that no preventive maintenance whatsoever was included in the contract and that if we wanted it we had to pay extra for it—even though we were paying nearly $20,000 a year for "maintenance services"! Talks with the vendor led to a proposal stipulating that each week a repairman would run some tests for a fixed monthly cost. However, nothing in the proposal even mentioned which tests were to be run or for how long. That is how we decided to get involved ourselves.

We noticed that the first thing that the repairman did on coming was to run reliability tests to see if any anomalies could be detected. We found that we could do this easily. With no more background than that, we established a procedure whereby we would run overnight tests every week in the following rotation:

Memory	week 1
CPU	week 2
Discs	week 3

The reason for choosing the above tests was that an undetected fault originating in the memory, the CPU, or during the transfer of information to or from a disc had a good chance of becoming catastrophic for the system. This is the kind of fault we were after.

Faults originating from the card reader, the line printer, or the magnetic tape units could be detected almost immediately. Therefore, we adopted a wait and see attitude for these parts of the system.

At any rate, after several months of operation we saw that most problems were due to faulty memory boards, not from electromechanical components. Once we localized a fault in the system, we then isolated the bad component or unit and, if possible, reconfigured the system in a degraded mode of operation. This allowed us to send the bad component for repair, wait until it came back, and reinsert it in the system. We thought that with this solution we could benefit from having a stock of repaired and adjusted parts, but were reluctant to jump all the way into doing our own work.

By the time we developed do-it-yourself capabilities, we were almost at the end of our original maintenance contract and not ready to extend it. Also, prices had gone up. We were told that our original maintenance contract had been setup at two-year-old prices and that this year the vendor was seriously considering an increase.

We decided, therefore, to shop around for suitable maintenance firms willing to troubleshoot our equipment on an on-call basis. This solution promised to be much cheaper than the full parts and labor maintenance contract, and—given the experience we had been accumulating—it could be tried without risk. Suddenly we were maintenance people. The cyclic tests run on memory, CPU, and discs made us somewhat confident that the system would be fairly reliable.

Of course, the worst can always happen, such as an undetected bug which turns out to be uninterpretable by our diagnostics. The time required to diagnose an intermittent fault is potentially very long, but it would be for the outside serviceman as well. It was our experience that the first indication of a fault of any kind is the progressive destruction of the system software residing on disc. So as soon as we suspect something is getting worse, we re-create a system disc. (The re-creation of a user disc takes much longer, from one to two hours for a three-quarters full disc. However, this procedure is rarely necessary since we separated the user disc files from the system disc after noticing that the user disc rarely gets scratched.) Should a disc, or a processor, go down completely, we can load data onto the other disc and/or operate with a single processor. The possibility of the whole system going down at once is rather remote.

Once in a great while we faced a problem we were unable to trace to the hardware, operating system, software, or to the foreground/background method of operation. In these cases, if the problem does not disappear it soon becomes apparent if the hardware is at fault. If the hardware has a bug, it is certain to get worse; that may not be much of a diagnostic method, but it works.

We soon learned how sensitive computer systems are to temperature and to variations in temperature. A good way to prevent or postpone potential problems is to make sure that the ambient temperature of the computer room is constant and slightly cool. Regular checks should be made of the air circulation inside the racks in the area where there is a great deal of heat dissipation.

Another diagnostic tool we used is the test job. From time to time we run a few jobs which seem to exercise most of the software and hardware, then compare their output with known results.

Finally, we do send suspect memory boards to the manufacturer to be readjusted and margined.

These fairly simple procedures keep our system alive and well. If this method can be used for a central installation, why not for the DIS sites? Here supplier maintenance is often a complex issue, and the user has to be very careful with uptime and with keeping down the labor costs.

39

The Network Control Center

A primary cause of degradation and malfunction of a communications system is the environment. Concern for associated environmental factors is germaine to any electronic equipment.

Normally, the central computer site or the distributed host computers receive ample attention in this area. However, data communications systems which have distributed terminals, concentrators, and remote miniprocessors are commonly neglected. When the electronic devices are located at other than the central site, environmental concerns often do not receive the same priority of attention. Yet, distributed information systems require the same attention as the central installation.

Quite often the user is misled into this situation. To present a product in the most attractive manner to a prospective customer, the manufacturer makes statements such as, "it operates in a normal office environment," "no special installation needs," "just plug it in like a typewriter." As a result, the user thinks that the equipment has inherent immunity to its actual operating environment; in reality, it is highly susceptible to adverse environmental conditions. Figure 39.1 presents the total view of the user's relation to the physical and logical resources. The reason for studying, projecting, and implementing a network control center, NCC, lies in this fact and in the desire to provide automatic, not manual, control solutions.

Networks today involve hundreds of terminals. Projects are already under study for information systems with 3,000, 6,000, even 12,000 terminals. A thousand user-operated minicomputers will easily be involved in such network structures. From an overall service maintenance point of view, the network is only a component of an end-to-end customer service. Other components are the terminals, modems, network access channels, and so on. It is both unfeasible and inefficient to check such complex systems manually. The answer lies in the NCC, which is becoming a fundamental building block to achieving a division of responsibility.

Figure 39.1
User-oriented applications facility

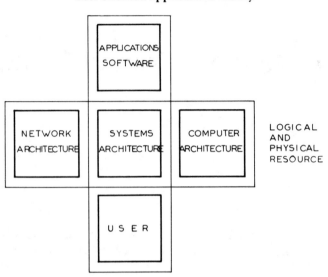

A basic, and very critical, issue for networks is never get out to diagnose; everything must be done on-line, whether it involves hard-level diagnostics, or a major part of the software. Also, the maintenance people should replace boards only when the client cannot do it. The object of NCC is the enhancement of these hardware and software engineering aims. A primary goal of design engineering is to produce a product that will function properly within set ranges of environmental conditions. Due to diverse topology and to operating conditions not always under control, the network architect cannot assume that conditions will vary over known ranges; actual conditions will occasionally exceed nominal ranges.

Major environmental factors include temperature and humidity which work together to attack electronic equipment; temperature is the more significant factor with today's component technology. Although not usually considered, dirt and dust particles can render subtle yet extensive damage to electronic equipment. In addition, there is primary power, proper installation, power stability, and power availability must be considered.

Environmental issues are not the only ones of a disturbing influence. Operational factors, too, contribute to equipment malfunctions, particularly, wrong operations and wear and tear. Furthermore, maintenance itself often leaves much to be desired in terms of performance. A study which we did at the General Electric/ Bull facility some years ago documented that one-third of the failures were hardware oriented, one-third had software reasons, and one-third were traced to prior intervention by the maintenance engineer. Notice, however, that the classic maintenance approach—undoubtedly influenced from the time of mechanical equipment—concerns itself with the wear and tear of the machine itself, hence, with hardware. Though still necessary, this concern is today inadequate.

Another reason for equipment failure is a combination of minor factors of which the most important is the impact of electrostatic effects on the magnetic recording media. We have had the experience of terminals with a cassette unit which does not register the transaction because of the electrostatic effect of the pavement. In another case, a cassette registered bit errors every time the nearby traffic lights changed.

A final cause behind equipment failure is quality histories (field operations and service) and the possibility of inference. The classic case is that quality records are nonexistent, incomplete, or written in a way which does not lend itself to extrapolation and inference. An NCC can correct this situation by offering the needed data base. The procedures and the streamlining required for the establishment of an NCC provide much more in terms of breadth and depth in the reorganization necessary for efficient, well-rounded maintenance operations.

Briefly, the benefits to be derived through on-line maintenance are the following:

1. Saves personnel.
2. Maintenance people become better acquainted with background and foreground failures.
3. Detailed planning reduces frustration for maintenance people and for users.
4. Provides for schedule changes as the need arises.
5. All spares are kept active, and boards are on continuous check-up.
6. Makes feasible a dynamic reconfiguration of the network.
7. Failure statistics are carefully maintained; examination and inference may be made on-line.
8. Hardware tracking is automated with a minimal use of the network for downline tests.

Environmental Factors

Adverse temperatures, as evidenced by extreme heat or cold, can cause a myriad of component weaknesses. All manufacturers specify an acceptable operating temperature range for their equipment, but most users consider operating temperatures as a factor only when the equipment is in use. They are not concerned with environmental temperatures when the equipment is dormant, such as during long night hours or weekends. However, just the fact that equipment is on creates the same susceptibility to temperature extremes as when it is functioning.

The mean time between failures for a given component will be reduced by 50 percent for every 10 degrees above the normal temperature.

The differential between room temperature and the temperature at the top of an electronic equipment cabinet is usually 10 to 15 degrees.

A minicomputer-based system with memory and associated electronics easily achieves a 15-to-20-degree differential. If that equipment is located in a room that on weekends reaches 95 to 100°F due to air conditioning shutdown, the cabinet temperature can approach 115 to 120°F.

Although not in use, the system's being powered leads to the same degradation and, eventually, permanent damage. This results in highly error-prone operation on Mondays and, ultimately, random and seemingly unrelated circuit failures. Users must be fully aware of all possible environmental extremes and either lower the equipment power or provide auxiliary air conditioning or heating equipment.

It is also important that a record of past temperature extremes be maintained, with room and cabinet temperatures monitored simultaneously. A temperature chart recorder should note all temperatures. Even inexpensive maximum-indicating thermometers are effective if read and reset on a frequent basis. Ideally, a temperature threshold alarm system for unattended equipment would alert personnel when preset temperature conditions are reached.

Humidity usually is not a major factor until condensation begins or the saturated air coupled with dirt and dust particles begins to exhibit a conductivity characteristic. However, continuing high humidity or interchanges of very humid and very dry conditions can create problems. At Washington State University* in the mid-sixties the maxicomputer exhibited effects of "silver migration," and it took three weeks of tests (and time out) to find the reasons and to correct them.

A high dirt or dust environment will first become evident in the filters located in the cabinet blowers. Frequent inspection and cleaning of these filters not only ensure that dirt and dust particles do not reach the electronic components, but also provides for free air flow through the equipment. If the internal air flow is impeded, the temperature differential will increase dramatically. A moderately dirty filter could easily raise the differential over 30 degrees.

Under extreme conditions, high humidity coupled with a dusty or dirty atmosphere can produce a conductive solution that condenses on electronic components, causing a component to literally destroy itself. For example, an electronic system that experienced chronic failures was found to have a virtually imperceptible coating of "dust" on each board. Isolation of equipment in a closed room with directly filtered air outlets or vents is ample precaution.

The environmental factor of primary power is another matter. The first concern here is correct grouping of the circuits, which is the most common cause of system malfunctions if done improperly. While this may seem self-evident, it is not unusual to find a significant potential existing between the primary power neutral lead and the actual frame ground. It is normally assumed that within a building's electrical distribution system this interconnection is properly maintained, yet in a

---

*Pullman, Washington. This is a point where the High Sierras of the Pacific Northwest and the Nevada Desert meet.

multistory building a significant difference can develop. For instance, in a given installation when a minicomputer's magnetic tape peripheral was turned off the minicomputer's memory of information was mutilated. In effect, the system was "floating," inviting any kind of spurious power signal to invade the primary system. The assumption that the primary power was properly terminated and would maintain that termination led to this failure.

Though every well designed power supply will compensate for nominal power fluctuations, it is not unusual to have relatively common power variations that exceed the tolerances of the equipment's power supplies. In such environments, auxiliary primary power regulation equipment—which is relatively low cost— should be installed at all sites having unattended or multiple device dependency such as remote concentrators or remote input–output processors. This level of precaution is usually not warranted at a remote interactive terminal, but it may be necessary to a remote job entry (RJE) terminal site.

If actual power outages are a reasonable, or even remote, probability, and the associated application's operational sensitivity is totally intolerant of such outages, an uninterruptible power supply (UPS) must be considered. Economic factors heavily influence a UPS decision. If a UPS is to be implemented, care should be taken to include all critical system equipment and devices.

Unfortunately, the impact of environmental factors is appreciated only after the damage has been done; in retrospect, the appropriate attention would have been relatively easy. A poor operating environment can reduce the finest designed equipment to valueless junk. Remote sensors, however, cannot handle everything. While a remote temperature system, for instance, integrates nicely with a network control center, humidity and power supply, not that easy to automate, call for inspection procedures. Tymnet, for example, has instituted teams with clear-cut missions for inspection at the client level. This involves the customer's premises in general and checks on humidity and power supply, as well as suggestions for the correction of power failures.

A Maintenance Architecture

Control of environmental factors and supervision of critical system components— terminals, hosts, concentrators, modems, access channels—and the network itself will be exercised by the network control center. It will operate as a test and repair center, responsible for the maintenance of all data services in the geographical area under its authority.

The basic maintenance architecture calls for this center to integrate physically the personnel involved in all aspects in its territory, and to provide the ability to centralize maintenance aspects effectively. This includes customer trouble reporting, testing, service implementation, and quality analysis of end-to-end customer data service. These four points summarize the advantages which on-line network maintenance offers. The end-to-end service is a prerequisite for all on-line systems.

Customer quality service starts with the logging of errors. It proceeds with error monitoring and analysis—the two pillars on which diagnostics rest. It is enhanced by the possibility of downline maintenance.

Both preventive (systematic) and failure maintenance may be assisted through automatic on-line procedures, for example, network supervisory activities, fault isolation, and maintenance dispatching. Maintenance dispatching minimizes the time required both for the location of spares and for the allocation of scarce, expensive maintenance personnel. In the Tymnet network control center, for instance, the optimization of maintenance personnel is done by specialization and by location. Inventory management is on the NCC computer. All spares are distributed; common spares attract particular attention.

For fail-soft purposes network reconfiguration is done on-line at the NCC by a simulator. The simulator projects possible solutions, and the chief maintenance engineer decides on the alternatives. Maintenance schedules are established one month in advance; schedule changes, as the need arises, are computer assisted. The scheduling of people, including addresses, etc., so that maintenance personnel can always be identified, is also done by computer. This level of detailed planning is explicit enough to give minimum trouble to the operations of the Tymnet network and of the subscribers.

The computer, though it can be of great assistance, cannot do everything. A well-planned understructure is necessary, and this involves procedural issues. At Datapac (Bell Canada), for instance, not only is the maintenance force dedicated to the network but it is upgraded and re-evaluated continually. The same is true of maintenance procedures. There is little paper orientation; all data is passed into memory and kept at the network control center for retrieval and examination.

Quality histories kept on a data base not only permit investigations by management, but allow the maintenance engineer to interrogate, examine, and run diagnostics before visiting the subscriber's premises. This is very important for the future development of on-line applications, their maintainability, and dependability. It is also a good means for cost reduction in the maintenance operation itself. Bell Canada has 2,000 men performing maintenance work. Computerization has brought a savings of 10 to 15 percent in personnel costs or between 200 and 300 men per year. Not only is this enough to pay for the on-line solution, but also service has improved greatly. The network control center is the "beyond the human capabilities" extension of the network supervisor. Maintenance dispatched from this center covers preventive maintenance coordination, fault isolation and repair dispatching, replacement schedules, and spare parts management. Reconfigurations are made online through a simulator as are inferences. Changes are made through cathode ray tube displays. Scheduled interventions are run on a computer and are made one month ahead of time. Failure statistics on all units are kept very carefully and demands on manufacturing are made accordingly.

The correction of power failures has been greatly assisted through this data base. Power failure reasons were found to be the single largest improvement in reliability. In one case, the node was on the same line with the elevator.

Figure 39.2
Datapac overall network maintenance architecture

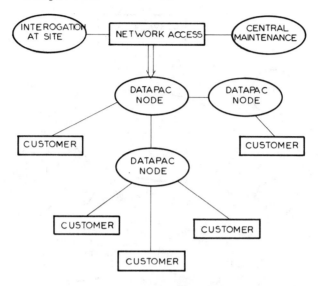

The next most important fact in improving reliability has been the tracking of failures to uncover their reason and dispatching accordingly by specialized personnel. However, at least one NCC found it necessary to discontinue hardware tracking; many signals were interpreted by the remote computers as commands (and the overhead was heavy).

Figure 39.2 identifies the overall network maintenance architecture at Datapac. The network control center organization is shown in Figure 39.3.

The computer-run data base includes quality statistics, failure rates by equipment and its components, and downline maintenance capabilities. Both the end equipment (terminals, concentrators, hosts) and the lines as well as the modems are part of this capability. Tymnet, which uses exclusively Bell System data sets, considers the modem and the line to be one in terms of maintenance responsibility.

The soft-copy interactive terminals which access the quality history data bases are given to clerks answering customers' demands, hardware/software analysts for correlation studies, maintenance supervisors, experts to conduct tests by way of instrumentation, and dispatchers (expediting the maintenance services).

The software answers key questions concerning all trouble within a given section (current and historical trends); the specific trouble in which sections are currently; trends analysis; and the current application and its historical trend.

The new generation of tests, in terms of systems, methods, and programs, is applications oriented—and not only toward the equipment and the software. Tests and analytical functions are performed on intelligent terminal services, node services, and classic telephone services. Furthermore, an *optimizer* available on-line allocates resources as failures occur.

Figure 39.3
Datapac network service center

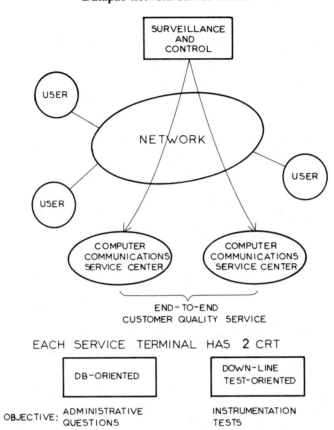

EACH SERVICE TERMINAL HAS 2 CRT

Implementing the Maintenance Architecture

The implementation of a maintenance architecture calls for hardware, software, and procedural solutions.

The hardware requirements are the computers at the network control center, the data base media for the described data collection, storage, and retrieval activity, the input–output and the lines and the modems.

The software requirements may be divided into two classes. The first group is the basics, which include telecommunications software, drivers, downline loading, upline dumping, loopbacks, and supervision software. The second group is the applications, the main object of which is inference by means of the data in the data base. Other applications issues are scheduling, dispatching, failure analyses, and inventory management. Many of these applications-oriented programs lead to or require the construction of simulators.

In the basic software we have included downline loading programs. These are needed for execute, memory checks, and read responses. Another important feature is the static and dynamic testing of modems and terminals. Line monitoring and error statistics are absolutely essential. At the NCC the tester must be presented with historical logs, and should be able to request special failure and problem reports on video.

The reliability of the lines is a major subject in itself. Both dependent failures and the variability of line characteristics must be considered. The major source of dependent failures is the use of old standard equipment. The variability of line reliability characteristics makes impossible the achievement of a true real-time application. This is not an issue which affects only the new generation of networks. If anything, the older star-type networks are more exposed to it.

The Danish Savings Banks have 3,000 terminals grouped through 1,000 terminal concentrators on line. Each time the Danish PPT switches from cable to radio linkages from Copenhagen (where the computer resources are) to Jutland, it throws the transmission system out of synchronization. This requires very elaborate procedures to balance the system again.

All over the world, wherever real-time solutions are used, extreme variability of the line reliability parameter is a disturbing factor. Such variability stems from a number of reasons. First is the tremendous variance in the age of the equipment; typically, the life cycle of telephone equipment is 10 to 20 even 30 years. In addition, an equally broad variation exists in the kinds of technologies used; this problem is related to the preceding one and is aggravated by colossal investments in telephone equipment.* Other reasons are a barely controlled situation in equipment environments, and a well-known variability in error rates.

It is essential that many of the controls be done not only *centrally* but also in the field through interactive terminals. It is exactly these improvements which result in labor savings and higher quality service. To reach this goal, organizational and technological problems have to be overcome. The organization must change as the network topology and service structure change.

The procedural aspects of reorganization are the most critical. In Datapac, for example, they involve four issues.

The centralized report function: This is responsible for receiving, routing, tracking, and disposition of all customer trouble reports.

The centralized dispatch function: Its authority includes the direction and control of all personnel involved in outside installation, repair, and preventive maintenance activities.

The centralized analysis function: This is responsible for network surveillance, information analysis, customer service studies, and correlation of network and customer service problems.

*Some $130 billion in the United States alone.

The centralized test control function: Its goal is controlling the end-to-end testing and sectionalization of impairments to all data services emanating from and entering the operating area of the service center.

The object of the procedural reorganization is to mechanize as quickly as possible the repetitious test setup and execution functions in order to allow the tester to spend more time in the analysis of test results and the resultant human decision-making function. Emphasis has thus been placed on the mechanization of the test function and the automated access of the testing equipment to customer service, across the board of the function and of the units involved in such tests.

Let us recapitulate. The new procedures provide a paperless test-center operation. The data base of the network control center stores equipment records on each customer's service, history logs, and information on the progress of all outstanding impairments. The system provides a trace of progress on all outstanding troubles, allowing field forces and management to analyze and obtain a picture of all controlled maintenance activity in real time. This is done interactively and is video-based. The on-line system is designed to accommodate three types of user control: centralized testers which can initiate tests; tests initiated by installers or repairmen from remote points in the network and accomplished by calling the system over the network and communicating via a keyboard interactive terminal or via a special hand-held keyboard device; and the history retained by the system of all tests performed and their results for later administrative analysis.

40

Network Diagnostics and Monitoring

The systems solution presented in the preceding chapter is both technical and managerial. As such, it incorporates loopback tests, network element testing, connection tracing, off-line diagnostics, and automatic fault diagnosis. We have also spoken of networking loading, centralized versus distributed network management, and data communication tests. These comprise the component parts of a solution which goes beyond the simple models we have known in the past.

A *loopback test* involves a different philosophy of running a maintenance function than what we are familiar with. The idea is to have every line within a system able to be turned around and sent back to itself, for instance, the terminal to itself, the terminal to the modem, the terminal to the front end, and the terminal to the host. Failures do occur, and we must be able to isolate the location. This is the essence of diagnostic tests.

Data entered from the keyboard pass through the transmit portion of the terminal to the modem interface. The modem's output data flow is connected to the terminal's input or receive section. Test data are then returned through the DTE devices to output printer or CRT display.

In the loopback mode many of the internal electronic circuits of the terminal must be involved and verified. Functions like parity, communications timing, and buffer operations should be included and tested.

Loopback data flow should be inherent in the modem associated with the remote terminal. Ideally, the modem test signal should pass through the entire modulator and then be looped back through the demodulator.

Let us take as an example the way loopback tests may be implemented with lines, modems, and multiplexers. At the line level this involves carrier responsibilities, self-tests on private or leased lines, analog circuit testing of the parameters, of bandwidth, delay, jitter, phase shift and procedures for such tests (including the needed agreements with telephone companies). Primarily at this level there is also protocol testing—emulation, test messages, and control traps—and digital throughput testing—trapping the entire exchange.

Modems require both analog and digital loopback, self-testing methods, and digital circuit testing of the parameters of clock, data timing, controls, delays.

Loopback tests implemented with multiplexers involve high-speed trunk, operational environment, secondary channel, difficulties of trunk testing (such as format, timing, local and remote), and terminal and host interfaces. This last refers to local versus remote loopbacks, timing considerations, bit/byte, independent testing, interface cable problems, and different control settings.

In general, *network element testing* involves different considerations, starting with subsystem isolation versus location diagnostics and working inward versus outware possibilities. Subsystem isolation brings up a second element—procedures. Procedures regard remove and replace, remote switching to alternative modules or subsystems, and centralized versus remote testing environment.

Fault isolation is a good approach by which users can learn how to do their own testing; utilities are also helpful. After identification of the element or board which is not performing, replacement may be done locally since most current board designs are plug-in/plug-out.

Coping with line failures is a little more complex. We must study routing alternatives such as end-to-end; with loading points—queues, percentage idle, percentage of input–output; circuit downs; and retries. The monitoring of failures must include the number of block transmissions, location of circuit downs, and the number of retries.

Connection tracing typically involves forced configuration, traced configuration, point-to-point identification of switched circuits, constant monitoring of pathways, and requirements for load analysis and billing.

Off-line diagnostics pertain both to manual testing (remove and replace, loopbacks, test configuration) and automatic testing (preprogrammed data patterns, network simulators, isolation of suspected subsystem or module).

Loopback tests are the basic ingredient for *automatic fault diagnosis*, which, in turn, must provide for both normal failures and catastrophic ones. If the CPU, the front end, and so on should lose power, an automatic switch line (hot switch) must be able to channel resources to backups. This calls for hardware and software support. The hardware must monitor circuit parameters, detect circuit quality, and conduct tests on throughput, turnaround, and channel operations. Correspondingly, the software should, keep connect statistics, permit remote loopbacks, monitor error detection, and test alternative routing. Terminal and host channels must be tested and a location detection facility provided. The latter should foresee monitoring of error detection and correction, alternative routing selection, and isolation of computer failures.

Finally, network access protection involves access methods including open or closed network, locations of access points, hardware/software methods for invoking network control, and trunk and interface circuits (private dedicated service, switched private or public service). In addition, it entails host and network interface (access check, network control) plus use of network services, more specifically scheduling, billing, loading statistics, and diagnostic services.

Applications with Remote Diagnostics

In this section we shall discuss the line and terminal and host monitoring techniques as applied by two users, Bache Halsey Stuart Shields Inc. and First National Bank of Seattle, and by two manufacturers, Digital Equipment Corporation and Intertel. These exemplify pragmatic approaches and document what needs to be done by the way of implementation.

Some years ago, Prudential/Bache, one of the largest stockbrokerage firms in the United States, had in operation a real-time system, based on two Univac 494, which had managed a centralized starlike network since the mid-1960s. These machines coordinated worldwide the Bache communications facilities, with a dual minicomputer installed in London for interfacing. However, the system was scheduled to change in the late 1970s in order to combine the information systems into one network, aiming to reduce people, cut down hardware costs, extend the life of the software, and unify maintenance. They also want to make available a growth capability for the next five years, while integrating their files. Their operations managers have to consult four different volumes of paper to find some information. What they want is to get the information in one shot on the screen from *one* data base, whether centralized or decentralized.

The other important network Bache had was the minicomputer-run configuration for its branch offices. This is most interesting since it is a significant development from a former Telex service. Some 150 branch offices are covered by this network, all former Telex users. There are four to six videos per branch office projecting market information. Another application is under study to include customer information, thus integrating with the real-time applications.

Apart from the videos, the present configuration includes two printers: one for the branch office and the other for the Bache news service. Not only did this approach improve the efficiency of the operation, but it also reduced the costs. Bache referred to a $100,000 cost reduction per year as compared to the teletype operation, and the results, management said, were much better.

Still greater savings would materialize from the projected reduction of paper work through the use of soft copies. Ply-paper alone for computer output costs one million dollars a year.

The part of Bache's network most relevant to our subject here is the communications control center built to manage the on-line maintenance operations for the aforementioned branch office minicomputers and terminals. The following functions are ensured: control over communications, monitoring of all circuits, failure logging, on-line testing, and maintenance scheduling.

The communications control center was operated by two Incoterm minicom-

Figure 40.1

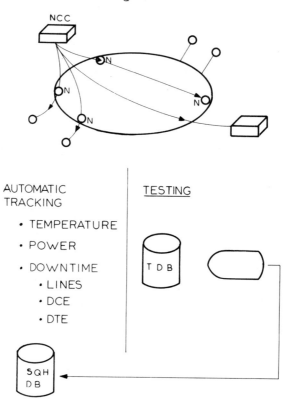

AUTOMATIC
TRACKING

* TEMPERATURE
* POWER
* DOWNTIME
    * LINES
    * DCE
    * DTE

TESTING

puters operating twenty-four hours a day. Another Incoterm minicomputer handled the news-wire function at night.

Figure 40.1 illustrates the network control center operation. Data collected during the automatic tracking of the critical performance variables extend over the lines; the DCE and the DTE are stored for later retrieval as the need develops. These statistics on quality history (SQH) are supplemented by a test data base (TDB), a data base in which is stored the results of downline tests.

The network control center works twenty-four hours a day. This is necessary for an operation tuned to round-the-clock use requirements. The network works through the night and prepares receipts at each branch office using a 180 CPS printer. In other words, there is a considerable amount of broadcast traffic run by automatic modems throughout day and night hours. The operation allows all branch offices in the morning to find already compiled the data relative to clients, commodities, margins, name and address confirmation, and stock exchange notices.

Some statistics may help establish the profile of this operation. A large branch office of Bache has about 22,000 customers, 200 executions per day, 370 to 400 inputs per day, and an execution ratio of 60 to 65 percent. The reports the typical branch office receives are divided into three main categories.

Listing of all active customer accounts that have a credit or debit balance: One of the offices stated that there are 200 interrogations per day on behalf of the 40 executives working in that office.

Cash-run activity identification: This report indicates the activity in an account as of a particular date. It has roughly 100 inquires per day. A distinction should be made as to the subject of the report, namely, stocks, bonds or commodities.

Margin status and requirements: Margin status particularly concerns the client's buying power; it is calculated on house requirements, above current stock value.

A new study projects these reports on an interactive basis. This will complete the changeover at Bache, since the firm has been moving from Telex to high-speed network, and on to a distributed information system. It also underscores how dependent the company is on its data network and the precautions to be taken for its maintenance.

To enhance the on-line maintenance capabilities, biweekly meetings are held involving AT&T (for the circuits and the modems), General Telephone and Telegraph (for the minicomputers), Bache communications experts, and branch office people (as users). These meetings are vital, having had a great impact on facing day-to-day problems and, in the more general case, on all data communications use. Among the activities taking place in the course of these meetings are rating of performance, reliability evaluation, extrapolations based on the analysis of the log tape, examination of repetitive problems, review of performance evaluation, statistics by type of problem, type of equipment, type of circuit, and reaction of devices to high duty use.

We shall follow this type of service more accurately with the following examples.

Examination of a typical banking environment is the objective of the next case study. Seattle First National Bank installed a control and diagnostic system that isolates data communications problems remotely. It is part of a dedicated on-line banking system able to diagnose and monitor data communications and data transmission in branches throughout the state.

The network diagnostic control system (and the corresponding modems and support data transmission equipment in each branch) provides the bank with systems control and monitoring for all stations in the bank's on-line network. From the central location the NCC gives the bank a window into its analog and digital communications: it identifies that portion of the system which is malfunctioning and provides the ability to restore operations through alternative facilities.

Besides automatic diagnostic test and control functions, the NCC isolates local problems when they occur. Its automatic scanning feature monitors the bank network, providing on-line diagnosis without operator intervention. Should a failure occur, the system alerts the operator with an audible alarm and a message on the console's screen. The operator can then isolate the problem and, when possible, use restorative features to correct the failure with a minimum of downtime.

Some of the malfunctions at a branch location that are reported to the central system are loss of a data terminal's ready signal, loss of carrier from the central site, and loss of data set ready signal. Based on its diagnostic capabilities, the NCC can then perform such restorative features as dial backup of four-wire telephone lines, hot transfer for all remote modems upon command, and modem streaming detection and disabling.

The equipment consists of a microprocessor-oriented diagnostic and control system that operates out of the main channel bank. It allows off-line testing and on-line telemetry functions by scanning all lines and modems on a continuing basis. At the Seattle office the NCC addresses and monitors modems of 2.4 KBPS at each branch, along with multipoint diagnostic master units. The latter operate in conjunction with each modem and permit the diagnostic, monitoring, and restorative features of the system.

Again in the late 1970s, Digital Equipment Corporation, DEC, application was at the remote diagnostic level. To be able to use remote diagnosis of system malfunctions—within the 11/70 environment—users have to provide a dedicated voice-grade telephone line and a data access arrangement.

The remote computerized diagnosis system is composed of three elements.

Electronic console: A microprocessor-controlled unit that performs system diagnostic procedures and communicates with the remote host computer.

Service response line: A 24-hour toll-free telephone service that makes the initial determination of whether to attempt remote diagnosis.

Digital diagnosis center: The place where the host computer communications equipment and the engineering staff are located.

The electronic console is used in place of the regular PDP-11/70 front panel, allowing users to initiate operating commands through the system terminal. When a system malfunctions, the user dials the toll-free number to contact the service response group, which then arranges for remote diagnosis and reaches the appropriate field service office to schedule a service call. Configuration files are used to determine proper parameters and diagnostic procedures for specific systems. The console also allows the remote host system to log problems for each installation so trends may be identified and flagged.

The above-mentioned system has been operated, and maintained by DEC, but NCC systems are also offered to the ultimate user for proprietary operation. An example is Intertel's fully automated diagnostic and control system able to follow up 160 lines and 6,400 drops of data networks. Such networks may contain point-to-point, multipoint, and multiplexed transmission facilities, and distributed processors. Most combinations of four-wire transmission facilities can be serviced.

Intertel's system has four operating modes.

In the first, automatic network configuration learning (self-learn), a processor at the central site can query the system automatically, learn its configuration, and build a directory without operator intervention.

With background monitoring or automatic monitoring, AM, the system can operate on an unattended basis, checking continually the status of all lines and drops in the network to determine what changes are taking place. Scanning of a network with 10 lines and 20 drops per line occurs in less than 60 seconds. In pinpointing problems, the system makes diagnoses based on events or status changes then displays full details in English with data recorded simultaneously as a printout.

The third mode is automatic predictive maintenance, APM. The system is user programmed to automatically initiate on- and off-line in-depth testing at specific times of the day. Results are recorded by the printer, allowing completely unattended operation during off-hours. Hard-copy records may be used as an indicator of trends in equipment performances for predictive failure analysis.

In a comprehensive, manually initiated test and control mode, the user initiates a test directly by keystrokes on the console keyboard. Results are shown on the console display and may be recorded by the printer.

The architecture, like that of a distributed system has three types of processors: central (CP), satellite (SP), and remote test (RTP). Keeping processing as close to the source data as possible improves data transmission efficiencies and speeds.

The controller is based on a firmware-driven, multiple-processor design. The central controller consists of a CP connected to a system bus. Operator input–output devices connect directly to the CP through serial interface ports.

Also connected to the system bus are multiple SPs, which control operations in self-learn and AM modes and also serve as interface to the user's network. Each SP behaves much like a front-end processor, and is responsible for inquiry–response polling of all RTPs connected directly or indirectly over telephone lines to its ports.

The RTP continuously performs fourteen tests at each remote drop to accomplish status check. Polling of all lines occurs simultaneously in parallel. Thus, the longest time to scan a network is governed by the line with the most drops, not by the number of lines.

Primary system interface is through an operator console from which operations for all ports, lines, and drops can be controlled. It comprises a keyboard and display. The console together with a record-only printer constitute the work station.

The modular structure, processor power, memory capacity, and input–output support may be upgraded.

Finally, in the late 1970s, specific interest has also focused on other arrangements. Indeed, there has been a birth of a new telecommunications industry—specialized common carriers, SCC. These carriers, regulated by the FCC, offer private-line voice and data service, primarily between large urban areas. While the marketing impetus for SCCs has been mainly for voice applications, a cable system can quite easily interface to these analog circuits.

sccs provide interstate microwave radio channels between central city locations. It is now necessary to connect the microwave radios located in a tall building (say, the Empire State) with the customer's location, say, Wall Street. This portion of the circuit, while only a small fraction of the overall circuit mileage, comprises the telecommunications manager's nightmare—the local loop; it is this section of the circuit that tends to cause a majority of the recorded outages.

Presently, the Bell System provides these local loops for the sccs, probably at an economic loss because of the amount of maintenance required. There are many requests for increased tariffs for these loops by Bell System companies operating across the country.

While it might be uneconomical for a cable television company to provide a single loop between microwave hub and customer, it would seem quite possible and plausible for a cable system to provide loops for multichannel customers or those with broadband requirements. An example could be local interconnection of a broadcast studio to the ultimate user.

User-operated local loops* create many maintenance problems which the general industrial and trading company is simply not equipped to handle. Here again, computer-run, on-line maintenance procedures—able to hookup to professional maintenance operators—seem to have a bright future.

A Case Study with the Danish Savings Banks

On-line maintenance on a limited scale, gaining the maximum advantage of the resources available for processing purposes, is exemplified in an application by the Danish Savings Banks. This teleprocessing and data processing application encompasses 1,000 branch offices; an equal number of terminal concentrators and data collection if maxicomputers or lines are down (with a one-cassette capability for local journaling); a concentrator which can handle up to six terminals, and is programmed to handle format control, check digit, and so on; 3,000 teller terminals, roughly 80 percent at the windows and 20 percent in back-office operation, each with a mini-video display, hard copy, keyboard, and passbook device.

An average of 700,000 transactions are handled on-line per day. The maximum has been 1,520,000 on-line transactions in one long workday. The normal work load is augmented by some 300,000 clearance and other items to the one million per day level. The system handles on-line a total of three million central information file names—of which a little over two million are distinct customer entities. (The balance is accounted for by area and bank variations.) Including clients, there are slightly less than four million accounts.

Two maxicomputers handle the traffic and batch operations (originally IBM 168 and 158, changed to Amdhal). Each of the front ends, done by Collins, is capa-

---

*Over the years, local loops have been a weak spot. Those belonging to telephone companies have usually been poorly serviced because of a lack of competition.

Figure 40.2

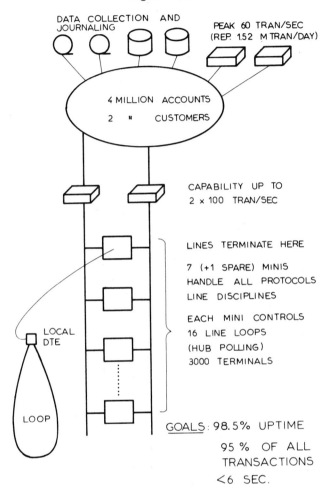

DATA COLLECTION AND JOURNALING

PEAK 60 TRAN/SEC
(REP. 1.52 M TRAN/DAY)

4 MILLION ACCOUNTS
2 " CUSTOMERS

CAPABILITY UP TO
2 x 100 TRAN/SEC

LINES TERMINATE HERE

7 (+1 SPARE) MINIS
HANDLE ALL PROTOCOLS
LINE DISCIPLINES

EACH MINI CONTROLS
16 LINE LOOPS
(HUB POLLING)
3000 TERMINALS

LOCAL
DTE

LOOP

GOALS: 98.5% UPTIME
95 % OF ALL
TRANSACTIONS
<6 SEC.

ble of handling 100 transactions per second (2 x 100). The mainframe handles roughly 70 transactions per second; the current peak is 60 transactions per second. Loop management is also done by Collins; see Figure 40.2. Each controls up to 16 line loops. Some 90 loops run the aforementioned 3,000 terminals. Hub polling is the discipline being used. The same principle is applied in the maxicomputer and front end loop.

The telecommunications network involves 40,000 kilometers of leased lines at a cost of about one million dollars per year with only 0.5 percent time out. The total system strives for 98.5 percent uptime, 95 percent of all transactions to have delays of less than six seconds (all sorts included), and about two transactions per terminal per minute at peak time.

Figure 40.3

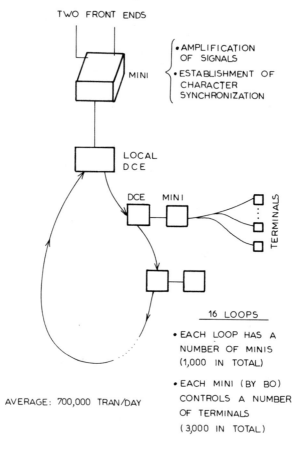

The applications are divided into thirty subsystems: 90 percent of the programs are common to all banks, 10 percent are dedicated. As the application evolves, the object is to integrate user subsystems; current accounts, savings, and loans are the first ones chosen for integration.

The terminal concentrators, too, will change. The specifications being considered call for ten-megabyte discs at the minicomputer, one type of teller terminals, two types of back-office terminals, inquiry capability, and ability to handle automatic teller machines.

The maintenance application is as follows: All terminals are mapped on a panel located in the control room. Data is fed to the panel by each PDP for the loops which it controls; see Figure 40.3. The status of the loops and of the concentrators is indicated. Failure of a loop activates an immediate reaction from the centralized control room towards the PTT (a direct, private line has been installed for this purpose). Failure of a terminal concentrator calls for corrective action on behalf of the manufacturer. In both failures the need for repetitive (and often inefficient) telephone calls between the branch office and the center has been eliminated. Delays are nonexistent.

At the central location, the modems interface with the PDP via printed circuit board with test capability. This front end also handles amplification of signals and establishment of character synchronization. If character synchronization is assured, the lights are switched off the map. If not, the lights are on, bringing the controller's attention to a deficiency. This is one of the major problems of all on-line installations; telephone companies often switch between, say, coaxial and radio links, without informing the client—and synchronization has to be re-established within seconds.

Though the prevailing protocol is hub polling, front ends can be programmed to handle any line discipline. In this particular solution, the external loop concentrators incorporate a fairly extensive ability for acting as gateways.

Index

Access System, 110–111
Alohanet, 80
Ansi, 251, 252
  and process-level protocols, 258
  and session control, 255–256
Arpanet, 62–63, 475
  connectivity, 314
  features, 80–81
  and IMP-to-IMP, 235
  services, 178
automated teller machines (ATM), 440–441

baseband
  defined, 100
  and LAN, 318
baud, 85
Bell Telephone, 15, 16
bit, 23
bit error rate (BER), 73–74
  see also errors
bit-oriented protocols, 197, 218
  discussed, 198, 200, 202
  frame sequence and acknowledgment, 207–208

in a loop, 208–209, 211
  SDLC, 202, 203, 204
  transmission, 209, 211
  XDLC, 200, 208, 219, 237, 242, 479
    basic characteristics, 200
    fields, 202–204, 207
    objectives, 211
bits per second (BPS), 86
biocomputer, 18–19
broadband
  defined, 100
  and LAN, 318
byte stream protocol, 113

central processing unit (CPU), 4
  architecture, 157
CEPT, 266–267, 278, 279
circuit switching, 371, 373–378
  characteristics, 373
  polling, 376–377
  principles, 188–189, 195
  selecting, 377–378
coaxial cable
  and cable networks, 103–105
  grounded, 101

installations, 100–102
  and LAN, 319
  ungrounded, 101
code conversion, 78–79
communications
  model, 41
computers
  defined, 126
  history of, 284–285
  and software, 33–34
computer system
  availability, 508–510
  life cycle performance, 506–507
  maintenance, 521–525, 530–532
  portability, 515–520
  preventive maintenance, 525–527,
    528
  reliability, 508–510
  repairability, 527–530
  and software, 511–515
concentrator
  defined, 154
  line adapters, 155
connections
  basic phases, 189, 192–194
cost, 24
  and future systems, 37–40
  of intelligent and nonintelligent
    workstations, 37
  reductions, 23

Danish Savings Bank, 550–553
datacomm engine
  levels of, 166–169
data communications
  implementation, 460–461
  jargon, 85–86
  and on-line applications, 46
  three main classes, 50–52
  user levels, 44–45
  wideband, 53
Datagrams, *see* network

Datapac, 332–336
  gateways, 334–336
data processing
  factors of, 43
  and on-line applications, 46
data terminal equipment (DTE), 149,
    192, 193, 232, 456, 481
  and layered network, 367
  and network commands, 463
  and operational commands, 233–
    234
  and X.25, 239–240, 241–242
DECNET, 229, 299, 301, 308
Digital Equipment Corporation, 548
distributed data base, 5
distributed information system (DIS),
    1, 6–7, 9, 33
  elements of, 30
  vertical and horizontal, 9–12
distributed operating system, 5–6
distributed processing, 5
downline loading, 456

electronic funds transfer (EFT)
  depository transfer checks (DTC), 415
  discussed, 414–416
  and foreign exchange, 417–421
  in retail area, 416–417
electronic mail, 407, 413–414
electronic message systems, 52–53
  and LAN, 53
Erland algorithm, 92
errors, 485–486, 488, 497
  bit error rate, 483–485
  cyclic redundancy check, 483
  discussed, 479–480
  error detection and correction (EDC),
    482–483
  hash total, 481
  parity check, 481
  reduction, 480–482
  and software, 513
  and voice-grade lines, 486–487

fiber optics, 105–107
field effect transistors (FET), 17
Firestone Tire and Rubber Co., 355
floppy disc, 121
foreign exchange (FX), 91
frequency-division multiplexing (FDM),
  75–76, 152–153
front-end (FE), 156, 169
  and central resources, 159–161
  control of, 10
  functions, 160
  network control center (NCC), 159
  processor (FEP), 157, 159
  tasks, 161–165
front-end processor (FEP), *see* front-
  end (FE)

IBM, 51, 63, 180, 208, 283, 394–395
  basic levels for electronic office, 45
International Standards Organization
  (ISO), 301–305
Intertel, 548–549

Josephson technology, 24
journaling, 327, 391–392
  and auditability, 499–500
  and failure isolation, 496–498
  procedures, 492–493
  and recovery and restart, 493–496
  and security, 498

line controller, *see* terminals
link
  framing, 217, 218
local area networks (LAN), 36–37, 310,
  313–314
  and coaxial cable, 100–102
  connectivity, 314–316

cost/effectiveness, 321–323
discussed, 320–321
and packet switching, 316–318
and PBX, 98
and satellites, 111
see also electronic message systems
loopback, 457
  test, 543–544

Manufacturers Hanover Trust, 405
mean time between failures (MTBF),
  503, 506
mean time between system interruptions (MTBSI), 506, 511
mean time of system interrupt (MTOSI),
  491, 511, 529–530
mean time to repair (MTTR), 506, 511,
  522
message
  fields, 401
  formats, 401
  systems, 398–400, 402–403
  technology, 397–398
  and user requirements, 403–406
message switching, 371, 378–381
  store and forward, 279–380, 381
Metropolitan Life Insurance, 405–406
microcomputer, 155
  evaluative criteria, 34–35
  see also modem
microelectronics
  current mode logic (CML), 19
  interfaces, 20
  microcoding, 20
  and paralytics, 20–21
  transistor/transistor/logic (TTL), 19
microprocessor, 3, 156
  defined, 126
  introduction of, 17
minicomputer, 2–3, 25
  compared to maxicomputer, 36

modem, 140–141
  conditioning, 138
  defined, 131
  equalization, 138, 140
  for microcomputers, 134
  noise and line losses, 135–136
  scrambling, 140
  transmission, 132
  types, 133
  user categories, 136–137
  at user sites, 141–142
multiplexers, 309
  defined, 151
  process of, 152–154
  stat mux, 152–154

network, 290–292, 352–354, 533–535
  architect, 350–351
  connection and transmission, 233–234
  data encryption standard (DES), 308–309
  Datagrams, 230, 232, 233, 234
  defined, 59
  element testing, 544
  end-user objectives, 331–332
  and environment, 535–537
  first generation, 285–286
  implementation techniques, 361–365
  interfaces, 292, 351–352
  layered, 347–350, 365–368
  levels of, 225
  and message systems, 404
  packet assembly/disassembly (PAD), 296–297
  pipelining, 228
  protocols, 351–352
  remote diagnostics, 545–550
  requirements, 358–361
  routing, 226–229, 329–331, 459
  second generation, 287–288

  third generation, 294–297
  topological description, 326–327
  topological solutions, 327–329
  value-added network (VAN), 287, 288–289, 292, 310–311, 317–319, 355–356
  virtual circuits, 230–232
  see also Datapac; X.25
network architecture, 338–339, 351, 357
  capabilities, 346
  CITINET, 338
  design, 345
  host, 339–340
  for maintenance, 537–542
  nodes, 339–341
  protocols, 341–344
  switch, 339
network operating system
  basics, 463–464
  data maintenance, 472
  design, 464–466
  discussed, 468–471
  distributed operating systems, 477–478
  executive functions, 471–472
  server systems, 474–475
  software, 467–468
  system management, 472
  terminals, 472–473

on-line
  environment maintainability, 503
  maintenance, 550–553
  planning, 38
  terminal, 29–30, 31–32
Ontyme, 54–55

packet switching, 371–372, 381–383
  and error control costs, 480
  see also local area networks (LAN); polling and selecting

pel, 265
personal computer (PC), 3–5, 26, 36–37
  and modems, 134
personal identification number (PIN), 116
physical circuit, 216–217
pixel, 265
polling and selecting, 194–196
  packet switching, 196
presentation control, 279
  discussed, 264–265
  functions, 256–257, 278
presentation level protocol (PLP), 267, 269, 271–272, 278, 279
  C-set, 272
  G-set, 267, 272, 278
Prestel, 51, 267
private branch exchange (PBX), 63, 64, 91
  analog and digital, 94–95
  assessment of, 65–68
  and cost control, 95–96
  and modems, 134, 135
  services, 96–98
  unit charges, 68–69
protocols, 187, 197, 226, 257
  access methods, 176–177
  binary synchronous communications (BSC), 180, 182–183
  defined, 173–174
  higher levels, 219–221
  host-to-host, 236
  IMP-to-host, 236
  IMP-to-IMP, 235
  layering, 215
  node-to-node, 234
  observance of, 261–263
  procedural requirements, 178
  process level, 258
  reliability, 174–176
  second-level, 217–218
  synchronous and asynchronous, 179–180
    and terminals, 183–186

user-level, 223
  see also bit-oriented protocols; network architecture; X.25
Prudential/Bache, 545–547
pulse code modulation (PCM), 106

random access memory (RAM), 119
read only memory (ROM), 119

satellite, 107–109
  British Universe network, 111, 113–114
  master antenna television (SMATV), 109
Seattle First National Bank, 547–548
session control, 253–255
signal, 86
software, 478, 518
  communication functions, 449–450, 452–454
  and database support, 457–458
  development, 451–452
  and network maintenance, 540–541
  system design, 458–460
  see also computer system; network operating system
standard interfaces, 142–149
switching
  computer-based, 90
  crossbar, 90
  functions, 88–90
  space-division, 74–75
  and storage elements, 90–92
system designers, 2
System Network Architecture (SNA), 299, 301, 329, 363
  compatibility, 307
  discussed, 305–307
  and LAN, 319
systems architecture, 338–339

system, transaction-based
  links, 391–393
  requirements, 395–396
  structural changes, 393–395
  TNS, 387–389

telecommunications
  factors of, 44
  as management discipline, 59
TELEMAIL, 408–413
telephone, 61, 63–64
Telex, 71
terminals, 127
  defined, 116
  DTE, 119–123
  and line controller, 123–126
time-assignment speech interpolation
  (TASI), 81–83
time-division multiplexing (TDM), 76–
  77
  intelligent TDM, 83–85
  and multiple access (TDMA), 80
transistor, 16

UNIX, 16
upline dumping, 457

value-added network (VAN), *see* network
very high-speed integrated chips
  (VHSIC), 15
videotex, 423–424
  Bank of America, 445–446
  Bildschirmtext, 426–436
  development of, 425–426
  First Bank System, 437, 438–444

workstation (WS), 7

X.25, 137, 197, 244–245, 344
  communications session, 241
  defined, 238–241
  discussed, 237–238
  flow control, 245, 247
  internetworking, 248–250
  and LAN, 315
  and multiplexing, 153
  and networks, 293, 296
  and SNA, 307–308
  and virtual circuits, 230, 232
  see also data terminal equipment
XDLC, *see* bit-oriented protocols